THE RHETORIC OF SCIENCE

THE RHETORIC OF SCIENCE

*A Study of Scientific Ideas and Imagery
in Eighteenth-Century English Poetry*

———

WILLIAM POWELL JONES

———

UNIVERSITY OF CALIFORNIA PRESS

Berkeley and Los Angeles 1966

University of California Press
Berkeley and Los Angeles, California

Copyright William Powell Jones 1966

Library of Congress Catalog Card Number: 66-19187

Printed in Great Britain

To Marian
and our increasing tribe

Preface

THE PURPOSE OF THIS BOOK is to assess the influence of science ('natural philosophy' as it was then known) on English poetry of the eighteenth century. Although there is a continuity of ideas from the seventeenth century that carries over in part to the romantic poetry of the nineteenth century, the hundred years from 1701 to 1800 have a remarkable unity of subject matter in scientific poetry that changes with the developments of science but carries a continuous thread of ideas. The dramatic use of Newton as a symbol, especially in the series of long scientific poems after his death in 1727, has overshadowed other less spectacular uses of science in poetry. It was the newer astronomy after 1700, it is true, that led to the popular interest in that and other branches of science, an interest that was reflected very early in poetry as well as in periodical essays, sermons, and physico-theological books. Yet in the poetry that followed, Newton was only part of the picture, for it included not only microscopic study that aesthetically balanced astronomy but also various branches of natural history, medicine, and even the study of minerals and shells. The accelerated interest in natural history after 1750 under the influence of Linnaeus led to a revival of georgic poetry that consciously followed the scientific nature description of Thomson's *Seasons*. This merged almost imperceptibly with the more thoughtful nature poetry of Wordsworth: the declaration in the preface to the second edition of the *Lyrical Ballads* in 1800 marks the end of the century as a logical terminus to an era when science was freely accepted as a subject for poetry.

Many aspects of this subject have been ably studied, Newtonian, georgic, religious, and philosphical, but this is the first attempt to describe and assess the whole story of scientific ideas and imagery in English poetry of the eighteenth century. As such it is an essay in literary history and criticism, and only incidentally a chapter in the history of science or ideas. Because much of my primary evidence is difficult of access if not unknown, I have quoted freely though often only in revealing phrases or short passages. At the same time I have tried to analyze the material critically as poetry, especially where the scientific poetry reveals new aspects of poets well known in English literature, such as Pope, Thomson, Young, Smart, and Cowper. Wherever possible, I have quoted from the original editions in the British Museum, either the first edition or the most important revision. I have kept the original spelling and punctuation but normalized what often appears in this period to be a confusing capitalization that differs even in revised editions in the author's lifetime.

If this seems too ambitious a subject, it is because I have become convinced of its unity after many years of research. I began my preliminary studies in the 1930's as the result of my history of Thomas Gray's scientific research, and at that time I thought of limiting my work to the second half of the century. Without the glorious burst of scientific poems in the first half, however, the subject seemed to have little meaning. Though the influence of the telescope and microscope in this earlier period had been described in part, the encyclopedic quality of the longer poems and the aesthetic effect of the total picture had not been recognized. For this reason, after an interruption of three years of military intelligence and eight years of administration as Dean of Adelbert College of Western Reserve University, I undertook to write the whole story. I have had much help from the advice of friends too numerous to name, but I wish to thank especially Genevieve Miller and the late Richard Foster Jones for help in the history of science and ideas, as well as Thomas McFarland, Alan McKillop, and Kenneth MacLean for helpful suggestions. Some of the material in the book has appeared, in substantially different form, in articles duly acknowledged in the footnotes. The check-list of selected primary sources, which takes the place of a bibliography, should be useful to future research in the subject.

WILLIAM POWELL JONES

Western Reserve University
Cleveland, Ohio.

Contents

I

THE BACKGROUND OF
SCIENCE AND IDEAS

I

THE conflict between the visionary power of the artist and the analytical method of the scientist has led to the twentieth-century hostility of literature and science. This is what A. N. Whitehead calls 'the discord between the aesthetic intuitions of mankind and the mechanism of science', of which nineteenth-century English poetry is a witness.[1] This hostility did not exist, however, in the late seventeenth and early eighteenth centuries, when poets greeted the advancements of science with enthusiasm. This book tells the story of this enthusiasm, the influence of science on eighteenth-century English poetry, particularly in ideas and imagery.

The transition from the seventeenth-century confidence in science as proof of order in nature to the nineteenth-century hostility to science can be found in the profuse number of poems in the eighteenth century that lent a new rhetoric to science in an overwhelming desire to show the wisdom of God in nature. The subjects used for illustration changed during the century, gradually shifting after 1750 from astronomy and microscopic studies as the chief source of examples to natural history, but the faith in an orderly universe was still there at the end of the century. Before 1800 there was little determined hostility to science, only the con-

[1] *Science and the Modern World* (New York, 1925), p. 127.

I

tinuity of a skeptical attitude that illustrated the limitations of science because it could not give the answer as to how or why certain phenomena took place in nature.

The change in the attitude of eighteenth-century English poets toward science can be dramatized in the two extremes shown in attitudes toward Sir Isaac Newton, one by James Thomson in 1727 and the other by Blake at the end of the century. In the best of a number of poems on Newton's death, Thomson described Newton's scientific achievements and lavishly praised his ability to 'trace the secret hand of Providence' from the laws of motion. William Blake by 1800 had freely expressed his dislike of science by linking Newton with Bacon and Locke as symbols of material-istic analysis and experiment opposed to the spiritual world of imagination symbolized by Milton, Shakespeare, and Chaucer.

Between Thomson and Blake science had developed so rapidly that natural history became the only branch of science that was easily grasped by the poets. The soaring imagination that had sublimely written about Newton's orderly universe of limitless space and the equally harmonious world under the microscope now found its chief scientific inspiration in realistic description of numerous plants and birds. The story of this slowly developing rhetoric of science may be said to begin about 1700 when the use of telescope and microscope so fired the poetic imagination that science became the chief inspiration of a new kind of Biblical paraphrase and a new interest in sublime descriptions of the phys-ical universe. The real story, however, begins much earlier with Galileo and Bacon in science, and with Donne and More in English poetry.

Modern science began when Galileo and Kepler, with their research in astronomy and mechanics in the late sixteenth and early seventeenth centuries, demonstrated and perfected the theory of the universe which Copernicus had formulated in opposition to the older Ptolemaic system. In England it was Francis Bacon who gave the impetus to scientific research ('experimental philosophy') that bore fruit in the founding of the Royal Society. Bacon had in his writings, especially the *New Atlantis*, promoted the idea that scientists should pool their research, since the vast body of natural knowledge was too much for one man to attempt. The 'Invisible College', composed of devoted English scientists, met weekly in 1645 and as regularly as the confusion of Civil War would allow until 1662, when it received the patronage of the newly restored King Charles II and became the *Royal Society of London for the Promotion of Natural Knowledge.*

Meanwhile such poets as John Donne and John Milton showed the impact of the newer science on the creative mind, while Shakespeare, Spenser, and Sidney wrote with little or no awareness of the ferment around them. As early as 1642 Henry More was using science in his philosophical poetry, and after 1660 Abraham Cowley and John Norris of Bemerton followed his lead. Men of letters were closely associated with the Royal Society— Dryden, Waller, Denham, and Cowley—and conversely, the desire of scientists to simplify the language and make it more universal had a decided effect on changing prose style from the florid and decorative to the simple and straightforward.

Excitement was in the air around 1700 over the limitless possibilities of this new science, an excitement much like that of today when the prodigious discoveries in all fields of science, especially nuclear physics, stagger the imagination. At the end of the seventeenth century in Europe, the celestial universe seemed boundless: each new development in the telescope revealed new stars, and so it was self-evident that still further improvement in observation would show newer suns and systems. Ordinary men, theologians and poets in particular, studied astronomy and let their imagination play among the stars. Space travel was a frequent topic, at least in fantasy, and trips to the moon dominated the science fiction of the time. Speculation was abundant over what creatures inhabited this plurality of worlds revealed by the telescope.

Conversely, the stretching world of micro-organisms revealed by constantly improved microscopes appealed to the imagination. The under side of a leaf or a drop of water could hold myriads of living creatures that were just as orderly in their little world as the planets and comets in the celestial universe. If men could see so much with their present knowledge of optics, how much more would they be able to see with new optical improvements. The wisdom of God was apparent, and the boundless fertility of nature was staggering to the imagination.

And there was fear then, too, not that man would destroy himself through science, but that God, who had brought the elements of nature together into an orderly world, might at any moment put the process in reverse and unspin 'the web of nature' as a prelude to the Last Judgment. There was much in 1700 that looks like the 1960's, but there was one great difference: the layman then was an amateur scientist who could follow the new discoveries and even write about them. His imagination was stirred by this science that he called 'natural philosophy', and so it seemed sublime enough for poetry, even if the verse he wrote might not always be sublime or even worthy of being called poetry.

The seventeenth-century scientist himself was far from a specialist in the modern sense of the word. Robert Boyle, discoverer of the famous law of gases, wrote many books on physics and theology as well as chemistry. Sir Isaac Newton was not only mathematician and university science professor but also inventor of a reflecting telescope, efficient Master of the Mint, and author of books on theology and ancient history. Many of the scientists, moreover, were also collectors of many kinds of things, of skeletons, plants, mummies, stuffed crocodiles, and all kinds of natural monstrosities, as well as such cultural things as books, manuscripts, and objects of art. Ironically, they became known to writers and men about town, however, as *virtuosi* or specialists, and so they were ridiculed for not being 'gentlemen'. The pattern is best known in Shadwell's play, *The Virtuoso*, in Pope's *Dunciad*, and in Swift's picture of the Royal Academy of Lagado in Book III of *Gulliver's Travels*. The sequel is also interesting, for the butt of much of this ridicule was Sir Hans Sloane, a wealthy physician who, when he died, left his great collection of books and specimens to become the nucleus of the British Museum.

The new science that had been developing in the late seventeenth century, in spite of this unsympathetic reception by some writers, opened up vast new realms for the play of the imagination that had a tremendous impact on literature. With the improvement of the telescope and the founding of observatories at Paris and Greenwich, such astronomers as Huygens, Flamsteed, and Halley were able to improve upon the early work of Kepler and reveal a universe in the skies that stretched to new stars which could be shown to be new suns for new systems like the solar system. This earth, which was formerly the center of the universe, became a mere speck in a plurality of worlds, each of which was believed to be inhabited by reasonable creatures, some of them undoubtedly of a higher intelligence than human beings. The

4

earliest fantasies of a world in the moon, an imaginary voyage to which furnished the plot for a number of books,[2] now stretched in poetry to include distant galaxies and systems. Most important of all to the imagination, Newton demonstrated by his laws of motion that this telescopic universe was orderly and harmonious, by proving mathematically that the orbits of planets and stars, and even comets, could be calculated with precision. He became to the poets the symbol of the new science that magically revealed the wisdom of God in creating and setting in motion a world that, though mechanically perfect, still required divine direction. By 1700 the microscope had also been so improved as to reveal, at the other end of the Great Chain of Being, an orderly universe in miniature that showed God's watchful care in the small animals in a drop of pond scum as much as in the vast stretching world in the skies.[3]

II

The new scientific movement symbolized by the formation of the Royal Society in 1662 was dominated by a fervor for experimentation and collecting of data from observation of nature that was inspired by Bacon. At the same time it was keenly interested in philosophical ideas: it rejected the debilitating theory of the decay of nature in favor of the idea of progress; it developed a faith in the method of direct investigation that led to a break with the authority of Aristotle and the ancients and an attack on the scientific ideas of antiquity; and finally it weighed carefully the

[2] Marjorie Nicolson, *A World in the Moon*, Smith College Studies in Modern Languages, Vol. XVII, 1935-6.

[3] On the relation between science and imagination in the eighteenth century, the most significant work was done by Marjorie Nicolson in several studies reprinted in *Science and Imagination* (Ithaca, N.Y., 1956). Alan D. McKillop, *The Background of Thomson's Seasons* (Minneapolis, 1942), pp. 1-88, summarized many scientific poems and earlier scholarly research, including several good articles by Herbert Drennon. Many other scientific poems are described in other contexts in the first two volumes of Hoxie N. Fairchild, *Religious Trends in English Poetry* (New York, 1939, 1942) and in Dwight L. Durling, *The Georgic Tradition in English Poetry* (New York, 1935). Bonamy Dobrée, *The Broken Cistern: the Clark Lectures 1952-53* (London, 1954), pp. 52-103, is suggestive in nature, while Douglas Bush, *Science and English Poetry* (New York, 1950) and B. Ifor Evans, *Literature and Science* (London, 1954), have little of value for the eighteenth century. See also John Butt, 'Science and Man in Eighteenth-Century Poetry', *Durham University Journal*, XXXIX (1947), 79-88, and H. H. Rhys (ed.), *Seventeenth Century Science and the Arts* (Princeton, 1961), especially pp. 3-28.

new ideas, especially Cartesianism, with varying results. The impact of the new philosophy upon thought, and later upon religion and literature, is of the greatest importance to our subject of science and poetry in the eighteenth century. The best account of the rise of the scientific movement in seventeenth-century England is probably Professor Richard Foster Jones's *Ancients and Moderns*, first published in 1936, and his later books and articles. He emphasizes the fact that the new science of that day not only encouraged discoveries based on experiment and observation but also, unlike that of our own day, ardently preached and defended the controlling ideas.[4]

The English reaction to the new mechanical philosophy of Descartes around the middle of the seventeenth century is an example of this intellectual movement among scientists in England. The dramatic appeal of matter as particles whirling in vortices, of the importance of the mind ('Cogito, ergo sum'), and of the infinity of life in a plurality of worlds (later popularized by Fontenelle) aided an early acceptance of the Cartesian doctrine by English scientists, courtiers, and the Cambridge Platonists. Within a short time, however, the suspicion of atheism arose, aided perhaps by the fact that Thomas Hobbes vigorously supported Descartes, and the writings of such orthodox scientists as Robert Boyle began to attack Descartes' notion of a physical universe that was mechanistically determined and therefore seemed to have no place for God.[5]

Paradoxically, a good example of the early acceptance of Descartes, Henry More's *An Antidote against Atheism* (1652), is also a startling instance of the orthodox praise of science as a means of discovering the uniformity, beauty, and harmony of the natural world, not only in the celestial phenomena of Descartes but also in the more familiar minerals, plants, and animals. Such proofs of a

---

[4] R. F. Jones, *Ancients and Moderns: A Study of the Rise of the Scientific Movement in Seventeenth-Century England* (2nd ed., St. Louis, 1961), p. 184. On the changing ideas to 1700, see Victor Harris, *All Coherence Gone* (Chicago, 1949).

[5] Cf. Jones, *op. cit.*, p. 185: 'The atomical, the Epicurean, the corpuscularian, the mechanical, and the Cartesian philosophy were terms which possessed in common the fundamental idea that all physical phenomena are the result of matter and motion, matter consisting of minute atoms or corpuscles. This philosophy, as developed by Descartes, was first embraced in England by the Cambridge Platonists, who, however, were animated less by scientific than religious motives, in that, eschewing Bacon's separation of science and religion, they wished to reconcile the two.'

'knowing principle, able to move, alter, and guide the matter according to his own will and pleasure' revealed to More a God whose 'visible footsteps' could be traced by science. This enthusiasm for science symbolized by Descartes appears in More's summary of the scientific activities of the seventeenth century, written before the founding of the Royal Society:

> For there being so many notable objects in the world to entertain such faculties as reason and inquisitive admiration, there ought to be such a member of the visible creation as man, that those things might not be in vain; and if man were out of the world, who were then left to view the face of heaven, to wonder at the transcursion of comets, to calculate tables for the motions of the planets and fix'd stars, and to take their heights and distances with mathematical instruments; to invent convenient cycles for the computation of time, and consider the several forms of years; to take notice of the directions, stations and repedations of those erratick lights, and from thence most convincingly to inform himself of that pleasant and true paradox of the annual motion of the earth; to view the asperities of the moon through a dioptrick glass, and venture at the proportion of her hills by their shadows; to behold the beauty of the rain-bow, the halo, parelii and other meteors; to search out the causes of the flux and reflux of the sea, and the hidden virtue of the magnet; to inquire into the usefulness of plants, and to observe the wisdom of the first Cause in framing their bodies, and giving sundry observable instincts to fishes, birds, and beasts?[6]

The attacks on Descartes began early in England. In 1663 Boyle proclaimed in *The Usefulnesse of Experimental Natural Philosophy* the combination of religion and experimental science that was later to become the foundation of orthodox physico-theology. In the second essay of this book he made this plain by praising the new science 'on the ground that it incites men to devotion, since experiments and observation, especially with the aid of such instruments as the telescope and microscope, reveal the power, wisdom, and goodness of God as seen in his marvellously contrived creations'. The fourth essay specifically attacks Descartes's

---

[6] 2nd ed. revised and reprinted in *A Collection of the Philosophical Writings of Dr. Henry More* (London, 1662), pp. 37–85. See Paul R. Anderson, *Science in Defense of Liberal Religion* (New York, 1933), especially chaps. 4 and 5. More's later attacks on Descartes are discussed in Alexandre Koyrè, *From the Closed World to the Infinite Universe* (Baltimore, 1957).

theory on the ground that, while it successfully explained the physical universe, the logical inference arising from it was that it left no place for God. In other words Boyle believed what he thought Descartes denied, namely that God created the world, imparted motion to matter, and continued to operate the machine of the world.[7]

Thomas Sprat in his *History of the Royal Society* (1667) and a number of other scientific writers of the Restoration period attacked Descartes for basing his philosophy too much upon conjecture and not enough on experiment. To them the atheistic implications in Cartesian materialism revealed by Hobbes made it necessary to distinguish between their philosophy and Descartes's. All scientists believed in the methods of experimental philosophy, whereas the mechanical philosophy was theory with which they might or might not agree.[8]

These apologists for the new science in the late seventeenth century were devout men of religion who saw no difficulty in reconciling data from observation of nature with natural religion itself. The best examples of the continuity of the idea that science furnishes the aptest illustrations from nature for the wisdom of God are to be found in the prose writings of the scientists themselves and in the poetical paraphrases of certain parts of the Bible. Thomas Sprat, Joseph Glanvill, Walter Charleton, John Ray, and Robert Boyle were among the eminent writers on science in the late seventeenth century who tried to show that there is a God demonstrated by nature, whose power and wisdom we should be led to admire from a study of the natural world. They cited parts of the Bible, particularly Job and the Psalms, as models for the praise of God in nature. John Ray led the way for many scientific poems by his famous book, *The Wisdom of God as Manifested in the Works of the Creation*, which appeared in a number of enlarged editions after its first appearance in 1691. Probably no one was

---

[7] Jones, *op. cit.*, pp. 201 ff. For a fuller account of Descartes and his influence on later thought, see E. A. Burtt, *The Metaphysical Foundations of Modern Physical Science*, (rev. ed., New York, 1951), and J. S. Spink, *French Free Thought from Gassendi to Voltaire* (London, 1960).

[8] Jones, *op. cit.*, p. 322: 'The mechanical philosophy was merely one explanation, widely accepted, to be sure, and destined to revolutionize opinions of nature, of the data furnished by the experimental philosophy; and . . . the collecting of authentic data, which show how nature acts, and which thus enable men to command nature for the satisfaction of their own needs, was more important than the devising of hypotheses as to why nature acts so.'

more effective in linking science and religion than Boyle, especially in the lectures he endowed to defend Christianity against unbelievers. These lectures, delivered from 1692 to 1722 and later collected under the title, *A Defence of Natural and Revealed Religion* (1739), included summaries of scientific opinion and the latest scientific discoveries by such philosophical writers as Richard Bentley, Samuel Clarke, William Derham, and William Wollaston.[9]

Sir Isaac Newton should be included with these scientists who defended religion. Among the important discoveries of seventeenth-century science was Newton's universal law of gravitation, from which the laws of motion were propounded by which the orbits of celestial bodies could be mathematically demonstrated. Newton was essentially a scientist who said himself that he was able to discover 'the cause of those properties of gravity from phenomena' and therefore he would 'frame no hypotheses'. Yet he too was a religious man like his friend Boyle, and so, though he made no mention of God in the first edition of his famous *Principia* in 1687, he allowed his editor Roger Cotes to add to the second edition in 1713 the belief that there was a First Cause, a Creator who made the laws of motion, put the universe in order, and has kept it ever since.[10] Though he would have nothing to do with metaphysics, the influence of his own assumptions on subsequent thought was great, leading to ideas that Newton, himself the author of theological treatises, would have rejected.[11]

The growing conflict between the scientist and the man of genuine religious convictions did not affect the orthodox views of Newton or of many scientists of his day, and certainly not those of the theologians and poets who followed him and made of his demonstrations of an orderly universe a sort of new religion that took as its main theme a rhapsodic praise of the power, wisdom,

[9] See my article, 'Science in Biblical Paraphrases in 18th Century England', *PMLA*, LXXIV (1959), 41–51, especially pp. 42 f.

[10] E. W. Strong, 'Newton and God', *Journal of the History of Ideas*, XIII (1952), 146–67, summarizes previous scholarship on this subject. A good early study is Herbert Drennon, 'Newtonianism: Its Method, Theology, and Metaphysics', *Englische Studien*, LXVIII (1934), 397–409.

[11] E. A. Burtt, *Metaphysical Foundations*, p. 236, summarized Newton's influence: 'It was of the greatest consequence for succeeding thought that now the great Newton's authority was squarely behind that view of the cosmos which saw in man a puny, irrelevant spectator . . . of the vast mathematical system whose regular motions according to mechanical principles constituted the world of nature.'

and goodness of God.[12] This kind of poetic Newtonianism refused to acknowledge that Newton had shown a mechanical universe that left God with little to do. The poets of the eighteenth century expressed their admiration of Newton with repeated verboseness, the praise that Pope, with his usual conciseness, put into a single couplet:

> Nature, and Nature's Laws lay hid in Night:
> God said, *Let Newton be!* and All was *Light.*

Modern commentators can see the mistake that Newton made in mixing the two levels of discourse, the mechanical and the religious, but the popularizers and the poets, struck by the sublimity of the new conception of the universe, could see no inconsistency.[13]

III

We are not concerned here with understanding or trying to present the scientific data involved in the discoveries of this period, of Gilbert or Harvey or Boyle or Newton, or even of the new discoveries made possible by technical improvements in optics used in telescope and microscope. The historian of science may show that the genius of Newton was that of synthesis, since all the data needed for his laws were already published, and the historian of ideas may show that Newton's theology was outdated and that the unconscious metaphysics arising from the assumptions of his laws of gravitation and motion were to influence later thinking to a degree and in a manner that would have horrified Newton. Yet in his own day Newton was best known for proving what the poets already believed, that God had created an orderly universe, and for dramatizing the impact upon the imagination already made by the telescope. Now for the first time man could calculate the motions not only of the solar system, the orbits of the moon around the earth and of the earth and other planets around the sun, but also of distant systems and even of seemingly erring comets. This scientific proof of an orderly universe gave a new

[12] For the historical background of the influence of science on religion, see Roland N. Stromberg, *Religious Liberalism in Eighteenth-Century England* (London, 1954), especially pp. 26–33.

[13] See John Dillenberger, *Protestant Thought and Natural Science* (New York, 1960). p. 122.

meaning to the older praise of God in the creation, which they had been chanting in church services for more than a hundred years, and added new metaphors and illustrations from science to Biblical paraphrases of the glory of God declared by the heavens.

Newton's ideas were made available to the general reader around the turn of the century by the various writings of scientists with a theological turn of mind. Most prominent of these before he turned to odd heresies was Newton's successor at Cambridge, William Whiston, especially in *A New Theory of the Earth*, first written in 1696 but revised in several other editions. An example of the usefulness of this book to the poets is the imaginative comment on the fixed stars that follows a summary of the state of knowledge of the subject: 'But then as to the nature of the fix'd stars, 'tis in all probability the same with the sun's; and so each of them may have their respective systems of planets and comets as well as he has. Which things, considering that the number of them is continually found to be greater, according as the telescopes we use are longer and more perfect, do vastly aggrandize the idea of the visible universe; and ought proportionably to raise our admiration of the Great Author of the whole to the highest degree imaginable.' [14]

Another commentator on Newton quoted by imaginative writers is George Cheyne, whose *Philosophical Principles of Natural Religion* (1705), after chapters on the physical laws of nature, on gravity, and the pagan philosophies of nature, includes chapters on the existence of a deity and 'the proofs for the being of a God arising from the contemplation of the humane structure'. In his preface Cheyne acknowledges his debt to Newton, 'that great inventor and improver of most of our modern philosophy and geometry', as well as to Newton's other interpreters, Roger Cotes and William Derham. Atheism, he concludes, 'may be eternally confounded, by the most distant approaches to the true causes of natural appearances'.

Roger Cotes, the brilliant young Cambridge mathematician who died young, was largely responsible for the improvements made in the second edition of Newton's *Principia*. The correspondence of Newton and Cotes between 1709, when Bentley got Newton's consent to a new edition, and 1713, when the work was published, shows what great labor lay behind Cotes's comparatively brief

[14] *A New Theory of the Earth* (4th ed. rev., London, 1725), p. 33.

Latin preface to the edition, in which he summarized the arguments against 'some persons and those of great name, too much prepossessed with certain prejudices' and added the belief, presumably Newton's, that a divine mind was the first cause of the effects discovered by science.

The third edition of the *Principia* (1726), a handsome folio in large type printed by the Royal Society,[15] had the distinction of a poetic eulogy in Latin by Newton's friend and fellow scientist, Edmund Halley. For a summary of the laws of motion by a learned astronomer, the descriptive portion is very concise, beginning

> Intima panduntur victi penetralia caeli,
> Nec latet extremos quae vis circumrotat orbes.

To continue in what is apparently the first English translation, that of Francis Fawkes in 1761, we now know 'what course the dire tremendous comets steer', the seemingly erratic motions of the moon and its effect on tides. Like other poets, Halley makes Newton the favorite of the muses, 'Newton, that reach'd th' insuperable line, The nice barrier 'twixt human and divine.'

The death of Newton in 1727 seemed to inspire a number of popularizations of his works. The first English translation of the *Principia* was published in 1729 by Andrew Motte, younger brother of Benjamin Motte, who was best known as the publisher of *Gulliver's Travels*. Andrew had helped his brother in 1721 edit a three-volume abridgment of the *Transactions of the Royal Society*, 1700–20, and in 1727 had himself written 'an easy and familiar' explanation of the laws of motion. Motte's translation included not only the additions contained in the second and third editions but also the first English version of the pertinent parts of Cotes's preface. A sample from the conclusion of this famous preface summarizes much of the Newtonian physico-theology that was the main theme of the long scientific poems to follow: 'Without all doubt this world, so diversified with that variety of forms and motives we find in it, could arise from nothing but the perfectly free will of God directing and presiding over all. From this fountain it is that those laws, which we call the laws of Nature, have flowed; in which there appear many traces of the most wise contrivance, but not the least shadow of necessity. These therefore

---

[15] The copy from the library of George III (BM 31.g.7) is sumptuously bound in red morocco with the royal crest on the cover.

we must not seek from uncertain conjectures, but learn them from observations and experiments.' From Newton's example the close relation between religion and science, that part of natural philosophy which depended on experiment and observation of data, became well established. By the middle of the century it was a commonplace to say that the way to understand God was to study the works of nature.[16]

Yet the full impact of Newton's discoveries on poetry waited for the theologians and popularizers. At first the popular accounts were written by the divines, particularly the inaugural series of Boyle Lectures given by Richard Bentley in 1692 and William Derham's *Astro-theology: or a Demonstration of the Being and Attributes of God, from a Survey of the Heavens* (1751), the sequel to his own Boyle Lectures (*Physico-theology*) on the wisdom of God as shown by man, animals, and other things seen on land. Perhaps the two books of Derham, together with William Wollaston's *The Religion of Nature Delineated* (1722), were the physico-theological writings that most influenced poetry, and so their ideas will be summarized later. But the number of scientific popularizations of Newton increased after his death in 1727.

In 1728 Henry Pemberton's *A View of Sir Isaac Newton's Philosophy* appeared, a work now best known for the first printing of the inept eulogy of Newton in verse by Richard Glover that contains the phrase 'Newton demands the muse'. In 1735 an English translation of W. J. s'Gravesande's Latin lectures at Leyden was published in London as *An Explanation of the Newtonian Philosophy*. In 1737 the youthful Francesco Algarotti, later the friend of Thomas Gray and protege of Frederick the Great, fired by Voltaire's interest in Newton, printed his popularization of the *Optics* as *Il Newtonianismo per le Dame*, which the learned Elizabeth Carter was to translate in 1739 as *Sir Isaac Newton's Philosophy Explained for the Use of the Ladies, in Six Dialogues on Light and Colour*, her first contribution in a long life devoted to science and scholarship. Newton's Scots disciple, Colin Maclaurin, had prepared his *Account of Sir Isaac Newton's Philosophy* before 1728, but

---

[16] See a later Newtonian treatise, Alexander Campbell's *Chain of Philosophical Reasoning* (London, 1754), p. 40: 'Natural philosophy has been always supposed to lay a sure foundation for natural religion, by leading the mind in a satisfactory manner to the knowledge of the Author and Governor of the Universe. To study nature, is to search into God's workmanship, every discovery in which reveals to us a new part of his scheme, whose works are so manifold and hard to be comprehended.'

it was not published until 1748. Benjamin Martin included elementary Newtonian physics among the topics in his many science books written for the layman, yet he also wrote *A Panegyrick on the Newtonian Philosophy* in 1749.

Not all the writings on Newton were favorable. The strangest early opponent, John Hutchinson in his *Moses's Principia* (1724), and the later opposition recorded in William Jones's *Essay on the First Principles of Natural Philosophy* (1762) were repeated in the encyclopedias as late as 1842.[17] The serious refutation of Roger North in his science notebook in the British Museum (Add. MS. 32,546), as far as I know, was never published. The ideas arising from Newton's physics were well established, however, by 1750 and continued through the century in the writings of James Ferguson.

IV

Astronomy was only one of the branches of science that contributed to this physico-theology that excited the poets of the early eighteenth century, though it continued, probably because of its sublime setting, to be one of the most influential. Microscopic study, human physiology, and botany were also popular sources of illustrations of divine wisdom in nature, and occasionally minerals, animals, and insects were added. Even Fontenelle's astronomical dialogues for learned ladies, *Conversations on the Plurality of Worlds*, first published in France in 1686 and later widely known in England, included a section on the value of the microscope for exploring the universe.[18] From 1704 encyclopedias began their popularizations of general science in England, with John Harris's *Lexicon Technicum*, followed in 1710 by a supplementary second volume and in 1728 by the two folio volumes of Ephraim Chambers' *Cyclopaedia, or an Universal Dictionary of Arts and Sciences*.[19] The use of dialogues for instructing amateur scientists was continued in John Harris's *Astronomical Dialogues between a Gentleman and a Lady* (1719) and in the various editions and translations of Pluche's *Spectacle de la Nature*, over half of which was

[17] *Annals of Science*, VII (1951), 365–370.
[18] The first critical edition of this work, that of Robert Shackleton, Oxford, 1955, gives its history and scientific background.
[19] See Arthur Hughes, 'Science in English Encyclopaedias, 1704–1875', *Annals of Science*, VII (1951), 340–70, and subsequent issues.

devoted to insects and the rest to birds, animals, fishes, and plants.

The most prolific of the early popularizers of general science was Benjamin Martin, who in the forty years from 1733 published at least forty works, most of them compendiums of science for amateurs of all ages and both sexes. Perhaps his best known work was *The Philosophical Grammar*, published in at least seven enlarged editions after its first appearence in 1735. This compendium describes itself as 'a view of the present state of experimental physiology, or natural philosophy' and includes in its four parts somatology (doctrine of the universal properties of nature), cosmology (celestial bodies), aerology (air, winds, meteorology), and geology (earth, minerals, waters, plants, animals). By 1743 he could say, in his preface to *A Course of Lectures in Natural and Experimental Philosophy, Geography, and Astronomy*, that science is now fashionable and 'to cultivate this study, is only to be in taste, and politeness is an inseparable consequence'. This idea was repeated in his *General Magazine of Arts and Sciences* beginning in 1755, which he reprinted under the title of *The Young Gentleman and Lady's Philosophy*, containing scientific experiments and dialogues illustrated with plates and poetry. In addition to his books and lectures, Martin kept a shop for optical instruments and advertised in his books that he could repeat the numerous microscopic views mentioned and could furnish every experiment and instrument in hydrostatics and mechanics. All this is useful, he said, to study religion and poetry, for even insects under the microscope 'loudly declare the wondrous skill and wisdom of their maker'.

The popularizations of science made by Martin illustrate with a cross-section what was going on with other popularizers in England, that the books were written for the instruction and entertainment of amateurs, especially ladies and young people, that the instruction extended to moral and religious applications that included the physico-theological ideas of the poetry of the time, and that the tastes in science were changing even as the subjects used to illustrate science in poetry were changing. During the early part of the eighteenth century the ladies studied the stars and tried to understand Newton. From 1740 to 1760 the microscope, which had been already much talked about, came into vogue for actual experimentation by amateurs. After 1760 the chief polite branch of science is botany, supplemented by a certain amount of other natural history, especially birds. These shifts in amateur scientific pursuits were not only important to the social history of the times. They also had a profound influence on the poetry of the late eighteenth century that has not been fully recognized. The full documentation of this popular interest in science must wait for a separate study, but the transfer of ideas from science to poetry cannot be explained without knowing something of the impact of the study of microscopic life and natural history on amateurs. Let us begin with the microscope, an instrument designed for scholarly research but used by amateurs for amusement and by poets and theologians for moral teaching.

The discoveries of the little world of nature under the microscope became the amusement of ladies and young people from about 1740.[20] Henry Baker wrote several popular guides to microscopic study, summarizing the research of Hooke and Leuwenhoek, but his work can be shown best in *The Microscope Made Easy* (1743). Dedicated to the President of the Royal Society and designed to make the discovery of truth by means of experiment 'easy, intelligible, and pleasant', this handbook dramatized the fertility of nature by showing in a drop of water creatures so small 'that a million of them are less than a grain of sand', in male semen 'millions of millions of animalcules', and in the internal structure of a gnat or louse a sublime idea of 'the infinite power, wisdom, and goodness of Nature's Almighty Parent'. We should not, Baker reminds us, be ignorant of the 'capitals in nature's mighty volume', which he identifies as 'bears, tigers, lions, crocodiles and whales, oaks and cedars, seas and mountains, comets, stars, worlds and suns', but to understand the basic principles we must also become 'master of the little letters likewise, which occur a thousand times more frequently'.

In 1746 the elder George Adams published *Micrographia Illustrata*, a serious handbook with numerous folding plates illustrating experiments with the microscope. Natural philosophy had by that time become so greatly improved, he said, that few persons with liberal education 'are wholly unacquainted with the value of it', but one should avoid the mistake of pursuing only the big and obvious, since the smallest works are perfect in their kind and show infinite wisdom and power as much as the largest. 'The more

---

[20] For the earlier history of the microscope and its influence on literature, see Marjorie Nicolson, *The Microscope and English Imagination*, Smith College Studies in Modern Languages, XVI, 1934-5, reprinted in *Science and Imagination*, pp. 155-234.

we enquire into nature, the more excellent she appears', and there is no way better than with the microscope, where beauty of color combines with amazing variety.

John Hill helped greatly to popularize natural history, particularly the microscope, with his *Essays in Natural History and Philosophy, Containing a Series of Discoveries, by the Assistance of the Microscope* (1752) and with his diverting periodical essays called *The Inspector* that appeared from March 1751 in the London *Daily Advertiser*. He wishes, he said, to improve the use of the microscope, which was already much esteemed for the way in which it leads to useful knowledge, pleases the imagination, and 'renders the whole life one continual act of adoration'. There is a pleasing and familiar air about Hill's microscopic experiments: fungus from the American Grove in Goodwood, coral from the bottom of the sea, stagnant water from the pond behind Montague House, sand from Minorca, and an American moth in the Chelsea Apothecaries' Garden. All such experiments, Hill insisted, were brought in, not as digressions but to introduce general principles. Writing as 'The Inspector' Hill introduced diverting scientific expeditions to teach as well as entertain: a conducted nature tour on Primrose Hill, and a study of the aquatic creatures on Hampstead Heath ready to turn into flies. But he was careful to point out the distinction between natural history, with its childish delight in collecting and observing, and natural philosophy which challenges the highest human understanding.[21]

After 1760 the most popular subject for scientific study was natural history, especially botany. The Englishman has always loved flowers and birds and some animals, and he could always justify his use of them in poetry by citing Virgil's *Georgics*. Yet the difference is that in the eighteenth century, as with the celestial bodies and the invisible world of microscopic animals, the poets put new life into their georgics and their Biblical paraphrases by using sharp imagery and apt illustrations from the latest discoveries of science.

Until the middle of the century the birds and flowers and insects and quadrupeds were usually thrown in with other scientific

[21] As late as 1787 the younger George Adams, in his own *Essays on the Microscope*, occasionally quoted poetry or came to a philosophical conclusion about the almost infinite number of intermediate degrees in the universal chain that 'unites all beings, connects all worlds, and comprehends all spheres'.

proofs of divine benevolence and omniscience found in astronomy, microscopic research, and human anatomy. Botany, it is true, had developed early as a science in England, partly because of the interest of medicine in establishing various botanic gardens at great expense, and partly because of the perennial interest in gardening for home, kitchen, and parks. Both interests had accelerated considerably with increasing exploration of foreign lands and the consequent knowledge of exotic plants that came from describing them in travel books and actually importing them for English collections.

It was not until the middle of the eighteenth century, however, that natural history, under the impetus of the new classification scheme of Linnaeus, became an established branch of study with amateurs as well as scientists. After 1760 the scientific study of plants, birds, quadrupeds, and even insects became the polite avocation of clergymen, writers, and ladies, and for this study the term 'natural history' came to be used to distinguish collecting and observing from 'natural philosophy', the general term for all science in the earlier years of the century but used in the late eighteenth century to designate the more theoretical branches of physics and chemistry. Popularizers like Benjamin Martin, John Hill, and Thomas Pennant fed the avid followers of Linnaeus with books, articles in magazines, and numerous compendiums devoted to the new developments in natural history. Gilbert White's *Natural History of Selborne*, which later became a sort of Bible for those amateur naturalists who noted the first blossoms of spring and the last appearance of the swallows before winter, was at first a publisher's venture made up of actual letters by a parson in a little Hampshire village describing rural life for the scientists in London. John Aikin helped to show that natural history was a respectable subject for poetry, and Thomson's *Seasons* furnished the model.

Up to 1750, then, natural history got general treatment in the compendiums of science, with very little in zoology and mineralogy and more on botany. Of these popular handbooks the most widely read were probably the two translations of Noël Antoine Pluche's *Spectacle de la nature* and Benjamin Martin's *The Philosophical Grammar*.[22] An example of the changes taking place in the

---

[22] For documentation of some early popularizations of science, see Gerald Dennis Meyer, *The Scientific Lady in England 1650-1760* (Berkeley, 1955).

growing popularity of natural history may be seen by comparing two of Martin's publications. *The Philosophical Grammar* (1735), as we have seen, treats plants and animals as merely part of 'geology', which is itself one of four divisions of science. On the other hand, Martin's *General Magazine of Arts and Sciences* (1755–1763), reprinted in several editions after 1759 as *The Young Gentleman and Lady's Philosophy*, devotes one of its three scientific sections to 'a survey of the principal subjects of the animal, vegetable, and mineral kingdoms'.

The magazines began early to cater to the new taste for natural history. In July 1752 the *Universal Magazine of Knowledge and Pleasure* proposed 'to give a compendious system of natural history illustrated with copper plates of the most curious animals, vegetables, and minerals, in their natural colours'. By 1760 at least four magazines had followed suit: the *Grand Magazine of Universal Intelligence*, the *Lady's Magazine*, the *Royal Female Magazine*, and the *Royal Magazine, or Gentleman's Monthly Companion*. And the *Imperial Magazine, or Complete Monthly Intelligencer* announced in its opening number in 1760 that it would give a copper plate of a Chinese pheasant and follow with other curiosities, since of all the employments of man, 'there is none which conveys so much real advantage, as well as solid pleasure to it, as the enquiring into the nature and properties of the things about us'.

The elegant world was furnished with a series of handsome illustrated folios of natural history by Sir John Hill, two of which came before 1760, *A General Natural History* (1748) with sections on fossils, plants, and animals, and *The British Herbal* (1756). In 1759 Benjamin Stillingfleet, who as the original 'bluestocking' did much to interest the learned ladies of London in science, published his *Miscellaneous Tracts relating to Natural History*, which included translations of Linnaeus and other scientists designed 'to make known more generally how far all mankind is concerned in the study of natural history, and thereby to incite such as are properly qualified ... and encourage that branch of knowledge'. A sample of the scientific dictionary available to poets after 1760 can be seen in the six volumes of *A New Accurate System of Natural History* written by Richard Brookes, M.D., to supply for the average person 'a complete cheap, and commodious body' of this most certain of all sciences. The inquirer is at first bewildered by 'the multitude of Nature's productions', he begins, but greater study 'points out a similitude in many objects which at first appeared different', and so the mind rises from minutiae to general considerations, until at last 'it finds Nature in almost every instance acting with her usual simplicity'. The compendium ends, as it began, with the philosophical conclusion that 'in proportion as we increase our knowledge of natural causes, the more elevated idea shall we have of him, who is the author of them all'. Yet in the six volumes of detailed science the poet and other amateurs had descriptions and names, not only of the birds and flowers used in their nature poems but also of all other branches of natural history.

In the last four decades of the century popularized natural history appeared in profusion, highlighted by the books of John Hill and William Curtis on botany, of Thomas Pennant and George Edwards on zoology, and of Sir Joseph Banks on the natural wonders of foreign lands.

V

It is now time to take stock of the leading ideas that appear in theological treatises, in popularizations of science, and in literature. The creative writing of the early eighteenth century in England is filled with the praise of God in the creation, illustrating from science the wonders of the universe that show the power, goodness, providence, omniscience, and other attributes of the Supreme Being. This theme and its variations were repeated in poems and essays, developing lyrically what the scientists themselves had said earlier in their efforts to refute the charges of atheism hurled at them. Paraphrases of the passages of Scripture dealing with the glories of nature became more numerous and more ecstatic as they used the discoveries of the new science to illustrate their various examples of God's wonders. Many 'poetical essays' developed the physico-theological themes, nearly all of them leaning heavily on how science had revealed with new vigor the wisdom of a Creator who could form so vast and yet so orderly a universe. Many long poems on moral subjects used science to illustrate order, providence, and divine wisdom. And even the less pretentious lyrics and shorter poems often included stock scientific illustrations as metaphors in developing other themes. The poets were elaborating what they found in the standard physico-theological handbooks, and so the progression is a natural one, from the ideas formulated by the theologians and scientists in the seventeenth century to the popular compendiums and finally into literature.

The theological writing of the early eighteenth century is so profuse and complex that I shall limit my sample to two writers that are known to reflect the kind of scientific thinking that interested the poets, William Derham and William Wollaston. They were themselves following such scientists as Boyle and Ray, who, as we have seen, took pride in their orthodoxy. Boyle was so anxious to assert the orthodoxy of science that he endowed lectures in defense of Christianity against atheists, 'theists', and other 'notorious infidels'. The first series of Boyle Lectures was given by Richard Bentley in 1692, beginning with two sermons refuting atheism and deism in general, followed by three showing how the structure and origin of human bodies refute atheism, and three entitled 'A Confutation of Atheism from the Origin and Frame of the World', a summary of scientific opinion on the creation of the universe, including Newton's laws of gravitation and motion.

The most popular of the Boyle Lectures was probably the series of sixteen sermons delivered in 1711–12 by William Derham and published separately and widely as *Physico-theology*. Although this work bore the subtitle 'A Demonstration of the Being and Attributes of God, from His Works of Creation', it dealt only with 'a survey of the terraqueous globe'. He promised another work on the heavens, which appeared as *Astro-theology* in 1715 but in 1726 he admitted in a preface to the fourth edition of *Physico-theology* that, while he had made progress on a further survey of the waters, he had not enough leisure to finish it. The two companion published volumes together served as a sort of science handbook for divines and poets alike, standing for many years as the epitome of what was now to be known as 'physico-theology'. The two books are filled with scientific data, references to voluminous scientific reading, and accounts of Derham's own experiments, but their real purpose appears in the conclusion that scientific inquiry into nature is commendable, since it shows that infidelity is unreasonable and since it excites obedience, gratitude, and adoration of God.

Derham summarized in *Astro-theology* the new discoveries of Newton under such headings as the magnitude of the universe, the number of the heavenly bodies, their situation, their motions, their figures (mostly limited to the solar system because of the power of telescopes), the usefulness of attraction or gravity in maintaining orderly motion, and the qualities of light and heat. Each section concluded with the firm assertion of the wisdom of God, but one example will be enough to show what appealed to the imagination of the poets:

> But in this our scheme we have a far more extensive, grand, and noble view of God's works: a far greater number of them; not those alone that former ages saw, but multitudes of others that the telescope hath discovered since; and all these far more orderly placed throughout the heavens, and at duer and more agreeable distances, and made to serve to much more noble and proper ends: for here we have not one systeme of sun and planets alone, and only one habitable globe, but myriads of systemes and more, of habitable worlds, and some even in our own solar systeme, as well as those of the fixt stars. And consequently if in the sun and its planets, altho' viewed only here upon the earth at a great distance, we find enough to entertain our eye, to captivate our understanding, to excite our admiration and praises of the infinite CREATOR and Contriver of them; what an augmentation of these glories shall we find in great multitudes of them! in all those systems of fixt stars throughout the universe, that I have spoken of.[23]

When Newton became a sort of symbol of the proof of God's power and omniscience, his new laws of motion and gravity, demonstrating the regular movements of the planets, stars, and even comets, became the stock examples of the glory of God in numerous poems. This new spirit of mingled science and religious fervor, later known as Newtonianism, can perhaps be seen more clearly summarized in William Wollaston's *The Religion of Nature Delineated* (1722).

The existence of a Deity approaches demonstration, Wollaston said, from the fact that the motions of the heavenly bodies must be accounted for 'either by one mighty Mover, acting upon them immediately, or by causes and laws of His appointment'. Attraction and gravitation are but effects, and we must look for their cause: 'What a vast field of contemplation is here opened! Such regions of matter about us, in which there is not the *least partical* that does not carry with it an argument of God's existence'. The infinite wisdom and power of the Almighty designer are revealed by the grandness of this world, of the sun with its vast magnitude, heat and distance, of the chorus of planets moving about it (some with secondary planets, 'and probably all possesst by proper inhabitants'), of the comets, and of the fixed stars, not made for their feeble light but 'to convince him, that they are rather so many *other suns*, with their several regions and sets of planets about them . . . to shew that if the world be not infinite, it is *infinito similis*; and therefore such a magnificent structure, and the work of an infinite Architect'.

With the help of telescopes and microscopes, Wollaston continued, we extend our knowledge of the great variety of nature and are given 'fresh reasons to believe that there are indefinitely still *more and more* behind, that will for ever escape our eagerest pursuits and deepest penetration'. Wollaston cited scientific evidence of design and thought to indicate the Almighty Mind behind the universe prescribing uniform and steady laws so as to form 'a just and geometrical arrangement of things' that could not be the work of chance. This God who has given existence to the world also governs it by His providence. We glibly talk about Nature and take an unaccountable liberty in the use of the word, he concluded, but in no sense can Nature 'supersede the being of a Deity'.

The ideas of Wollaston, centering on the basic conception of a powerful and beneficent God whose wisdom is shown in nature, occur over and over in the writers of the eighteenth century. Even before Wollaston they can be found, expressed most clearly perhaps in the prose essays so popular in that period. It is scarcely a coincidence that in the two years between 1710 and 1712 the same theological interpretation of the new science appeared in many writers of prose essays, some well known and others obscure, but all concentrating on this new message, in the essays of Lady Chudleigh, Shaftesbury, and Needler, and in the periodical essays of Addison and Blackmore, culminating in the ambitious poem, Blackmore's *Creation*. This is the same period as Derham, who stems from Newton, Boyle, and Ray. Shaftesbury is too well known for quotation, but let us see how Lady Mary Chudleigh in 1710 can express herself with the same enthusiasm and with more use of science.

'Of Knowledge' advises courses of study that will impart insight 'into the useful parts of learning', leading us from effects that show power, wisdom, beauty, harmony, and order, to the cause, 'the Divine Original, to the unexhausted Source, the Foundation of all Perfection'. The new science will show the variety of nature, Lady Chudleigh continues, and 'instruct us heedfully to consider all her wonderful productions, and trace infinite wisdom and power thro' the immense space, from the heights above, to the depths below; from the glorious orbs which roll over our heads, to the minutest insect that crawls under our feet'. She amplifies the idea in her essay 'Of Love' by showing how science can reveal the degrees of divine perfection from astronomy to microscopy:

> Wherever we cast our eyes, we may see them displaying their charms; by day shining in the glorious fountain of light, by night glittering in ten thousand stars, sparkling in gems, pleasing the sight in gold, delighting the eye in lofty trees, in the admirable colours of fruits and flowers, in the florid green of plants and grass, and in the amazing mechanism of insects and reptiles, those surprizing and inimitable finenesses which by the help of glasses are discoverable in their minute bodies, usefully entertaining it with the exact proportion of parts, and the wonderful variety of shapes in birds, beasts, and fishes.

Lady Chudleigh shows how this can be put to religious use by the praise of contemplation in her essay 'Of Solitude', running through creation from man to 'the sensitive and vegetative kingdoms' to inanimate things and finally to the glory of the celestial universe.[24]

The periodical essays helped to popularize the ideas derived from science, and in this field, as in many others, no paper was more successful than the *Spectator*. In an early paper (121) Addison called attention to the remarkable manifestation of divine providence shown in the instinct of common animals like the hen or mole and wished that the Royal Society would compile a body of natural history, which would show the wisdom of God even though it could not possibly be complete: 'Besides that there are infinitely more species of creatures which are not to be seen without, nor indeed with the help of the finest glasses, than of such as are bulky enough for the naked eye to take hold of. However, from the consideration of such animals as lie within the compass of our knowledge, we might easily form a conclusion of the rest, that the same variety and goodness runs through the whole creation.' A

[24] Mary Chudleigh, *Essays upon Several Subjects in Prose and Verse* (London, 1710), pp. 9 ff., 180 ff., 235 ff.

paper on cheerfulness (387) shows the delights that arise from contemplation of nature, whether in the beauty of bird-song and flowing water or the harshness of wild rocks and deserts: 'In short, the whole universe is a kind of theatre filled with objects that either raise in us pleasure, amesement, or admiration.'

Nowhere did Addison glorify 'the authors of the new philosophy' better than in one of the final papers on imagination (420). Here he finds the study of 'metals, minerals, plants and meteors' appealing to the fancy, but the contrasting worlds revealed by the microscope and telescope lend a sublime touch to the imagination as it rises from the green leaf that swarms 'with millions of animals, that at their largest growth are not visible to the naked eye' to the vast space between Saturn and the fixed stars where the prospect is so immense that it puts the imagination 'upon the stretch to comprehend it'. Addison concludes that the imagination is defective in not being able to comprehend such extremes, but before he does so he takes us on a sublime excursion, first into the unfathomable space beyond the reach of telescopes where, lost in a labyrinth of suns and worlds, we are 'confounded with the immensity and magnificence of Nature', and then into the perfection of the little world surrounding 'an animal, a hundred times less than a mite', where we may discover 'a new inexhausted fund of matter, capable of being spun out into another universe'. In nature we see, nevertheless, the best arguments for the existence of God, and so it becomes a matter of faith and devotion which can only be expressed properly in poetry, as in the verses he added to *Spectator* 420 in praise of God as revealed in nature, beginning 'The spacious firmament on high'.

Addison often used science to illustrate his papers but we have space only for two more that are almost completely given to scientific topics. The first is a rhapsody on the Great Chain of Being (519) that extends from the infinity of little animals on a green leaf, to the 'numberless kinds of living creatures' on the earth, to the inhabitants of the stars. It becomes almost a hymn to plenitude when he pictures 'the exuberant and overflowing goodness' of God in the diversity shown by the almost imperceptible gradations in nature: 'The whole chasm in nature, from a plant to a man, is filled up with diverse kinds of creatures, rising one over another, by such gentle and easy ascent, that the little transitions and deviations from one species to another, are almost insensible.' The last paper on science (543), inspired by the reading of Blackmore's *Creation*, shows how the human body, and the physiology of animals as well, can reveal divine wisdom and providence as well as the more demanding discovery in a 'whole planetary system' made by a Newton 'who stands up as the miracle of the present age'.

Richard Blackmore's *Lay-Monastery* in 1713 devoted many of its periodical essays to science, and some of his papers give scientific examples of how God is to be seen in nature. One essay (5) shows the great fertility of nature under the microscope; since 'every plant and animal breeds numberless insects, every drop of water and piece of earth is a nest of minute living creatures, and a little pepper-corn is crowded like a populous city, with inhabitants, we cannot but conclude that the regions above are equally peopled'. The Divine Author is to be seen in this endless variety combined with 'a regular and beautiful subordination' of the chain of being, illustrated not only by differences in creatures but in such similarities as that of the cat to the tiger and lion, of the ape and ourang-outang to man. Another paper (19) illustrates God's perfection by the economy of nature with such examples as the life-giving warmth of the sun or the power in a small seed to sprout, grow, and produce new seeds to multiply itself.[25]

The essays and letters of the ill-fated Henry Needler (1690–1718) are full of the way that the scientific study of nature reveals God. He wrote a rhapsody on nature in 1709, two years before Shaftesbury's *Characteristics*, and another after reading Shaftesbury. His 'familiar letters' also contained discussions of Newton and Locke and a letter on spermatic worms that praised the advances in science made possible by the microscope and telescope. The best of his essays, 'On the Beauty of the Universe,' gives his aesthetic justification for poems based on science, not only in depicting the celestial universe but also plants, animals, and even insects as evidence of the wisdom and goodness of God.

The prose rhapsodies of Mary Chudleigh, Henry Needler, and Richard Blackmore, as well as the more famous essays of Addison and Shaftesbury all belong to the same intellectual milieu in which Derham's *Physico-theology* belongs. The fact that Lady Chudleigh

---

[25] *The Lay-Monastery, Consisting of Essays, Discourse, etc. published singly under the Title of the Lay-Monk* (London, 1714). The essays cited appeared on 25 Nov. and 28 Dec. 1713. Nos. 31, 32, and 40 discuss color as suggested by Newton's *Optics*.

and perhaps Needler anticipate the others matters little, for the ideas were already abroad in the writings of Boyle and Ray and the various interpreters of Newton. Pomfret's judgment day poems, Prior's *Solomon*, and John Reynold's scientific poem on death showed that poetry was already feeling its way toward extensive poetical essays on the subject. In this larger picture Shaftesbury appears as one of a number of writers around 1710–12 who, for lack of a better term, might be called Newtonian.

Certainly there is no dichotomy between the influence of Newton and Shaftesbury. The influence of Shaftesbury seems to me to be in the application of Newtonian order and especially benevolence, to the moral world of man. Many moral poems that stem from this aspect of Shaftesbury portray the idea of moral harmony with much more scientific imagery than does Shaftesbury. Even Thomson's *Seasons*, whose very eclectic nature and overcharged sentiment seem often to stem from Shaftesbury, added much of this element, as well as his special praise of 'generous Ashley', in later revisions of the poem even after the Newtonian science had been well established. For this reason I take it for granted that many poets, especially the writers of moral poems with scientific interest, are consciously following Shaftesbury, often it is true at second hand through Thomson, but that their scientific imagery comes from various scientific sources, the astronomy from Newton, the world of microscopic life, human anatomy, mineralogy, and natural history from many books and experiments, as well as from that careful observation which is the result of the scientific method.

The ideas represented by scientists, theologians, and essayists were repeated in poetry during the eighteenth century with profuse variation. Yet the main theme is that all the works of the Lord praise him and magnify him forever, to use the words of the Book of Common Prayer in the *Benedicite* chanted in the Morning Prayer by the Church of England. First the heavens declared the glory of God as the telescope revealed more and more of what seemed to be an infinite celestial universe. With the improvements in the microscope, however, another world of amazing plenitude showed a similar orderliness at the other end of the Great Chain of Being. Elaborating on the ideas found in the books of physico-theology, the poets saw the element of the sublime in these contrasting worlds and played up the great range of God's power stretching from the most distant star to the minutest insect. Yet their examples from the world of nature are intended to be representative of all things animate or inanimate, on the land, in the waters, in the skies, celestial, earthly, human, brute, plant, bird, insect, or microscopic creature, it mattered not what. The choice of example, in the earlier comprehensive physico-theological poetical essays at least, depended upon the poet's knowledge of science and his enthusiasm for the subject. For this reason it becomes difficult to illustrate any one branch of science in poetry, for most of them, at any rate the longer poems like Blackmore's *Creation* and Thomson's *Seasons*, include a variety of examples, from planet to primrose, from elephant and whale to silkworm and bacteria, from man to nightingale. For this reason, it seems most logical to summarize here the ideas found in the poems influenced by science and then to show, in rough chronological fashion, how the poems themselves first use science to put new imagery into old themes, and then learn to versify the new science in a new and often sublime way.

Some of the prevailing ideas in the physico-theological poetry in eighteenth-century England may be briefly summarized as a sort of rough guide to the analysis of individual poems. The list is suggestive and not intended to include many variations.

1. *Order.* The universe is orderly and harmonious, set in motion by a divine Creator. The orthodox scientists and most of the English poets believed that God personally watches over the universe and will dissolve it by fiat at the last judgment. The followers of the mechanical philosophy, especially in France, believed that God set the great clock of nature in motion and does not need to watch it. This order is dramatized in the scientific poetry of two contrasting worlds:

   a. The telescope has opened up a vast celestial universe that Newton has shown mathematically to be orderly. The orbits of moon, planets, and even comets can be calculated. The fixed stars are suns for new systems like the solar system, and this earth is a mere speck among many such worlds. The moon, planets, and probably other worlds beyond are believed to be inhabited by reasonable creatures, for it is presumptuous of man to assume that God would create such an elaborate universe just for him.

   b. The microscope also shows an orderly system but in miniature and reveals God's watchful care in the small as much as in the vast.

2. *Plenitude.* By analogy there must be still more left undiscovered

28

in a universe that seems infinite in both directions. Since God is in personal control, the universe to the orthodox cannot really be infinite, but a plenitude of forms is evident in an incredible variety in nature. Two common metaphors are related:

a. The Great Chain of Being, very influential in the thought of the period,[26] the graded scale of nature ranging from microscopic life to plants and animals to man to God, was interpreted variously by the poets as a symbol of order and design, of complacent conservatism, and of restraint of the pride of man. The poetic interest in misfits or missing links is listed below under scientific puzzles.

b. The book of Nature, a commonplace for plenitude, lies open to all, and in its pages the wisdom and beneficence of God may be read.

3. *Providence.* Discrepancies in nature can be explained only by assuming that God is good and provides what is best in the long run. Evil was necessary to fill out the divine scheme of plenitude,[27] for the very abundance demanded by the Great Chain of Being had to include imperfections as well as good things. This acceptance of partial evils reconciled with universal good led to the early doctrine of optimism that was rejected by Voltaire and other French writers, especially when applied to the Lisbon earthquake of 1755. The most common examples in English poetry of evil or harshness in nature reconciled by Providence are the following:

a. Violence as shown by earthquakes and hurricanes

b. Inequalities of climate as shown by the frozen north and torrid jungles

c. Mountains, even before they became a source of aesthetic pleasure, were believed to be the source of much good to man in spite of their harshness.[28] The most common illustration of the usefulness of mountains was as the source of underground streams.

4. *Puzzles of nature*

a. Instinct in animals paralleling reason in man.

b. Curiosities in the gradations of the Great Chain of Being, such as the resemblances of apes to man or those apparent mixtures of animal and plant, the polyp, the Tartarian lamb, and the sensitive plant.

5. The limitations of science in not being able to answer the fundamental questions as to the cause behind the effects it observes.

[26] A. O. Lovejoy, *The Great Chain of Being* (Cambridge, Mass., 1936).

[27] Lovejoy, 'Optimism and Romanticism', *PMLA*, XLII (1927), 921-45, reprinted in revised form in *The Great Chain of Being*.

[28] Marjorie Nicolson, *Mountain Gloom and Mountain Glory* (Ithaca, N.Y., 1959).

The picture of Newton and other scientists finding the answers only after death is common in English poetry.[29]

6. Patriotic praise of Britain, a dominant poetic theme in English poetry after the Peace of Utrecht in 1713, appears in many scientific poems. Nature has played a part in England's world position because a temperate climate is virtually free of violent storms and earthquakes and because British commerce is based on the use of winds and scientific aids to navigation.

This chapter has attempted to give a cursory background of the new science that began in the seventeenth century and of the ideas derived from that science, but only as much as seems necessary to understand the English poetry of the eighteenth century influenced by science. It does not pretend to explain the scientific discoveries or even the metaphysics of the basic philosophy of the period, yet it does try to take into account these momentous events as they enlarged the imagination of the poets or influenced the religious and scientific thinking of the age. It does not try to show the close interchange of ideas between England and France. Here much could be shown, it is true, in the way of similarities at the outset: the almost simultaneous founding of the Royal Society and the Academie des Sciences, the influence of Descartes on Hobbes and Newton and the converse influence of Newton on later French thought, the vogue in England of the early popularizations by Fontenelle and Pluche, the widespread vogue of popular science and natural history in France paralleling what we have seen in England.[30] Yet the dramatic manner in which the French thinkers, particularly Voltaire and La Mettrie, accepted the mechanistic assumptions of Newton's discoveries and consequently repudiated the benevolent God and personal providence that was so dear to the English scientists and poets[31]—this makes the chief difference between the thought and literature of the two nations after the middle of the century.

The full story of several other phases of popular science in this period must wait for other studies. In addition to the handbooks,

[29] See my fuller study, 'The Idea of the Limitations of Science from Prior to Blake', Rice University *Studies in English Literature*, I (1961), 97–114.

[30] This has been well documented in Daniel Mornet, *Les Sciences de la Nature en France au XVIIIe Siècle* (Paris, 1911).

[31] Richard S. Westfall, *Science and Religion in Seventeenth-Century England* (New Haven, 1958), pp. 20 ff., concludes that the English scientists saw no conflict between orthodox Christianity and their mechanical conception of nature; they merely reinterpreted the concept of providence.

for example, there was a wide use of encyclopedias, periodicals, lectures, and demonstration classes, many of them especially designed for ladies and young people. From about 1760 there was profuse publication of colored plates to illustrate birds, flowers, quadrupeds, insects, shells, and other aspects of natural history, an important combination of art and science. Large collections of natural objects, alive and dead, were amassed by those with means, and the private collections of the *virtuosi*, ridiculed by neo-classical writers, were often very extensive and some became the basis for public museums.

The interest in the natural history of foreign lands that began in the seventeenth century with the scientific sections of travel books led to the extremely profuse importation of exotic plants, as well as some animals when possible, from all parts of the world. At first arranged privately through agents or commercial ships and later through elaborate and expensive expeditions organized for scientific study, the English imported exotic plants and cultivated them in their greenhouses and gardens, the Society of Apothecaries at their 'physic garden' in Chelsea, the royal household in their great botanic gardens at Kew. Along with the popularization of natural history in England there arose a serious study of science by amateurs with literary bent, and from the accurate observation of nature by writers like Thomas Gray and George Crabbe there came an understanding of nature that was to have a great influence on English literature, even though these two scientist-poets did not introduce much science into their poetry. The influence is best seen in *The Natural History of Selborne*, written by an obscure parson in a Hampshire village to his prominent scientist friends in London, but observed so accurately and written so well that it was to become a sort of Bible for later students of natural history as well as a companion for poets who wrote about nature.

The full story would indeed require more than one book. The present study will put its emphasis on the scientific poetry of the eighteenth century in England, beginning with the sublime excursions into outer space and ending with the primrose by the river's brim, beginning with encyclopedic physico-theology of poetical essays and ending with short lyrics on flowers, birds, and other aspects of the quiet English landscape. All have essentially the same message, that the attributes of the Supreme Being— goodness, power, omniscience, eternity, immensity, and others,

all of them asserting wisdom and providence—may be seen in the
works of the creation, in the physical world which is, in this study
at least, the same as NATURE. And so I shall attempt to show the
poetry that does just this, wherever possible by actual quotation of
the poems themselves but usually by description and summary.

II

THE CONTINUITY OF
OLD IDEAS AFTER 1700

MANY English poets were interested in science before 1700, and some account must be taken of them in order to understand what was new when natural philosophy began to captivate the popular imagination from 1709 to 1712 in the essays of Addison, Shaftesbury, Needler, Blackmore, and Lady Chudleigh and to furnish the subject for long poems by Reynolds and Blackmore. As in later times some of the poets were amateur scientists but did not see the value of using science as a subject for literature. Sir Thomas Browne belongs here, and perhaps Dryden. At the same time other poets, like Henry More, Abraham Cowley, and John Norris of Bemerton, used the science of their day to make their poetry more vivid. Milton, Drummond, and Rochester have also been cited in this class,[1] and something might be said for including George Herbert, since John Reynolds quoted him often in the notes to his scientific poem, *Death's Vision* (1709).

The chief evidence of continuity from the seventeenth to the eighteenth centuries, however, is in the ideas that go far back but received a new emphasis from contemporary scientists and philosophers, particularly the religious ideas that are associated with an orderly universe and with the allied theme of the wisdom of

[1] R. B. Crum, *Scientific Thought in Poetry* (New York, 1931), especially chap. III.

God manifested in nature. A distinguished scientist like John Ray could lend a new fervor with his book on the subject, and Robert Boyle with his own writings and the influence of the lectures that he endowed. The long scientific poems glorifying God came after 1709 and were multiplied after Newton's death in 1727, but the new spirit was to be seen soon after 1700 in the scientific illustrations used in numerous Biblical paraphrases. This sort of thing was natural to the English people who attended the services of the Church of England, where regularly at morning prayer psalms and chants developed the theme of praise for the wonderful works of God in nature.

The counterpart to this positive attitude to science may be seen in two negative factors that also continue from the seventeenth century. One of these is an offshoot of the Pyrrhonism of the age of Dryden, the skeptical attitude toward knowledge that translated itself into much questioning of the ability of science to explain such mysterious natural phenomena as instinct in animals, the origin of the universe, or the color of flowers. The other negative element to continue is the literary expression of a more pronounced hostility to science because of its lack of decorum. This fruitful source of satire on science was prolific from the early days of the Royal Society and became concentrated largely on the members of that august body. The early eagerness of Bacon's followers to acquire new material from all possible sources led to indiscriminate collecting of odd and miscellaneous objects that aroused the antagonism of those who considered themselves 'classical gentlemen'. The story of this body of literary satire from Butler to Swift has been often told, and indeed its best examples are in the prose of plays and fiction, yet a completer account of it in this chapter will show its relation to the larger story of science as it affects literature. Of the three aspects of continuity in the rhetoric of science, let us begin with the poetry in praise of science, first as seen in three seventeenth-century poets and then as reflected in Biblical paraphrases.

I. SCIENCE IN POETRY BEFORE 1700

The influence of science on Donne and Milton is well known and in many ways makes a pertinent part of our subject. The scientific interests of Henry More have been somewhat neglected, however, and the most revealing of his poetry concerned with science is hard for the modern scholar to get at. For this reason a short sample of More's keen interest in science as early as 1642 will make a good introduction to later scientific poetry. This may be seen in the illustrations and imagery borrowed from science to explain his metaphysical reasoning in *Psychodia Platonica: or a Platonicall Song of the Soul*.[2] The enthusiastic cataloguing of natural history in the first of the four long poems, 'Psychozoia, or the Life of the Soul', heightens the Spenserian allegory in his description of the figure *Physis* (nature):

> Nothing in Nature did you ever spy,
> But there's portraid: all beasts both wild and tame,
> Each bird is here, and every buzzing fly;
> All forest-work is in this tapestry:
> The oke, the holm, the ash, the alpin tree,
> The handsome buzzard, th' eagle, and the py,
> The buck, the bear, the boar, the hare, the bee,
> The brize, the black-arm'd clock, the gnat, the butterflies.

The enthusiasm for science does not keep him from criticizing, in the second poem, 'Psychathanasia', Lucretius and especially atheists who think they are hid 'in the covert of dame Nature's cell' and after learning Nature's secrets 'laugh at religion as a mockery'. The third canto of this poem is entirely devoted to Cartesian astronomy bolstered by learned notes with diagrams: the imagination staggers in boundless space, yet the poet must never forget that the important revelation of science is in man's metaphysical notions of the Divine Mind behind it all. The metaphors of the poet foretell the enthusiastic sublimity of later poets who use Newton instead of Descartes, the 'inconceivable swift motions / In the equinoctiall stars' which are 20,000 times the size of the earth, the imaginary 'shiver cut off from the moon' that would not fall into our mouths but would soon 'make back to the centre from whence forc'd it was', or that series of questions that might have come out of the mouth of Job:

> That famous star nail'd down in Cassiope,
> How was it hammer'd in your solid sky?
> What pinsers pull'd it out again, that we
> No longer see it, whither did it fly?

[2] Reprinted as *Philosophical Poems* (Cambridge, 1647). The only complete modern edition is the very scarce 1878 reprint by Alexander Grosart in the Chertsey Worthies Library. A scholarly edition of the first of four long poems is that of Geoffrey Bullough, Manchester, 1931.

Again in his poem on the infinity of worlds, 'Democritus Platonissans', appended to 'Psychanathasia', More tackles that astronomical problem with far more imagination and philosophy than did Fontenelle's later dialogues. The very profuseness of the idea of plenitude challenges his imagination but leaves him in the end 'breathlesse, even quite confound', overwhelmed and drowned 'in this huge endless heape' of 'grass, flowers, herbs, trees . . . flies, birds, men, and beasts . . . sand, pearls, pebbles . . . leaves, quills, hairs, thorns, blooms'. The idea of infinity bothered the philosophers, yet the poet in More feels that we can approach the subject through the natural world that science observes, 'the broad breasted earth, the spacious skie / Spangled with silver light', and the bellowing seas. There are many other evidences in More's poetry of this use of science, but these examples are enough to show that in the seventeenth century poets were using science to defend religion, and doing it with a sublimity that made it easy for the followers of Newtonianism to continue the old themes with new zest and new examples from the newer science.

Abraham Cowley had an intense interest in science that occasionally came out in his poetry. 'To the Royal Society' (1667) commemorates this interest with Pindaric enthusiasm, not so much by the use of scientific imagery as by the great philosophic theme of faith that knowledge gained by experimental science will set men free. The example of Bacon had given courage to members of the Royal Society to search for truth, a search that could not fail to show the glory of God in the universe. The fervor of the new science shows in the poem in phrases that describe 'the riches which doe hoorded for him lie / In Nature's endless treasurie', whether in the 'crowds of golden worlds on high' revealed by the telescope or 'the privatest recess / Of her imperceptible littleness' shown by the microscope. This knowledge and fervor can be traced in many scientific images in other poems by Cowley, but never so clearly as in his botanical writings.

The clearest expression of his views on science is perhaps in his prose description of an ideal scientific institute of advanced studies, *A Proposition for the Advancement of Experimental Philosophy* (1661). The proposed 'philosophical college' was to promote inquiry into the nature of God's creatures, since only mathematics and medicine were provided for in the universities. It would have twenty professors, four of them to travel and report, and sixteen scholars. There was to be considerable equipment, including chemical laboratories, stuffed animals and anatomical pictures, an apothecary, a garden for native plants and an experimental garden for the trial of whatever 'can be produced by art either for use or curiosity', a place for animals useful in zoological research, an astronomical observatory, and deep underground vaults for many experiments proper to such places. The professors were to lecture and investigate (new inquiries and tests of popular and received errors), to assemble data and print their achievements. Any profits would go, one-third to the inventor and two-thirds to the society. Each professor would have one scholar as helper and apprentice, and these scholars presumably also would be teachers of 200 boys who would study the usual Latin in writers on nature, accompanied by demonstrations in anatomy, zoology and botany.

Cowley's own proficiency in science was in botany, perhaps best expressed in English in 1666 in his Pindaric ode, 'The Garden to J. Evelyn, Esq.' This poem celebrates the combined joys of gardens and books that he and Evelyn both enjoyed, but the real culmination is in the way that botany reflects divine wisdom, since its flowers for beauty, its herbs for drugs, and its vegetables for food together produce the finest colours 'of the Creator's real poetry'. It is in the charming preface, however, that the real Cowley shows himself in thanking Evelyn for the use of his garden to satisfy partially his strongest desire to be 'master at last of a small house and large garden . . . and there dedicate the remainder of my life to the culture of them, and study of nature.'

This confession is a fitting prelude to Cowley's ambitious Latin scientific poem, a history of plants in six books. Sprat tells us in his *Life and Writings of Cowley* that the poet on his return to England took up the study of medicine to hide his real purpose, and so he soon retired into Kent to study plants and write his Latin poem. Cowley explained his purpose fully in his preface to the first two books, to ease his mind in time of trouble and also to celebrate 'the wonderful works of providence, for nothing is more admirable in nature than plants'. Realizing that the subject would be tedious and meager if treated nakedly, Sprat said, Cowley enlivened his materials by introducing circumstances 'of the places where his plants and herbs delight to spring; the seasons of

their flowering, seeding, and withering; their long or short duration; their noxious or healthful qualities; their figures and colouring;
all which he has managed with such dexterity of fancy, and unexhausted conceit, that each individual (as he has dressed and set
them out) appears with a different aspect and peculiar beauty'.[3]
The poem itself, in spite of its added coloring, is still essentially a
Latin didactic poem, but its lengthy lists of medicinal herbs in the
first two books, of flowers in Books III and IV, and of trees,
American, European, and British, in the last two books, are ample
proof that Cowley loved botany and, regardless of his own
modesty ('I, therefore, who am but a pigmy in learning, and scarce
sufficient to express the virtues of the vile sea-weed'), was an extremely proficient amateur.

John Dryden was also a member of the Royal Society and might
have given a great impetus to the use of science as a subject for
poetry. Only once did he express himself boldly in praise of
science, and that very briefly in his lines 'To my Honor'd Friend,
Dr. Charleton' (1663), where he includes the physician with such
scientists as Bacon, Gilbert, Boyle, and Harvey 'among th' asser-
ters of free reason's claim'. It is well known that Dryden respected
science and was a pioneer in the new prose style whose simplicity
reflected the desire of the Royal Society for clarity and preciseness.
Yet the scientific imagery that Dryden used in his writings was
borrowed, not from the new science but from the older pseudo-
sciences of alchemy and astrology.[4]

Among the late seventeenth-century poets besides Cowley and
Dryden who might have reflected the new discoveries of science
in his poetry was John Norris of Bemerton, the disciple of Henry
More. His skillful handling of varied verse forms, especially the
irregular 'pindarick ode', and his enthusiastic interpretation of
Platonic themes made him acceptable to the same readers that
were interested in the physico-theological poems of Reynolds and
Blackmore and in the Biblical paraphrases praising God in natnre.
Norris's *Collection of Miscellanies*, containing most of his poetry

[3] *Cowley's History of Plants, a Poem in Six Books*, translated from Latin by Nahum
Tate and others, London, 1795. The translation was printed in 1700 as the *Third
Part of the Works*.
[4] For an excellent summary of Cowley's use of science, see Robert B. Hinman,
Abraham Cowley's World of Order (Cambridge, Mass., 1960). On Dryden's use of
science, see Richard R. Griffith, *Science and Pseudo-Science in the Imagery of John Dryden*
(unpublished Ohio State University dissertation, 1956).

and some of his prose, was reprinted after 1687 a number of times and appeared in a ninth 'carefully revised' edition in 1730. There are a number of poems that would later have used scientific imagery, notably paraphrases of Job and Psalm 148, but there is no indication of an interest in nature that goes beyond everyday observation until we come to 'A Divine Hymn on the Creation', where the new astronomy appears with the 'lucid whirlpools' of the Cartesian theory. The harmony imposed by God on the 'seeds of being' in the 'empty waste', the 'plastic spirit' that fermented the formless mass, and 'nature's boon, where no errata's found', all testify in this poem to the scientific rhetoric of Norris.

The unspinning of nature at the last judgment, a theme that was to become very popular, gives Norris an even better opportunity to introduce scientific images, and so we are not surprised to find 'The Consummation' reprinted several times in *A Collection of Divine Hymns and Poems upon Several Occasions.*[5] Here is a foretaste of the scientific picture of the creation in reverse that Aaron Hill was to use deliberately in 1721: At 'nature's great passing-bell' the universe takes alarm, the sea tries to run underground, the earth shakes to the center, the sun is arrested, and general confusion reigns:

> The stars forget their laws, and like loose planets stray.
>   See how the elements resign
> Their numerous charge, their scatter'd atoms home repair,
> Some from the earth, some from the sea, some from the air.

Nature, the vivid description continues, lies 'sick of a strong fever', as the subterranean fire causes the mountains to sweat, the sea to roar, and waves of fire to roll until 'the earth's girt round with flames and seems another sun'.

The only direct comment on science comes, however, in an occasional poem, 'To Dr. Plot, on his Natural History of Staffordshire', where he commends Plot's contribution to a notable series of encyclopedic compendiums of local English science and antiquities. They are dull souls who do not learn to praise the Maker by studying the 'fair-writ volume' in which Nature takes such care 'to write in such a splendid character'. The stanza in

---

[5] The 3rd ed. (London, 1719) indicates its scientific interest by appending in full John Reynolds' 'Death's Vision: a Philosophical Sacred Poem'.

praise of scientists is worthy to be placed with Cowley's 'Ode to the Royal Society' among early tributes to science:

> They only can this tribute duly yield
> Whose active spirits range abroad,
> Who traverse o'er all Nature's field,
> And view the great magnificence of God:
> They see the hidden wealth of Nature's store
> Fall down, and learnedly adore;
> But they most justly yet their tribute pay
> Who don't contemplate only, but display;
> Comment on Nature's text, and to the sense
> Expose her latent excellence,
> Who like the sun, not only travel o'er
> The world, but give it light that others may adore.

2. SCIENCE IN BIBLICAL PARAPHRASES

It was quite natural that science should appear in religious poems, for the philosophers and the scientists themselves were saying before 1700 that the wisdom of God is shown in nature. It is not surprising then that the Biblical paraphrases should be the first poems in the eighteenth century to show extensive use of imagery and illustrations from the new science. Paraphrases of selections from the Bible and the Apocrypha were common in England in the seventeenth century. Some of these selections were particularly good for the scientists to use in defending science against atheism. The Psalms are full of the praise of God in nature: 'The heavens declare the glory of God, and the firmament showeth his handi-work.' The English people not only read the Bible, but those who attended the services of the Church of England heard regu-larly chants of praise to God for the creation. In the Book of Common Prayer the most widely attended service is Morning Prayer, in which passages from the Old and New Testaments are read, a psalm is sung, and three chants precede the prayers, the middle one always a chant of praise, either the *Te Deum Laudamus* or the *Benedicite omnia opera Domini*. Some of the psalms jubilantly glorified God in nature, notably Psalms 104 and 139, but the *Benedicite* of the second chant in Morning Prayer was the Anglican high point of Biblical natural history.

The importance of the *Benedicite* to the church may be seen in the excerpts in Latin used in the decoration of the ceiling of the choir of St. Paul's Cathedral. Its importance to the scientists, along with Psalm 104 and other nature psalms, is apparent in the fact that Sprat and Cowley specifically refer to these Biblical evidences of the wisdom of God in nature. The *Benedicite*, often called 'The Song of the Three Children' because it is taken from the account of the Hebrew children in the fiery furnace as told in the apocryphal book of Daniel, is an ecstatic hymn of praise for all created things, a chant that reaches the sublime in the simple translation of the Prayer Book done in the reign of Edward VI. 'O all ye works of the Lord, bless ye the Lord: praise Him and magnify Him forever,' the chant begins and from there builds up to a glorious climax through a succession of natural phenomena that invited scientific comment in the paraphrases after 1700. The Hebrew poet calls on all creation to magnify the Lord forever in triumphant tones, sun and moon, stars, showers and dew, ice and snow, lightnings and clouds, mountains and hills, green things upon the earth (Cowley quotes this in the preface to his *History of Plants*), whales and all that move in the waters, and so on to man as seen in the example of the three Hebrew children enduring the ordeal by fire for their God. The parade of nature is made to order for the new feeling that science is a help to religion in refuting atheism, and so it is a fitting beginning for our description of scientific poems after 1700.

Lady Mary Chudleigh was perhaps the first poet to add an interest in science to Biblical paraphrases. In 1703 her version of the *Benedicite* begins in the heavens in lyric praise of God's works and then descends to the earth.[6] In her description of the celestial universe she has used, she says in her preface, Descartes's theory of vortices surrounding the suns or fixed stars. In the poem she reaches the sublime in her description of the plains of pure light invisible to the naked eye,

> Whose bounds exceed the utmost stretch of thought,
> Whose vast unnumber'd worlds in fluid aether roll,
> And round their radiant centers move.

Everything extols the wisdom of God, who made 'and still pre-

[6] 'The Song of the Three Children Paraphras'd', xiv + 73 pages numbered separately, added to her *Poems on Several Occasions* (London, 1703); 3rd edition corrected, 1722, pp. 143-233.

serves the mighty whole', the sun that gives life to the earth, the moon with borrowed light, and the stars like suns 'whose light and heat attending planets share'. On earth the harshness of nature appears in earthquake, hurricane, and scorching heat, but with these inequalities God had also given good things. In her description of plants and animals, lyric praise replaces scientific imagery, but when nature dissolves in the last judgment she brings science to her aid in depicting the confusion heightened by ten thousand meteors, hot exhalations, fish swimming to land, birds with singed wings, and beasts struggling in death. The song then returns to the good earth, where mountains (source of rivers and minerals), green things, whales and fish, birds, and beasts all show God's goodness to man. At the end the theological theme overwhelms the scientific, but Lady Chudleigh, both here and in the essays already described, was one of the first to show that science is a fitting subject for poetry that is often sublime.

An extensive paraphrase of the *Benedicite*, published in 1724 as *A Paraphrase on the Song of the Three Children, in Irregular Stanzas*, is a good example of the use of the material and imagery of the new science to enlarge the simple praise of God in nature. 'O ye heavens' becomes twenty verses describing unnumbered orbs and 'agile worlds of light' that rove 'through a variety of figures . . . yet keep unwearied their unerring way'. Each phrase of the chant becomes a marginal rubric for the 44 stanzas that extend to 25 pages. The science is incidental to the praise of God: 'the fine mechanick motions' of the stars; heat, 'chief spring of Nature's wonderful machine . . . without whose vigorous energy' the earth would be a lifeless mass; frost that enriches the soil and pre-pares for next year's crop; huge mountains, 'beauteous, tho' vast, noble deformities', that yet are useful for providing minerals and unexhausted rivers; the variety of form and usefulness of 'all the green things'; the whales, 'lawless tyrants' that feed upon the smaller fish, 'who by uncounted millions multiply'; fowls of the air known not only for their beauty of plumage and song but also for their instinct in building nests and migrating; and the beasts who are taught by 'secret, native instinct' to carry out the purposes of nature. The science is less than in Blackmore's *Creation* already known or Thomson's *Seasons* yet to come, but the continuity of the praise of God for his created works is sharply shown in this

42

enlargement of church services, where the chorus swells in exaltation, 'Praise Him, and magnify Him forever!'[7]

Metrical versions of the Psalms, because of their use in church services, are common in English poetry, but only those in praise of God for his creation lend themselves to scientific paraphrases. It is understandable that the most common of these would be Psalm 104 with its glorification of Jehovah stretching out the heavens like a curtain, laying the beams of his chambers in the waters, making the clouds his chariot, walking upon the wings of the wind, and generally parading the works of nature. The appeal of this psalm to poets with scientific interests can be seen in at least four versions in the eighteenth century, of which one by Richard Bullock in 1750 furnishes the most revealing example.[8]

This paraphrase accentuates the scientific knowledge shown in the verses by copious footnotes containing explanatory summaries of recent scientific discoveries. For example, the variety and fecundity of nature are shown in the verses:

> Thy pow'r with life and sense all nature fills,
> Each element with varied being swells,
> Race after race arising view the light,
> Then silent pass away, and sink in night.
> The gift of life thus boundlessly bestow'd,
> Proclaims th' exhaustless hand, the hand of God.

The note expands this idea with a summary of microscopic experiment:

There is hardly any substance in nature, that is not the habitation and receptacle of some one or other species of living creatures. Every different plant nourishes its proper family of insects. All kinds of substances when turned to a state of corruption, swarm with life. The air is plainly an inexhaustible store of eggs, or stamina of animalcules of different kinds: for one cannot set in the sun-beams for any considerable time, a little paste, infusion of pepper, hay, flowers, leaves, or almost any vegetable substance,

[7] London: Edward Lathbury, 1724, folio, 32 pages. The dedication, signed Edm. Massey, ascribes the poem to 'the pious and learned Mr. Lepla' of Finchingfield, Essex.

[8] For other paraphrases of the *Benedicite* by Anne Winchilsea and James Merrick, of Psalm 104 by E. W., Thomas Blacklock, and Thomas Fitzgerald, and of other psalms by Mary Masters and Helen Maria Williams, see my description in *PMLA*, LXXIV, 44 f.

but it shall be impregnated with thousands and millions of animalcules imperceptible without a microscope; all of different forms, sizes, and manners of life, and all completely and elegantly formed in all their parts.

The scientific prose essay appended to the poem amplifies still further the illustrative science and the ideas of the wisdom, goodness, and power of God shown by science, in this instance twelve specific experiments for the microscope which serve to demonstrate the enormous plenitude of nature and the ability to exhibit 'in an imperceptible point, as well as in an unbounded sphere, the perfections and attributes of an infinite God'.[9] In an even fuller way the astronomical discoveries have revealed the power and wisdom of God, but all the science of earthly man cannot equal what will be revealed to us after death when we join the sagacity of a Newton and the memory of a Clarke and then improve this genius with an 'endless, undisturbed, and uninterrupted duration, for pursuing knowledge'.

The tradition reached its highest point, however, in the later poems of that wasted genius, Christopher Smart. His own metrical versions of the entire Psalms contain almost no elaboration for they were written to carry out his desire to reform the Prayer Book. But in his Seaton Prize poem for 1756, *On the Goodness of the Supreme Being*, he became 'Israel's sweet Psalmist' himself who alone 'with musical persuasion drew' the hills, rocks, and floods and gave voice to hail and snow. In the same year he wrote his *Hymn to the Supreme Being* in the mood of the Psalms, and in 1763 nobly caught the spirit of David in that magnificent blend of natural history and praise of God, *A Song to David*. Here he pictures David 'with harp of high majestic tone' enriching his psalms to God with such samples of created nature as the 'clust-'ring spheres' in the sky and on the earth trees, plants, flowers, birds, fishes, beasts, and gems. The adoration section is like that of the Prayer Book's *Benedicite* but with Smart's own array of examples from the world of nature: polyanthus, almond, humming bird, ounce, pheasant, ermine, sable, swordfish, ostrich, gier-eagle,

---

[9] *An Hymn to the Creator of the World, the Thoughts taken chiefly from Psalm CIV, to which is added in Prose, An Idea of the Creator from his Works* (London, 1750), pp. 6, 38–41. The prose essay is devoted chiefly (pp. 20–37) to the celestial universe, where the wisdom of God has been demonstrated by the scientific discoveries of 'the incomparable Sir Isaac Newton'.

whale, bullfinch, sugar-cane, cocoanut, orange, and in the skies the constellations and the 'planet's ring'. The native and the exotic crowd together to adore the Creator, the damson and pineapple as well as the squirrel and the robin, the English countryside blending with the natural history of Tahiti and the West Indies.

And this is itself but a prelude to the ecstatic marathon of madness, science, adoration, and autobiography that was only recently published for the first time, *Jubilate Agno*. Here all the patriarchs, including the three children of the Prayer Book and numerous other people, strangers and friends alike, come with innumerable beasts and birds and fish and insects and plants to rejoice in the Lamb of God, the beetle and the butterfly mingling with the baboon and the camelopard. In this strange medley of science and fiction, the scientific paraphrases of the Anglican Book of Common Prayer reached a literary perfection that glorifies their cruder beginnings.[10]

The Book of Job also appealed to the poets with its own questionings about the ruler of nature. William Broome (1712) made Job sound like a lyrical Boyle lecturer in his scientific comments on the mysteries of nature, such as tides, dew, flowers, sun, moon, stars, winds, comets, hail, snow, and rainbow, and in the perennial question of how this beautiful universe came from the womb of nothing.[11] A sample will show how the religious poet is inspired by science without knowing much about science:

> Say if thy hand directs the various rounds
> Of the vast earth, and circumscribes its bounds,
> How the revolving spheres amid the sky,
> In consort move, and dance in harmony?
> Why the ebb and flow of tides, why the lark's song, the odor
> of blossoms,
> Say, why the sun arrays with shining dyes
> The gaudy bow that gilds the gloomy skies?

[10] *The Collected Poems of Christopher Smart*, ed. Norman Callan, 2 vols. (London, 1949) is the most nearly complete edition. The introduction and notes by Robert Brittain to his edition of selected poems (Princeton, 1950) contains the best criticism of Smart's poetry as well as a summary of previous scholarship. The best edition of *Jubilate Agno* is that of W. H. Bond (Cambridge, Mass., 1954), acknowledging the contribution of W. F. Stead when he published the poem for the first time in *Rejoice in the Lamb* (London, 1939).

[11] 'A Paraphrase of Parts of the 38th and 39th Chapters of Job', *Miscellaneous Poems and Translations by Several Hands* (London: B. Lintot, 1712), pp. 102–8.

There is a touch of this attempt at the scientific sublime in Broome's paraphrases of Habbakkuk 3 (1710) and of Ecclesiasticus 43. In the latter the 'pow'r supreme' gave us the sun that measures time and seasons and calls sleeping flowers to life, the moon and stars, rainbow, thunderstorm, whirlwinds to lay whole forests low and tear up desert sands into drifts, snow and hail, stormy winter in the frozen north (a long vivid description of Arctic wastes where 'waves on waves in solid mountains rise, / And Alpes of ice invade the wondring skies'), and perils of the sea from storms and whales. The concluding hymn of praise is a prelude to many future scientific poems:

> Thus, Lord, the wonders of earth, sea, and air,
> Thy boundless wisdom, and thy pow'r declare; . . .
> For tho' this earth with skill divine is wrought,
> Tho' wondrous ev'n beyond the reach of thought,
> Yet in the spacious regions of the skies
> New scenes unfold, and worlds on worlds arise,
> There other orbs, round other suns advance,
> Float in the air, and run their mystic dance;
> And yet the pow'r of thy almighty hand,
> Can build another world from ev'ry sand.[12]

Edward Young added a special interest in natural history to the six pages of notes appended to his twenty-six-page scientific poem, *A Paraphrase on Part of the Book of Job* (1719). Among other things he added material on mountains, comets, and the solar system, and wrote copiously of such creatures as the lion and peacock. He defended in learned fashion his choice of the crocodile for Leviathan and the hippopotamus for Behemoth over the usual whale and elephant, arguing that since the descriptions in Job are close to what the naturalists say about Egypt it is probable that Moses wrote the Book of Job.

William Thompson, when he wrote in 1726 *A Poetical Paraphrase on Part of the Book of Job*, was not as scientifically accurate as Young but his poem was enriched by metrical discussions of rain, evaporation, and underground streams, of instinct in wild animals, and of exotic animals. He devoted sixty-eight lines to his des-

---

[12] W. Broome, *Poems on Several Occasions* (London, 1727), pp. 19–26, 151–160. His *Job* is reprinted, pp. 34–42.

cription of Leviathan but was more accurate in his picture of the ostrich:

> She, with head erect,
> And body upright rais'd, of stature tall
> And bulk enormous, with expanded wings,
> Two mighty sails outspread, sweeps o'er the earth
> With whirlwind rapture borne o'er hill or plain,
> Scorning the courser's speed, and rider bent
> On swiftest chase.

Inspired by the Bible but much freer in their treatment of the sublime scenes from nature are poems on the creation, when God called order out of chaos, and the last judgment, when nature was dissolved and all its threads unspun. The grandest treatment of the creation was before 1700, the sublime picture of the Mosaic hexaemeral tradition by Milton in *Paradise Lost*. After 1700 the creation is used as a lyrical inspiration for shorter poems of praise of God or as a part of longer poetical essays. John Dennis's paraphrase of *Te Deum*, used in his *Advancement and Reformation of Poetry* (1701) to illustrate the sublime in religious poetry, is an early example of the lyrics on the creation, followed by John Hughes' *An Ode to the Creator of the World* (1713) and two poems on the creation by Elizabeth Rowe. Almost any of the longer scientific poems described in the succeeding chapters might be called a poem on the creation, and the first long comprehensive scientific poem, that by Blackmore in 1712, even bears the title, *The Creation*.[13]

The poems on the last judgment are so numerous and so striking in their pictures of sublime horror heightened by scientific imagery that they become a startling phenomenon of the century.[14] The physical catastrophe of the prophet Joel quoted by Peter in Acts 2, 20 became the basis for lurid descriptions of the sun darkened and the moon turned to blood. Even before 1700, as we

---

[13] Jonathan Smedley, *A Specimen of an Universal View of all the Eminent Writers on the Holy Scriptures* (London, 1728), a summary of the earlier poetic and scientific accounts of the creation, quotes 102 lines from Blackmore. For the use of creation in other poems, see *PMLA*, LXXIV, 46 f., with these additions: *On the Creation of the World . . . a Divine Poem . . . to Mrs. Millington* (London, 1719), *A Paraphrase on the Creation, by a Young Gentleman* (London, 1744), and William Williams, *Redemption: a Sacred Poem* (London, 1796).

[14] See Norbert Sturm's unpublished dissertation (Western Reserve University, 1960) for a more complete picture of the social and literary manifestations.

have seen in Norris's 'The Consummation', poems on the last
judgment had enlarged the cataclysmic episodes and emphasized
the idea of the dissolution of nature by the use of vivid scientific
imagery. Theological and scientific treatises alike discussed the
judgment day and so it became naturally a subject ready made for
poets with scientific interests. The wild Jeremiads of the 'French
Prophets', the predictions of enthusiastic sects like the Methodists
and Moravian Brethren, and numerous tracts on the impending
judgment, full of frightening mathematical calculations, served to
keep the more ignorant populace in a constant state of seething
apprehension. Only by reading the *Gentleman's Magazine* or the
literary reviews can one realize the extent of this nervousness and
fear of doom. The poems on the last judgment are lurid enough
with their wild pictures of stars clashing in fury and all creatures
perishing in the grand conflagration, yet these sublime pictures
of horror seem almost sedate by the side of the more frightening
sermons and pamphlets of the time.

The whole background of early eighteenth-century thinking on
the last judgment can be seen in Thomas Burnet's continuation
of his very popular *Sacred Theory of the Earth*. Printed in a second
volume of later editions of the work, the continuation devotes
174 pages to Book III, 'Concerning the Conflagration', and 226
pages to Book IV, 'Concerning the New Heavens and the New
Earth'. Most of the eighteenth-century poems on the last judgment follow this pattern, but only the parts dealing with the
conflagration itself have any scientific interest. In Book III Burnet
summarizes all the evidence from the Bible, ancient writings, and
modern scientists having to do with the destruction of the sub-
lunary world by fire, its time, and the nature of the catastrophe.
There will be signs in the last days but they will come too late to
serve as a warning, for the darkening of the sun and moon,
earthquakes, the roaring of the sea 'and such like disorders in the
natural world . . . are the very pangs of death, and the strugglings
of nature just before her dissolution'. In great detail he describes
vividly the breakup of nature hastened by the miraculous divine
intervention, not only the darkened sun, the smoking mountain
tops, the dry rivers, the roaring sunken sea, but also the blazing
stars, the extraordinary number and nearness of big comets, the
air full of unusual meteors, and balls of fire rolling in the sky:
'the moon and the stars will be confus'd and irregular, both in

their light and motions; as if the whole frame of the heavens was out of order, and all the laws of nature were broken or expir'd'. This renewal of interest in a very old idea was helped by Burnet and by other more scholarly writers of physico-theology like John Ray.

Among the earliest of the poems on the last judgment are two Pindarics of John Pomfret, both in an exalted mood far removed from the Horatian quiet of his more famous poem, 'The Choice'. In 'On the General Conflagration and Ensuing Judgment: A Pindaric Essay', written in 1699, he depicts sublimely the strong convulsions that sinking nature must undergo as it dissolves, lighted to her tomb by darting lightnings, glaring meteors, 'vast sheets of flame and globes of fire'. In this poem the judgment itself is the important theme, though not until the setting has been vividly painted in terms of mad confusion, trembling Alps dissolving in volcanic fire, all living things gone, the sun turned dark, and the ocean become scalding hot. 'Dies Novissima: Or the Last Epiphany', a Pindaric ode written about the same time but not published until later, is even more startling in its detailed description of nature straying 'from her ancient order':

> Black thunder bursts, blue lightning burns,
> And melting worlds to heaps of ashes turns. . . .
> Reverse all Nature's web shall run,
> And spotless misrule all around
> Order, its flying foe, confound
> Whilst backward all the threads shall haste to be unspun.

The terror grows as the stars 'starting from their spheres, / In giddy revolutions leap and bound', and burning orbs 'unsupported, leave the skies', a fitting prelude to the approach of the mighty judge.

Still more precise in its description of the wreck of nature is the forty-page anonymous *Omega: A Poem on the Last Judgment* (London, 1708), in which with no light except where meteors or 'vast bearded comets, flaming dragons fly, / With firy lances, thro' the troubled sky', waters dry up, fish die, birds forget to fly, savages and beasts forget their wildness, and the earth becomes a sea of liquid fire. Probably in the same period, Elizabeth Rowe wrote, as companion to her two poems on the creation, 'The Conflagration: An Ode', in which she describes not only the

49

thunder, lightning, tornadoes, and volcanic eruptions like Aetna but also the definite disruption of Newtonian order:

> And now begins the universal wreck;
> The wheels of nature stand, or change their course,
> And backward hurrying with disorder'd force,
> The long establish'd laws of motion break. . . .
> Now mightier pangs the whole creation feels;
> Each planet from its shatter'd axis reels,
> And orbs immense on orbs immense drop down,
> Like scatt'ring leaves from off their branches blown.[15]

Edward Young made his version of this theme, *The Last Day* (Oxford, 1713), an early study for the melancholy pompousness of *Night Thoughts*. The yawning valleys, the impetuous winds that scatter the forests, and the ocean that roars as it sweeps over the land signal the destruction of nature: 'Time shall be slain, all nature be destroy'd, / Nor leave an atom in the mighty void.' After the blast from ten thousand trumpets signals the judgment, there is a deep silence 'As nature died, when she had groan'd her last'. Finally, there is destruction with 'dissolving elements and worlds in flame'. Nature shrinking at her approaching doom is accompanied by thunder, lightning, black clouds, winds, flames seen through smoke, hills rushing down to the valleys, flames spreading to the clouds, and sun, moon, and stars melting away: 'The devastations of one dreadful hour / The great Creator's six days work devour.'[16]

Samuel Catherall, in his sixty-six-page blank verse *Essay on the Conflagration* (London, 1720), treated the subject as an excuse for moral warning yet used science for some of his best descriptive passages. This second dissolution of the world will be ushered in, he said, by nature's powers, not by the sun quitting its regular course, for that 'would soon convert / Ten thousand worlds to one conflagrant mass', but by the central heat within the earth combined with other natural violent forces, 'volcano's, earthquakes loud, and meteors dire' to create eruptions like those of Stromboli, Aetna, Vesuvius, and the geysers of Iceland, but on a far grander scale.

All the early poems on the subject are pale beside Aaron Hill's

---

[15] *Miscellaneous Works in Prose and Verse*, I, 86–92.
[16] See Courtney Melmoth, *Observations on the Night Thoughts of Dr. Young* (1776), especially pp. 195 ff. on the last judgment.

The Judgment Day (London, 1721), for as he says in his preface, he is able with the aid of a friend to use the knowledge of 'Sir Isaac Newton's vast improvements' to let his fancy loose on this frightful topic and avoid the faults of other accounts that bring in too many faint images of law courts: 'But when I resolv'd to attempt the conflagration, I presently discern'd, that the horror of the imagery would be wonderfully heighten'd, by extending the design to a description and dissolution of the planetary systems, in all the amiable magnificence of our modern astronomy.' In the poem itself Hill first describes the beauteous heavenly fabric that is to be destroyed: on fancy's wings he rises 'through deep wilds of air' as millions of opening wonders dazzle reason's finite view with unnumbered globes that widen into flaming worlds:

> Millions of countless miles are lost between,
> And sick'ning thought grows tir'd, to stretch so far!
> How vast the concave spheres, which, hence, are seen!
> Th' enormous vaults, with wheeling worlds glow round!
> Rolling, sublime, they slide oblique, yet none their paths
> confound!

At the trumpet call the careful order breaks, the arrested systems stop their course, and 'the conscious planets . . . from their orbits bound'. On earth, 'the poles start sudden . . . And earth's snap'd axis, groaning quits its trust.' The vivid description of the chaos that follows is too long to quote, valleys heaving up, hills leaping into the sky, rivers rising into the sky and hissing against the hot lightning flashes that fall continuously. The ocean swallows the mountains and there is confusion among living things as lions float by on oaks, elephants paw the waves, birds fly frantically in screaming droves, and plunging whales spout the seas that steam from volcanic fires. The sun goes off its course and the planets, freed from attraction, drive with heavy speed until they hit a comet and add to the fire of lost worlds. Here is a short sample of the sublime horror:

> Involv'd, at length, th' attracted planets throng,
> And burn, confounded, with central suns;
> Tumbling, from ev'ry part, they strike, and thund'ring,
> rend along! . . .
> Down rain distilling suns, in liquid rills,
> Mix'd with red mountains of unmelted fire!

Hissing, perplex'd, with show'rs of icy hills,
And cat'ract seas, that roar, from worlds still higher;
Mingled, like driving hail, they pour along,
And, thund'ring, on our ruin'd system fall!

After Hill's lively treatment of the theme, the lengthy and very
diffuse epic of Thomas Newcomb, Rector of Stopham, *The Last
Judgment of Men and Angels, in Twelve Books, after the Manner of
Milton* (1723), seems very tedious indeed but the ambitious nature
of this 359-page folio poem is a good indication of the popularity
of the subject. Actually there is as much science in Newcomb's
praise of the creation in Book V as in the few places where cosmic
imagery depicts the end of the world. But 'the sad expiring groan
of nature' is the theme of the episode where hot nitrous vapours
work their way through caves in the earth until they gain 'a
dreadful passages through ten thousand wounds'. And the actual
picture of destruction comes to life for a moment with the sun
and moon darkened, and the air covered 'with direful meteors,
and the lengthen'd flame / That the huge comet draws', and a
thousand suns crashing flaming into the earth or rushing against
other orbs. This tiresome poem contains more of Milton than of
Newton, yet many passages in it reflect the use of science as a
background for celestial drama.

Joseph Trapp's contribution to the subject is fittingly the
second section of his long and gloomy poem, *Thoughts upon the
Four Last Things*, separately published in 1734 as *Judgment*. Trapp
had already showed, in his lectures on poetry in the science classes
at Oxford, that he was aware of the possibilities of using natural
philosophy in poetry, and here he put his ideas into practice. To
foreshow the dissolution of nature at the last judgment, he wrote,
the earth will stagger and the mountains reel 'cracking and
crashing, with a dreadul shock', the Alps will fall, the seas boil,
'strange lightnings whiz in air', and all the shooting stars, roaming
comets, and blue and red meteors will unite and shoot fire at each
other. After the judgment the wreck of nature will begin with a
roar like 'ten thousand Aetna's and Vesuvio's' and end with 'the
crush of lab'ring nature' and the rush of warring elements to their
ruin.

These are the chief examples of scientific poems on the last
judgment written before 1750, and good examples they are of how
effectively a popular theme can be made more vivid with what

Aaron Hill called the 'vast improvements' of Newton's science. There was a revival of interest in the subject in the 1750's, possibly as the result of the earthquakes that startled England in 1750 and destroyed Lisbon in 1755. John Ogilvie, for example, in *The Day of Judgment: A Poem in Two Books* (1753), is overwhelmed by the thought of 'ten thousand stars in one devouring blaze', of burning skies and 'boundless planets as they roll, / And burst the labouring earth from pole to pole', of the whirlwind driving the ocean over the land, and of a comet setting the great mountains on fire as 'nature labours with convulsive throws'. The earthquakes, Europe's most vivid reminder of the harshness of nature, became in later moral poems the most common scientific example used to explain divine providence in the distribution of seeming evil. Yet they reminded people of the last judgment, as in an anonymous *Poem on the Earthquake at Lisbon* (1755):

> With her last earthquake this round world shall rise,
> The sun shall lose his fires in endless night,
> And the moon turn'd to blood, glare horrid light,
> When comets dire shall sweep athwart the sky,
> And stars like leaves before the tempest fly.

In 1757 the last judgment was the topic for the Seaton Prize, the contest for the best poem on the Supreme Being already won five times by Christopher Smart, and two judgment poems were considered good enough to be published in the later collection, *Musae Seatonianae*. The subject continued to be popular at least until 1800, but in most instances after 1760 it was used as a passing theme in moral poems.[17] The many poems on the last judgment at the turn of the century, however, furnish perhaps our best example of the continuity of ideas used in eighteenth-century scientific poems.

The religious poetry of Isaac Watts makes a fitting conclusion to this section on religious continuity. Among devotional poets who reflected the divine worship in the church at the beginning of the eighteenth century, no one is better known than Watts.

---

[17] For other instances, see *PMLA*, LXXIV, 50 f. An interesting collection attests the popularity of the subject around 1750, *Dr. Young's Poem on the Last Day, translated into Prose . . . by T. Henry, A.M., to which are added Poems on the General Conflagration and Last Judgment, by Several Hands* (London: R. Thomson, n.d.). The collection includes the scientific poems of Young, Pomfret, and Rowe as well as Addison's *Resurrection* and four short poems of Isaac Watts.

His many short poems, hymns, and Biblical paraphrases were constantly reprinted to meet popular demands, but being short devotional pieces they did not lend themselves to an interest in science. An examination of one of his early collections, the second enlarged edition of *Horae Lyricae* (1709), shows nevertheless that Watts was aware of the new science and of the pleas of scientists like Boyle and Ray to let nature show the glory of God. The quotations from Job in his preface illustrate his plea for more of the sublime religious poems that John Dennis had recommended. The poems themselves abound in images from nature that reflect the new science: 'God's Dominion and Decrees' where wisdom 'guides the vast moving frame' and God regulates the stars and comets; 'Divine Judgment' with its vivid pictures of harsh nature, including two long stanzas on the polar world two decades before Mallet and Savage showed the way to Thomson; 'The Creator and Creatures' where seas and planets show the changes in restless nature that contrast with the order in God's 'vast designs'; 'The Law given at Sinai', a Pindaric miniature foretaste of later physico-theological poems; 'Sun, Moon, and Stars, praise ye the Lord', a version of the *Benedicite* supplemented by similar paraphrases of Psalm 148. These are a few examples chosen at random from one book of poems but they show that Watts was one of the first English poets to transfer the knowledge and spirit of science to lyrical praise of God.

3. THE CONTINUITY OF SKEPTICISM: THE LIMITATIONS OF SCIENCE

With his inquiring mind man has through the ages pushed forward the boundaries of knowledge, and yet he has been constantly reminded that there is still more that he does not know, that his phenomenal discoveries are but the effects of a cause that is still unknown. Especially in the eighteenth century the spectacular discoveries in the world of nature by means of the telescope, the microscope, the application of mathematics, and the geographical exploration of new regions, opened new vistas for the imagination to play in. But the theologians, and after them the poets, reminded the scientists that all their knowledge could not explain how these observed wonders came about, or what was the cause of these effects. Pope expressed well what oft was thought when, in his *Essay on Man*, he chided presumptuous man for his arrogance in measuring the tides and counting the stars. Yet it was not until Blake at the close of the century that the idea of the limitations of science reached a climax of belligerent attack that made it easy for some nineteenth-century poets to denounce science as the destroyer of imagination.

The idea of the vanity of human knowledge, at least as old in literature as the Old Testament book of Ecclesiastes, received a new emphasis with the scientific advances of the seventeenth century. The general distrust of human knowledge shown in the Pyrrhonism that questioned authority in many fields continued in the questionings of scientific poets in the eighteenth century, though it was probably colored by other threads of thought, such as the theme of forbidden knowledge portrayed in *Paradise Lost*, the fear that science would culminate in a purely mechanistic system that leaves out God, and the feeling that science is arrogant ('Presume not God to scan'). The word 'vanity' appears in the familiar writings on the subject—in the sixteenth century in Cornelius Agrippa's *De Incertudine et Vanitate Scientiarum et Artium*, in the seventeenth century in Glanvill's *The Vanity of Dogmatizing*, and in the eighteenth century in Prior's *Solomon on the Vanity of the World*. Yet the poets did not try to show the vanity of science, but to point out its limitations. In this they followed the lead of the orthodox scientists—Sprat, Glanvill, Charleton, Boyle, Ray, and even Newton—who, as we have already seen, tried to rid science of the charge of atheism by praising it for showing the wisdom of God in nature and at the same time freely implying its limitations. No scientific demonstration could explain the ultimate mysteries, the causes behind the riddle of nature. The poets were asking the same questions even before 1700, and they continued throughout the century but not in a hostile attitude to science, that is, not until Blake.

The first long poem to treat this theme seriously is Matthew Prior's *Solomon on the Vanity of the World, a Poem in Three Books*, published in 1718 but written by 1708.[18] As early as 1688, however, he had used it as the main theme of a schoolboy exercise, an ode on *Exodus* 3, 14. In this youthful prelude to *Solomon*, Prior accused foolish man of pride in knowledge, lust in learning, and

[18] *The Literary Works of Matthew Prior*, ed. H. B. Wright and M. K. Spears (Oxford, 1959), I, 306–85.

vanity in trying to explore the vast immensity of the universe. 'With dangerous curiosity' man tried, he said, to answer questions about the winds, tides, sun, and stars, only to build up hypotheses which soon became the 'jargon of the schools'. Only the 'pregnant Word' that called forth the universe, he continued, can give the answers, and only through faith in God can we see what 'all the volumes of philosophy, with all their comments, never could invent'.

Prior's longer poem, *Solomon*, takes up the searching questions of the wise king concerning knowledge, pleasure, and power, ending always with the conclusion that all earthly things are vain and the only solution is in religion with its praise of a Creator that is all wise, all powerful, immortal, and benevolent. Since the first book is devoted almost entirely to science or knowledge of the natural world, it deserves careful analysis as one of the best examples in the century of the theme of the limitations of science.

Solomon's discussions with his wise men are based on the assumption that to think is to be happy, for 'content of spirit must from science [knowledge] flow'. Almost immediately 'a thousand doubts oppose the searching mind' as he questions, without expecting an answer, the reasons for the operation of nature, first the visible things, then the origin of the earth and the nature of the celestial universe, and finally the nature of angels. Since the wise men cannot answer the numerous questions of his doubting mind, he blames his own curiosity and concludes that science is vanity.

Solomon begins with botany, the science that had developed rapidly during the seventeenth century along with astronomy. He knows the name and nature of every plant and tree, but there are so many things he does not know—for example, why the beech and fir are different in shape, why the oak sheds its leaves and the yew does not, why the specimens of the vegetable world differ in color, use, form, and ecology. He asks how fish breathe and choose the proper place to spawn, and how instinct teaches birds to build their nests, train their young, and migrate with the seasons. There are many things we do not know about the varied beasts and creeping insects around us, the duteous bee and fore-sighted ant, gnats and worms that have the same passions and physical functions as 'abject man' and differ only in shape and name from huge creatures like the whale and elephant or 'the crested snake, and long-tail'd crocodile'. Nature is so potent and varied that we cannot even comprehend the vast difference in size, much less pursue the myriads of ideas that great nature's power keeps secret from man. The actions of lower animals, whether the wild tiger and fox or the domesticated horse and dog, show that reason in man and instinct in animals are the same (an idea that is repeated in many poems during the period), and that man is wrong in thinking he is lord of nature and that all was made for his use.

Solomon next tackles the puzzling problem of the inequalities of nature in the torrid tropics and the frozen north, but surmises, as did most of the physico-theological poems later, that Providence dispenses secret good along with seeming evils. The strange animals and savages found in foreign lands by explorers are not so easily explained, but we should not label things with 'the pompous name of prodigy' simply because they appear more rarely to us. The one thing we can be sure of is change, whether in the erosion of mountains or of Egypt's pyramids. 'Are all things miracles; or nothing such?' the poet asks, and then cites as answer the everyday miracles of buds in spring and seeds of grain dying to multiply themselves in harvest. All such wonders are explained by a deity:

> From nature's constant or eccentric laws,
> The thoughtful soul this general influence draws,
> That an effect must presuppose a cause:
> And while she does her upward flight sustain,
> Touching each link of the continued chain,
> At length she is oblig's and forc'd to see
> A first, a source, a life, a deity;
> What has forever been, and must forever be.

After a patriotic digression in praise of the influence of Britannia beyond the seas, Prior leaves the earth and directs his curiosity into the skies, first to the solar system and the regularity of the sun, moon and planets, then to outer space where 'ten thousand stars' shine with such vast and varying light 'as speaks the hand that form'd them, infinite'. The order and harmony shown in the astronomical universe make it seem reasonable that each of these stars is itself a sun transmitting light to 'enliven worlds denied to human sight', new earths with new moons:

> And in that space, which we call air and sky,
> Myriads of earths, and moons, and suns may lie
> Unmeasur'd, and unknown to human eye.

Man is presumptuous to think that these 'worlds immense, unnumber'd, infinite' are made for his own delight. The smallest ant might as well say that Caucasus was made for his road, or the vilest cockle that the craggy rock was made to shelter him, or the whole ocean to quench his thirst. Solomon's speculation on the nature of angels who may be the inhabitants of these unknown worlds leads him to give his own answer in an ecstatic hymn to the Creator.

With this praise of the divine First Cause Solomon's scientific summary of doubts ends fittingly, but the rabbins and logicians continue to argue:

> To speak one thing, mix'd dialects they join;
> Divide the simple, and the plain define;
> Fix fancied laws, and form imagin'd rules,
> Terms of their art, and jargon of their schools,
> Ill-grounded maxims by false gloss enlarg'd,
> And captious science against reason charg'd.

Solomon listening to their debate is forced by reason to confess 'that human science is uncertain guess', lifting presumptuous eyes 'to what our Maker to their ken denies'. The brutal conclusion looks forward many years to Blake:

> Various discussions tear our heated brain:
> Opinions often turn; still doubts remain;
> And who indulges thought increases pain.

The theme of Prior's *Solomon* is that man-made things are vain—in Book I human knowledge and in Books II and III pleasure and power—and that the only answer is faith in God. While the questions directed to scientists in Book I seem to be entirely skeptical, they nevertheless give credit to science for showing that the universe is orderly and reveals the harmony of design of a benevolent and all-wise God. The final answer is not too different from what orthodox scientists like Boyle and Ray and Newton had said, and what the writers of many future physico-theological poems were to say, that science demonstrates the wisdom of

God in the creation of the universe but can never fully satisfy because it can never show how or why. When viewed in the light of this apparent dilemma shared by many other thinkers and poets of the time, Prior does not seem to me to consider contemporary science to be 'as materialistic, deterministic, and hostile to religion as the Lucretian doctrines'.[19] He expresses the doubts more fully and eloquently than other writers, but the overall attitude is that of gratitude to science for revealing the wisdom and power of God, the First Cause of these wonders that contain puzzles science cannot answer.

Prior's *Solomon* is the most complete poem on the limitations of science. Pope's *Essay on Man* is the best, but since it is also the best moral poem of the century to use scientific ideas it will be analyzed more fully below. Nevertheless Pope's larger theme of the paradox of man torn between great knowledge and sensual weakness, 'the glory, jest, and riddle of the world', ties in with the seeming dichotomy of the poets who praise science and at the same time taunt scientists with questions they cannot answer. Man may achieve the heights of scientific discovery, even 'instruct the planets in what orbs to run', and yet those superior beings who people outer space, knowing what man can never discover, would look on the scientist as a toy and show 'a Newton as we show an ape'. More verbosely and far less effectively Henry Brooke expands on the same ideas in his *Universal Beauty* (1735).[20] Let us see how this long poem is an example of the way the theme was treated in several physico-theological poetical essays that appeared in the decade after the death of Newton in 1727.

In the first of his six books, Brooke begins with an eloquent array of questions as to the how and why of the creation, presupposing a Divine Intelligence, 'mysterious thought . . . by space unbounded', who is swifter than light and ranges through the universe to 'new form old systems, and new systems change'. The futility of science to explain everything causes impatience with the intellectual efforts that would be unnecessary, Brooke says, if Nature could descend from its heights to 'Dispell the clouds that round our fancy stray, / The mist that damps our intellectual ray.' The vanity of learning appears in those who deny

[19] Monroe K. Spears, 'Matthew Prior's Attitude toward Natural Science', *PMLA*, LXIII (1948), 485–507.
[20] Chalmers, XVII, 337–65.

their God and obstinately refuse to recognize what they hear and see:

> While fondly thus prime reasoners you'd commence
> By literally exploding common sense . . .
> Approach, ye sages, to your parent Earth
> Much wiser than the clods on whom she lavish'd birth.

In Book II Brooke gives an extended answer to atheists who believe that the creation arose from the chance concurrence of atoms:

> Can atoms be omniscient, to discern
> (What human wisdom strives, but strives in vain to learn)
> What mode mysterious paints the purpling rose,
> What melts the current when Maeander flows?

Atheists cannot answer these questions, but if they would use their reason they could see in the boundless space of worlds on worlds that ' 'Tis order above rules that guides the plan, / And wisdom, far beyond what wisdom can.' Still the scheme is too great for human philosophy or science to grasp:

> For deep, indeed, the Eternal Founder lies,
> And high above his work the Maker flies;
> Yet infinite that work, beyond our soar;
> Beyond what Clarkes can prove, or Newtons can
> explore!

In the next three books Brooke continues the same praise of the great Maker whose works fill the book of nature, first with plants, then with animals, and finally with the myriad world of insects and microscopic creatures. In the beginning of Book V he sums up his theme of praise to Nature's God, and chides man for ignoring the evidence from the world of nature. But the vanity of science is never more apparent than when wild creatures outdo the scientists at their own game, and to this idea Brooke devotes all of Book VI. Let the botanist forego his art and watch the Cretan doe and other animals avoid poisonous plants. The bees are 'little virtuosi' who reduce the essential juice of flowers like chemists and build their waxen hexagons like geometricians. The wasp's nests and the beaver's houses defy the work of the finest architects, and the spider's intricate web squares the circle as she smiles 'o'er her great Newtonian rival'. These and other examples of divine wisdom furnish but the prelude, however, to the hymn of praise of the 'Sole Cause Essential'. Science has shown this divine wisdom in many ways, and the vanity lies only in the futility of believing it can ever explain all. In short, Brooke, like Pope and other poets of the 1730's, saw no inconsistency in glorifying physico-theology and at the same time attacking scientific rationalism.

Many poems that are now little known emphasize the general idea of anti-intellectualism, the vanity of human knowledge, but with a decided emphasis on the new science. Mary Leapor, that sensitive poet of nature who died in 1747 at the age of twenty-four, states the idea simply in 'An Enquiry': wisdom in vain tries to trace the boundless skies 'where doubled wonders upon wonders rise' and asks what kind of people inhabit the moon, 'What warms those worlds that so remotely shine? / And what can temper Saturn's frozen clime?' Even Newton's art, she says, cannot show a truth that is perhaps not fit for us to know, yet we can worship the Great Power that rolls the worlds and we can contemplate Him through the chain of being that stretches from the stars to microscopic worlds 'where little forests on a leaf appear'.[21]

Thomas Hobson showed a great knowledge of science in his *Christianity the Light of the Moral World*, published in 1745 but written more than eight years earlier. The discoveries of science, especially by Newton, are described in the verses and explained with specific references in the ample footnotes, and much credit is given to reason, which controls man's passions 'as Newton's sun the erring planets guides'. And yet when reason inquires why knowledge of the natural world was so long concealed, the poet reminds us that there are many questions science still cannot answer:

> Why men were not made angels, brutes not men?
> Why each revolving planet faintly shines
> With borrow'd lustre, and the sun his own?
> Tell how the central orb this system binds,
> Or how, self-balanc'd, high on nothing hangs?
> Even tell, why smallest atoms prone descend,
> Or sympathetic magnets forceful draw

[21] *Poems on Several Occasions* (London: J. Roberts, 1748), I, 196-200.

The trembling steel? . . . The known effects are plain:
The deep, mysterious Cause a Newton shuns.
These far evade the microscopic eye
Of all-exploring reason, unperceiv'd.[22]

Henry Jones's poem with a pretentious title, 'An Essay on the Weakness of Human Knowledge, and the Uncertainty of Mortal Life', sums up the mid-century point of view. Our weak sight cannot see the hidden secrets of nature, and so doubts and questions arise on the 'universal fabrick's laws' as well as on the smaller problems of stars, tides, winds, earthquakes, meteorology, geology, natural history, and psychology: 'Th' eternal Essence of one Atom show, / Then boast of Science, and how much you know.' 'Our prying eyes would pierce all nature's store', but this is a vain hope, for 'Newton's transcendent day must bound in night'. With an excellent couplet that anticipates Blake, the poet says that Nature asserts the Eternal Cause but the most infinitesimal piece of creation defies the scientist: 'The smallest worm insults the sage's hand; / All Gresham's vanquish'd by a grain of sand.' God's wonders are too often hid from proud man, the 'imperious emmet', because with his vain reasoning he 'sees so little of th' eternal chain'.[23]

Most of the poems, it can now be clearly seen, treated the idea of the limitation of science as a part of a larger effort to make man see that nature reveals the wisdom of God. Seldom were they hostile to science but only aware of its shortcomings. Even Prior, the one poet to treat the subject at length, praised the discoveries of Newton and other great scientists that showed the work of an all-wise God but could never explain the causes behind the miracles of nature. Many of the longer serious physico-theological works of the first half of the eighteenth century have no hint of distrust in science, while others bring it in very casually. For example, Moses Browne in his *Essay on the Universe* (1735), devotes over 360 pages of his poem to a scientific description of the world of nature, including 'Newton! vast mind! whose piercing pow'rs apply'd / The secret cause of motion first descry'd.' Then

[22] London, John Lewis, 1745. The footnote on p. 56 explains further that the fact of gravity and attraction 'is made extremely probable by Sir Isaac Newton. But what the physical cause of gravity or attraction is, the Newtonian philosophy does by no means pretend to explain or determine.'

[23] Henry Jones, *Poems on Several Occasions* (London: R. Dodsley, 1749), pp. 61 ff.

in conclusion, as he is about to call on all things in nature to praise the Creator, he begs the reader to close the book 'and ponder Nature's page'.

The same attitude seems to me to be true of Christopher Smart, even though *Jubilate Agno* (written in the 1760's but not published until 1939) contains, in its wild medley of natural history and autobiography directed to the praise of God, some passages that are close to Berkeley in their reflection of anti-Newtonianism.[24] The glory of God as revealed in nature and exemplified by science is the theme of five poems by Smart on the attributes of the Supreme Being, written between 1750 and 1755. Only one of these, *The Omniscience of the Supreme Being* (1752), allows Smart to treat the theme of the futility of science. It takes the usual form, though better expressed than before: 'proud reasoner, philosophic man' is taken to task for not knowing what animals know by instinct, and this reminds him of the vanity of learning:

> The venerable sage, that nightly trims
> The learned lamp, t'investigate the pow'rs
> Of plants medicinal, the earth, the air,
> And the dark regions of the fossil world,
> Grows old in following, what he ne'er shall find;
> Studious in vain! till haply, at the last
> He spies a mist, then shapes it into mountains,
> And baseless fabric from conjecture builds.

The migrating nightingale uses no science of navigation 'but instinct knows / What Newton, or not sought, or sought in vain.' Newton's science is insignificant compared to the omniscience of God, who was the light himself 'Ere yet Refraction learn'd her skill to paint, / And bend athwart the clouds her beauteous bow.' Yet Newton's ability to describe the things that show the glory of God is itself worthy of the greatest praise that can be given to human knowledge: 'Illustrious name, irrefragable proof / Of man's vast genius, and the soaring soul!' Smart took his fling at the pseudo-scientists in his satirical verses, and he mixed some irreverent distrust of rationalism with his ritualistic praise of the Lamb, but he did not reject the glory that Newton and other scientists had brought to man's imaginative concept of the vast and orderly universe.

[24] D. J. Greene, 'Smart, Berkeley, the Scientists and the Poets', *Journal of the History of Ideas*, XIV (1953), 327-52.

The most revealing poem on the futility of science between Prior and Cowper, however, is an obscure 19-page quarto in couplets, *The Vanity of Philosophic Systems: a Poem Addressed to the Royal Society* (1761). The poem begins with a plea to the 'sons of science, wisdom's chosen band' to leave their 'magazine of arts' built up from long experience in reading 'Nature's dark wilderness'. They are quick to understand but slow to believe, and so they must try a doctrine showing that God is the enlivening power that gave motion to the sun, moon, and stars.

> Pervading all things, yet to none confin'd,
> By wisdom working, with ideas fraught,
> Who moulded matter into being brought,
> United under various forms display'd,
> The atoms, fit or to be mov'd, or stay'd.

God moves everything and the scientist may describe the laws of motion, but the laws are futile 'unless the maker agitate the springs'. Philosophers have tried vainly to explain by building up systems based on second causes, deifying matter and setting up a 'journeyman to God' which they called Nature. The poet names the false systems of philosophy and rejects them all because they explain the effects but not the cause. Among the ancients, Strato and Epicurus only are represented, but among the moderns are Descartes ('with mechanick head . . . piec'd up one great clockwork of the whole'), dogmatic Hobbes, sagacious Newton, pious Malebranche, the short-sighted skeptics, and the 'minute philosophers', Berkeley's freethinkers. Since Newton is the only genuine scientist represented and since it is now well know that Newton was not interested in metaphysical speculation and added God as the First Cause in the second edition of his *Principia*, the poet's description of him is interesting:

> Sagacious Newton lost with pond'ring thought,
> To mathematick rules a system brought;
> God as an Eastern monarch, left for show;
> His Viceroy, Gravity, the God below.

The poet's attitude toward science is plainer in his plea to 'proud virtuosi' to cease their vain conjectures and stick to calculating where they are right, for 'attraction is no pow'r, but law alone'. They must remember that gravity and the tides are moved by one who presides over the moon, and that natural effects are manifest, steel to magnets, straw to amber, corks on water, 'but how—unknown'. If we look at the sphere copied 'by our late Archimedes, Orrery', we can see that motion is being continually applied, and if we need experiments we can clearly see that scientific laws proclaim a mind, a God 'who plan'd, preserves, and moves the whole machine'.

After 1750 the idea of the limitations of science had become a commonplace that could be introduced into poems that had little to do with science.[25] Late in the century the continuity of the idea can best be seen in the poetry of that mild-mannered rebel, William Cowper, who sympathized with science and praised its achievements but spoke out sharply against its pretenses and its willful attacks on religion. William Blake's trumpet call of deliberate rebellion late in the century marks a new era, yet his attacks on the spirit of science become more understandable in the light of earlier poems. Both poets serve as epilogue to the play that begins in 1700, and so they will be taken up later. The prologue, as we have seen, takes the form of mild protests against the pretense of too great knowledge, a form of anti-intellectualism that is closely tied up with the skepticism and distrust of authority of the seventeenth century.

4. SATIRE ON SCIENCE, 1660–1760

The only real hostility to science in literature appears in the ridicule of the *virtuoso* by the neo-classical wits. Even though most of this satire is in the form of prose, it deserves special study here as one of the best examples of the continuity of ideas from the seventeenth to the eighteenth century. The scientist depicted in literature as a comic type began soon after the founding of the Royal Society in 1662 and persisted well into the nineteenth century. Under the name of 'virtuoso' he became known chiefly as a collector of curiosities and a searcher for monstrosities in nature, and as such he became the object of literary ridicule in drama, prose satire, and comic verses. The early interest that reaches its

[25] For some examples, as well as a discussion of the theme in Cowper and Blake, see my article, 'The Idea of the Limitations of Science from Prior to Blake', Rice University *Studies in English Literature*, I (1961), 97–114, from which this section has been adapted.

high point in Book III of Swift's *Gulliver's Travels* and in Book IV of Pope's *Dunciad* reflects the classical gentleman's scorn for the one-sided specialist who lacks decorum. The literary interest of Swift's Grand Academy of Lagado, with its profuse burlesque of actual scientific experiments described in *The Philosophical Transactions of the Royal Society*, has tended to obscure the similar satire of William King and Henry Fielding in the early eighteenth century. To fill out the story of the scientist as a comic type and to relate it to the influence of science on more serious poetry, the history of the satire on science, 1660–1760, needs to be told here. The revival of this kind of raillery in the latter part of the century will be described in a later chapter.[26]

As early as 1667 Thomas Sprat in his *History of the Royal Society* warned 'the wits and railleurs of this age . . . that if they shall decry the promoting of experiments, they will deprive themselves of the most fertil subject of fancy'. Sprat sensed the power of 'these terrible men' to do more injury to science than the more serious opponents 'by making it ridiculous, because it is *new*'. Laughter, he continued, 'is the easiest and slenderest fruit of wit', and should be reserved for derision only of the extravagant, for 'while Nature has only form'd them to be pleas'd with its irregularities and monsters', it has given scientists 'the delight of knowing and studying its most beautiful works'.[27] Sprat was quick to recognize the possibility of satire and the danger to science of a too facile ridicule.

Sprat was probably thinking of Samuel Butler, for the laughable picture of Sidrophel in Canto III of the second part of *Hudibras* (1664) had already poked fun not only at the astrologer and pseudo-scientist but also by implication at the Royal Society itself. Hogarth's engraving of the Wizard's study (Plate XI) in 1726, with its bat and stuffed crocodile, its globe and books, and its mysterious diagrams, show that he thought of it as a satire on the virtuoso, and Zachary Grey's learned notes in his 1744 edition illustrate Hudibras in terms of contemporary science. The des-

---

[26] In addition to studies of Swift and Pope, see C. S. Duncan, 'The Scientist as a Comic Type', *Modern Philology*, XIV (1916–17), 281–91, Claude Lloyd, 'Shadwell and the Virtuosi', *PMLA*, XLIV, (1929), 472–94, Marjorie Nicolson, *The Microscope and English Imagination*, pp. 24–37, and Walter E. Houghton, Jr., 'The English Virtuoso in the Seventeenth Century', *Journal of the History of Ideas*, III (1942), 51–73, 190–219.

[27] Pp. 417 f.

cription of Sidrophel sets the tone for the virtuoso of later writings, who admired the rare and strange, even the monstrous:

> He had been long t'wards mathematicks,
> Opticks, philosophy, and staticks,
> Magick, horoscopy, astrology,
> And was old dog at physiology. . . .
> He made an instrument to know
> If the moon shine at full or no;
> That wou'd, as e'er she shone, straight
> Whether 'twere day or night demonstrate;
> Tell what her d'meter to an inch is,
> And prove that she's not made of green-cheese.

It is true that Butler's *Elephant in the Moon* was a more direct satire on the Royal Society, though its mistaking of a mouse on a telescope lens for an elephant is similar to Sidrophel's announcement that a paper-lantern on the end of a boy's kite was a 'dreadful wonder . . . A comet, and without a beard! Or star that ne'er before appear'd.' Yet *The Elephant in the Moon* remained in manuscript until 1757, when Robert Thyer printed two versions of it with notes to show further that 'Butler was a profest enemy to the method of philosophizing in fashion in his time' and that actual members of the Royal Society were being satirized in Sidrophel and the philosophers assembled to look at the moon through a telescope. In these verses and even more particularly in another satire never finished, Butler laughed at the 'virtuoso taste' of the Royal Society and its 'whimsical fondness for surprizing and wonderful stories in natural history'. In this fragment a hundred virtuosi ask curious questions of a learned man and pursue their 'learned speculations . . . to measure wind, and weigh the air', square the circle, or find the treble and bass in the braying of an ass.[28] Butler wrote a parody of a scientific paper in 'An Occasional Reflection on Dr. Charleton's feeling a Dog's Pulse at Gresham College' and in many other pieces he satirized pedants, scientists, and antiquarians.[29]

The first full picture of the new scientist as a comic type appeared in 1676 in *The Virtuoso*, a play written by Thomas Shadwell, the butt of Dryden's satire in *MacFlecknoe*. Nicholas Gimcrack, the experimental philosopher of Shadwell's play, is

---

[28] *The Genuine Remains in Verse and Prose of Mr. Samuel Butler . . . Published from the Original Manuscripts . . . with Notes by R. Thyer* (London, 1759), I, 1–56.

[29] *Ibid.*, pp. 404–10. See also *Remains*, I, 202–27, and II, 128, 179, 318.

busy with observation, experimentation, investigation, and the reconstruction of the natural world; in other words, he is striving to do what Bacon proposed to do, but this and other plays make this kind of scientist a fool because of his vain pursuit of useless knowledge, a pedant because he is a pretender to learning, and despicable because his vulgar interests were not those of polite London society. Gimcrack is not a mere collector of rarities; he studied twenty years on the nature of lice, spiders, and insects, spent £20,000 on microscopes to investigate the eels in vinegar and the cause of decay in cheese and plums, and engaged in his laboratory in various impractical experiments in chemistry, physics, zoology, and astronomy, nearly all of which can be traced to actual reports in the *Philosophical Transactions*. His female counterpart is Valeria in Susannah Centlivre's *The Basset-Table* (1705), who can talk of nothing but her experiments and discoveries, including the dissection of a dog and her pet pigeon, and is seen dissecting a fish in her laboratory.

The comic scientist appears in several plays after this, as Periwinkle in *A Bold Stroke for a Wife* (1718), Sophronia in *The Refusal; or, the Ladies Philosophy* (1721), and Lady Science in James Miller's *The Humours of Oxford* (1726), but the most famous of the stage satires on science in the eighteenth century is *Three Hours after Marriage* (1717), the combined efforts of three members of the Scriblerus Club, Pope, Gay, and Arbuthnot. In this play the character of Fossile is based on Dr. John Woodward, the well-known physician and author of an *Essay Toward a Natural History of the Earth*, but it might have been any scientist. Actually, the lively farce is a gross parody of medical language and of the aimless projects of a virtuoso. The action is more like that of a Restoration comedy than a satire, for it depends on disguises, mistaken identities, and bawdy situations, but the main comic scene, based on two would-be lovers taking refuge in a crocodile and a mummy in Fossile's museum, would remind the audience that science was still a subject for ridicule.[30]

The learned lady, a comic type in Moliere's *Les femmes savantes* or Thomas Wright's *The Female Vertuoso* (1693), turned to science in the eighteenth century. In real life she appeared as Elizabeth Carter, Mary Chudleigh, and Elizabeth Rowe, and in mildly

[30] A facsimile of the Dublin, 1758, edition, ed. by John Harrington Smith appeared in Augustan Reprint Society, 91–92 (Los Angeles, 1961).

satirical form in various plays or in such periodical pictures as that of Lady Lizard's young ladies in *The Guardian* reading Fontenelle's *Plurality of Worlds* while making preserves, 'dividing their speculations between jellies and stars, and making a sudden transition from the sun to an apricot, or from the Copernican system to the figure of a cheese-cake'.[31]

The most famous single poem ridiculing science is Dr. Samuel Garth's *The Dispensary* (1699), a mock-heroic that gave Pope ideas for his *Rape of the Lock*. This satirical account of apothecaries and physicians was so successful that it was reprinted many times and a complete key appeared in three editions as a separate book. The topical satire on famous physicians, the descriptions of diseases in the lower regions, and the mock-heroic use of syringes, emetics, cathartics, and pestles as weapons in Canto V more properly belong to the history of medicine, yet even here the wit of the poet often turns social history into satire.[32] The virtuoso, the scientist engaged in 'research', who appears in Canto II, is Horoscope (an apothecary usually identified as Dr. Barnard), who may be recognized from the following portrait as a worthy successor of Sidrophel and Gimcrack:

> Here, mummies lay most reverendly stale,
> And there, the tortois hung her coat o' mail;
> Not far from some huge shark's devouring head,
> The flying fish their finny pinions spread.
> Aloft in rows large poppy beads were strung,
> And near, a scaly alligator hung.
> In this place, drugs in musty heaps decay'd,
> In that, dry'd bladders, and drawn teeth were laid.

In an inner room 'globes stand by globes . . . and planitary schemes amuse the eye', while the sage himself in a velvet chair 'lolls at ease, / To promise future health for present fees'.[33]

[31] *Guardian*, 155, 8 Sept. 1713. See Gerald Dennis Meyer, *The Scientific Lady in England, 1650–1760* (Berkeley, 1955), especially chap. VII.

[32] For a summary of the background of the medical history in the poem, see Harvey Cushing, *Dr. Garth, the Kit-Kat Poet, 1661–1718* (Baltimore, 1906).

[33] *The Dispensary* is the most famous of several verse satires on physicians around the turn of the century. Others bound with it in a single volume in the British Museum (841, b. 84) are *Gideon's Fleece: or the Sieur de Frisk, an Heroic Poem . . . by a Friend to the Muses* (identified in MS as Dr. Guidot), London, 1684; *Androphonus: an Heroick Poem*, London, 1699; *The Duelist: a Poem address'd to Sir William Read*, (London, 1705); *Aesculapius: a Poem*, London, 1721 (a didactic poem on general science, ending with medicine); *Dr. Woodward's Ghost*; *Dr. Hannes Dissected*; and *Ietro-Rhapsodia: or a Physical Rhapsody*.

Many years before Swift wrote about the Grand Academy of Lagado, William King wrote a great deal of excellent prose satire on science, most of it aimed at Sir Hans Sloane, then Secretary of the Royal Society, and much of it a straight parody of actual articles in the *Philosophical Transactions*. The first of these was a long pamphlet, *The Transactioneer, with some of his Philosophical Fancies in two Dialogues* (1700). The first dialogue, ridiculing the style of Sloane's scientific writing and the versatility of his knowledge, is a close parody of Sloane in the form of a virtuoso's explanation to a gentleman that the *Philosophical Transactions* are largely the work of one man who is famous for his correspondence with learned men, for his skill as a physician, and for the sublimity of his style. He gives several examples as a burlesque of Sloane's casual manner of describing things that appear obvious, contradictory, or untrue,[34] and most of the quotations are close enough to show that King's ridicule was justified. The dialogue continues with praise of this universally qualified man, 'a great botanist, a great physician, a great philosopher, a great man, and a great naturalist'. Examples of his significant discoveries are a china ear-picker, nail paring instruments, brass tweezers, a straw purse, a fossil mandible, and an Irish giant. The second dialogue pretends to convey useful information by a transactioneer to a gentleman, again based on actual articles about shellfish (*Phil. Tr.*, XIX, 196), the scientist James Petiver (XIX, 393–400), medicinal herbs, monstrous births, microscopic flies armed with swords, the effects of hanging, the generation of fleas, and all sorts of natural knowledge but, says the gentleman, 'nothing that will make a man wise'.

In 1709 King continued his satire on Sloane and the Royal Society with several issues of a burlesque called *Useful Transactions*. The first issue, for January and February 1708/9, set the tone of burlesque in the preface: 'It may not improperly be said at present, that there is nothing in any art or science, how mean so ever it may seem at first, but that a true virtuoso, by handling it pilhosophically, may make of it a learned and large dissertation.' The present transactions are samples of what can be done: 'These

---

[34] For example, p. 4, Sloane's note to a letter on marble in Wales (*Phil. Tr.*, No. 252, XXI, 188) is cited in full; p. 7, another note of Sloane to a letter of George Dampier is quoted less exactly (XX, 52); and p. 13, Sloane's remarks on a man swallowing a stone (XXI, 192) are twisted and quoted out of context.

show that good housewives, tradesmen, boys, pedlars, semstresses, poets, gipsies, and indeed all sorts of professions may be useful to the world, if they study philosophy, and set their characters in a true light.' The contents include articles on samplers, natural observations on Llaudwwfwshwy (based on actual letters of Edward Lhuyd), honest millers, Grecian dances and plays, and an excellent satire on pedantry, 'A new method to teach learned men how to write unintelligibly.'

The second issue, for March and April, contained: 1. The eunuch's child. 2. Additions to Leuwenhoek's microscopical observations on the tongue, using material and a plate from *Phil. Tr.*, No. 315. 3. Migration of the cuckoos by Martin Cheapum, a delightful satire on adultery in various parts of London. 4. Observations on a piece of gut (based on *Phil. Tr.*, 314). 5. Consecrated clouts, a satire on Catholics.

The third and last issue is 'for the months of May, June, July, August, and September 1709, containing a voyage to the island of Cajamai in America . . . after the method used by Jasper van Slonenbergh, a learned member of the royal vertuosi of Great Britain, in the relation he has given of his voyages into those parts'. The title and preface of this issue show that King is here more particularly concerned with Sloane's travel account of his stay in Jamaica, which has more science than travel in it, for recent travel books show, King continues, that it is 'safer talking of ants, elephants, hedgehogs, and butterflies, than of persons of quality under the most secret disguises'. The preface explains Sloane's modest and humble style by the fact that philosophers must strive for truth rather than ornament. Many things that seem trivial at first, such as 'feeding of fowl, the education and discipline of swine, the making of beds, the untying of breeches, and loosening of girdles', contain great thought and depth of judgment, by means of which 'philosophers search into the recesses of nature'. King promised to continue his *Useful Transactions* 'monthly, as they sell'. Whether they did not sell or he felt he had achieved his main purpose, namely satire on Sloane, the third issue seems to be the last.

King wrote other satires on science, which were published in the first of his two-volume *Miscellanies in Prose and Verse*. The tone of them is apparent in his burlesque of Martin Lister's journey to Paris called 'A Journey to London in the Year 1698', and in several accounts of virtuosi (Doncaster with his pictures, Roman glass, tadpoles, and sticklebacks; Muddiford on a cat in an air pump; and Shuttleworth with his Scottish inscriptions, ass skin, snails, shellfish, frogs, and butterfly). King's playful disrespect for virtuosi pervades this passage on modern learning from his *Dialogues of the Dead*: 'I think, I have demonstrated, from the ditches, crevices, tadpoles, spiders, divinity, caterpillars, opticks, maggots, tobacco, flies, oranges, limons, cyder, coffee, and linnen-rags of the moderns, that the extent of knowledge is at this time vastly greater than it was in former ages'. And there are passages from other pieces in the *Miscellanies* such as the collection of briars and thorns from Chelsea Garden or the fairy-food in 'Orpheus and Eurydice', but the examples already given are enough to show that William King was a good satirist in his own right and a worthy inspiration for Swift and Pope.

From the same tradition an anonymous pamphlet, *The Art of Tickling Trouts* (1708), deflates the pride of learning among 'philosophical gentlemen': 'Next, come your nice philosophical gentlemen, who esteem themselves the only favourites of wisdom. . . . They'll give you the dimensions of the sun, moon, and stars, as easily as they wou'd do that of a flaggon or a pipkin: They'll give a punctual account of thunder; and all the other abstruser difficulties in physicks, without the least demur or hesitation, as if they had been admitted into the cabinet council, when Nature was midwif'd into the world. . . . But though they are ignorant of the artificial texture of the least insect; they vaunt however and brag that they know all things, when in deed, they are unable to understand the mechanism of their own body.'

The 'virtuoso' satirized by King and the playwrights was, it is clear, a seeker of the unusual, whether the monstrous in nature or the strange in coins, medals, or paintings. He thrived on curiosity and often spent great sums in collecting marvels until his museum became a treasure house of art and science. Sir Hans Sloane, the butt of much of this satire, actually amassed such a great collection that, ironically, it became the basis for establishing the British Museum. The virtuoso, male or female, was characterized by 'wonder and admiration for the rare, the strange, and the incredible'. This eccentricity made him vulnerable to the scorn of neo-classical followers of decorum, to the extent that the decline of the virtuoso movement from 1680 to 1710 was due, Professor Houghton believes, to the effectiveness of the satire.[35]

Swift and Pope were the best of the eighteenth-century writers to satirize science. Whether Swift opposed the scientists or respected science and merely satirized pseudo-scientists does not matter here.[36] His *Mechanical Operation of the Spirit* is a parody of papers in *Philosophical Transactions*, though it is more concerned with ridiculing religious enthusiasm than scientific experiment. His *Scriblerus Papers* contain a number of jibes at the scientists. Yet the enthusiasm of Swift's account of the experiments in the Grand Academy of Lagado is not accidental. The fervor of detail in the dozens of impractical projects shows that Swift was familiar with actual experiments described by members of the scientific societies of both London and Paris and that he deplored the unclassical mind that mixed Newton's laws of motion with accounts of monstrosities, odd medical case histories, and accounts of strange discoveries from all parts of the world.[37] The profuse examples, amusing as they are, add to Swift's serious purpose of showing the futility of too zealously pursuing knowledge without common sense: extracting sunbeams from cucumbers, plowing with hogs, teaching silkworms to weave, reducing human excrement to its original food, propagating a breed of naked sheep, composing books by the chance shifting of words on a machine, and disposing with words by using the things themselves. Swift in his best playful manner also brought political satire into the scientific experiments in Lagado: curing political corruptions by having attending physicians ready to give laxatives; reconciling opposing parties by sawing the heads of each of the leaders in half and exchanging the parts; discovering plots and conspiracies by examining the diet and excrement of all suspected persons. The rulers of Laputa, we remember, were excellent scientists and could manoeuver their Flying Island on magnetic principles but at the same time were so absorbed in speculation that they could

[35] Walter Houghton, *loc. cit.*, p. 214. Houghton emphasizes the fact that the true scientists were called 'natural philosophers' and that the scientific virtuoso was ridiculed, not because he collected rarities but because he showed no principle of selection with his indiscriminate collections.

[36] Herbert Davis takes the latter point of view in his review of R. Quintana, *The Mind and Art of Jonathan Swift*, in *Philological Quarterly*, XVI (1951), 187.

[37] A sampling of early French scientific periodicals may be seen in Thomas Gray's notebooks published in my *Thomas Gray, Scholar* (Cambridge, Mass., 1937), pp. 164-74.

not attend to everyday affairs and had to be reminded of the most ordinary things by means of flappers in the hands of servants. The virtuoso, as a miscellaneous collector of the strange for its own sake, may have largely disappeared by 1710, but Swift was clearly ridiculing the scientists whose zeal for experimentation and speculation led them to excess and away from the decorum of the classical gentleman. To Swift the Royal Society encouraged corrupt taste, and so he satirized its members playfully but also unmercifully.

This picture of scientists busied with vain and foolish experimentation must have been much in Pope's mind when he wrote the fourth book of *The Dunciad* to complete the revised version enthroning Cibber as the new king of the dunces in 1742. Just before the dread empire of Chaos is restored and 'universal darkness buries all', the followers of false learning parade before the goddess who has come to replace order and knowledge with dullness, and last to come are the scientists,

> A tribe with weeds and shells fantastic crown'd,
> Each with some wondrous gift approach'd the power,
> A nest, a toad, a fungus, or a flower.

They bring the rare flower and name it Caroline in honour of England's queen, and offer an ecstatic account of the discovery of a 'peerless butterfly'. The goddess hopes they may find inspiration in a humming-bird or 'congenial matter in the cockle kind', or let the mind wander 'in a wilderness of moss', or spend their time studying flies, learning only to trifle by seeing 'Nature in some narrow partial shape, / And let the Author of the whole escape.' Thus Pope, not as particular in his satire on science as Swift or others, gives to those who 'impale a glow worm' to gain the high honor of F.R.S. the dubious glory of the company of other dunces.

Some of the minor verse of the early eighteenth century approaches Pope in intensity if not in imaginative quality. In *Universal Passion* Edward Young wrote of the follies of mankind with a playful zest that makes this satire worthy of comparison with Pope's *Moral Essays* of the same period. He warms up to the ridicule of scientists in Satire II by depicting, among the victims of pride, Florio doting on a rare tulip and Tonson purchasing knowledge by the yard. In Satire IV (1725) he satirizes among collectors who 'for renown are singular, and odd' Sir Hans Sloane himself, 'the foremost Toyman of his time':

> His nice ambition lyes in curious fancies,
> His daughter's portion a rich shell inhances,
> And Ashmole's Baby-house is, in his view,
> Britannia's gold-mine, a rich Peru!

This year is the most insignificant since the Great Plague, for 'it has not brought us one new butterfly'. In Satire V (1727) the learned lady is ridiculed for her shallow pursuit of the new science in contrast with the ideal woman who never took the height of Saturn:

> The fair philosopher to Rowley flies,
> Where in a box the whole creation lies.
> She sees the planets in their turns advance;
> And scorns, Poitier, thy sublunary dance.
> Of Desagulier she bespeaks fresh air,
> And Whiston has engagements with the fair.
> What vain experiments Sophronia trys!
> 'Tis not in air-pumps the gay Colonel dies.
> But tho' to-day this rage of science reigns,
> (O fickle sex!) soon end her learned pains.
> Lo! Pug from Jupiter her heart has got,
> Turns out the stars, and Newton is a sot.

In 1730 Jonathan Smedley wrote some playful verses to a microscope, the 'wondrous machine' which can show an insect being formed or the embryo of a worm or the flea that disturbs Cynthia:

> See! with what monstrous port and stately pride,
> The pigmy swells, and tempts an awker'd stride;
> See his proboscis! see his well-hinged thigh;
> His lobster-legs; and see his eagle-eye.[38]

In 1733 James Bramston, answering Pope's satire on the man of fashion, ridiculed the scientific dilettante:

> Bears, Lyons, Wolves, and Elephants I breed,
> And *Philosophical Transactions* read,
> Next lodge, I'll be *Free-Mason*, nothing less,
> Unless I happen to be F.R.S.[39]

[38] *Poems on Several Occasions* (London, 1730), pp. 208–10.
[39] *The Man of Taste. Occasion'd by an Epistle of Mr. Pope's on that Subject.*

In 1735 Robert Dodsley made fun of the female scientist in his poem, *Beauty*:

> Study Sir Isaac at the Pastry School,
> And make Mince-Pies by mathematick rule.
> Know every art, and every science teach,
> Of nothing ignorant—but how to stitch.

In 1743 Henry Fielding added a close parody of the *Philosophical Transactions* to his other early satirical performances when he published in a pamphlet and later in his *Miscellanies*, under the guise of 'Philosophical Transactions for the Year 1742–43', an article with the revealing title, 'Some Papers proper to be read before the R——L Society, concerning the terrestrial Chrysippus, Golden-foot or Guinea; an insect, or vegetable, resembling the Polypus, which hath this surprising property, that being cut into several pieces, each piece becomes a perfect animal, or vegetable, as complete as that of which it was originally only a part. Collected by Petrus Gualterus, but not published till after his death'. Like Swift's *Mechanical Operation of the Spirit*, this paper uses a burlesque of scientific writing for a different purpose, here to call attention to the economic evils of money, its multiplication, miraculous powers, and sinister influence on mankind. Yet it is also an effective burlesque by its use of a popular scientific puzzle of the time, the polyp that seems to combine the animal and vegetable kingdoms, and by its imitation of actual scientific papers by Abraham Trembley, with plates, long quotations, and numerous reports of experiments, including a letter from Herr Rottenscrach in Germany.[40] Fielding followed Swift and Pope in deflating the pride of scientists and poking fun at their writings, and in the next decade Christopher Smart followed Fielding. The idea was attractive to the best writers.

Christopher Smart used images from natural history to support his serious poems in praise of God. At the same time, he castigated the shortcomings of science with all the vivacity of his satirical genius. This side of Smart has been neglected by modern critics,

---

[40] Fielding, *Miscellanies*, I (1743), 252–77. Henry Knight Miller, *Essays on Fielding's Miscellanies: a Commentary on Volume One* (Princeton, 1961), pp. 315–31, shows the close parody, relates this piece briefly with the tradition I have described, illustrates the vogue of the polyp, especially in Charles Hanbury Williams' poem *Isabella*, and cites (pp. 329–31) several other instances in which Fielding attacked the scientific spirit and the Royal Society.

though it is attested by many playful journalistic ventures and by his more ambitious *Hilliad* (1753), a satire on John Hill, the notorious but versatile scientist and writer. In Latin Smart wrote other satires on science which were later translated into English by Francis Fawkes under the titles 'A Voyage to the Planets' (a playful comic fantasy satirizing Fontenelle, written at Cambridge in 1741), 'A Mechanical Solution of the Propagation of Yawning' (satirizing medical quacks among others), and, best of all, 'The Temple of Dulness'. This sprightly fantasy displays atheistic Folly, ponderous Sophistry, mad Mathesis, and Microphile, the scientist who collects queer things and explores various microscopic wonders:

> On flies she pores with keen, unwearied sight,
> And moths and butterflies, her dear delight;
> Mushrooms and flow'rs, collected on a string,
> Around her neck, around her temples cling,
> With all the strange production of spring.
> With greedy eyes she'll search the world to find
> Rare, uncouth animals of every kind.

Her greatest joy Microphile finds in the wondrous Polypus who excels the curious crocodile, 'the weaving worm, and silver-shining shell':

> Lo! by the wounds of her creating knife
> New Polypusses wriggle into life.
> Fast as they rise, she feeds with ample store
> Of once rare flies, but now esteem'd no more.[41]

In 1751 the six books of Richard Owen Cambridge's lengthy satire on pedantry and science, *The Scribleriad*, were published separately. Inspired by Swift and Pope but lacking their ability, Cambridge poured into his tedious verses example of pretentious science, the polyp and the Surinam toad, sailing carriages and divining-rods, asbestos and asphalt, and finally electric friction machines producing a halo of light around a man's head. The engraved frontispieces set the tone of satire with their mummies, stuffed animals, aerial contestants, chemical apparatus, and electric sparks. Learned notes supply the scientific background, but even the prophecy of the submarine and airplane are not enough

---

[41] Chalmers, XVI, 261–3, has the same text as the 1761 edition of Smart. The version quoted here is that printed under Smart's poems in Chalmers, XVI, 82-8.

to lift the verses of the *Scribleriad* from bathos.[42] Nor can the social history of medical practice in 1752 occasionally afforded by the lengthy topical satire of *The Quackade* bring that imitation of the *Dunciad* from its deserved obscurity.[43]

[42] R. D. Altick, *Richard Owen Cambridge: Belated Augustan* (Philadelphia, 1941), pp. 101–19, provides a good summary of the poem.

[43] *The Quackade: A Mock Heroic Poem, in Five Cantos, by Whirligig Bolus, Esq.* (London, 1752). For other satires on the medical profession, see note 33 above.

III

SCIENCE IN POETRY:
THE NEW LOOK AFTER 1700

THE old ideas continued, as we have seen, into the eighteenth century, sometimes in praise of science in Biblical paraphrases, sometimes skeptical of science because it could not explain everything, and often vigorously in open ridicule of the Royal Society and science in general. In the Biblical poems something new was added, however, as the telescope and the microscope inspired the poets to refurbish the old themes with imagery from the new science. The time was ripe for a more extensive use of science that would lend to religious poetry the element of the sublime that John Dennis had asked for in his *Advancement and Reformation of Modern Poetry*. The time was ripe, and John Reynolds in 1709 produced the first consciously scientific long poem, *Death's Vision*. He showed his conscious purpose in the subtitle, 'represented in a philosophical sacred poem', as well as in his long scientific notes and in the preface calling for recognition of science as a subject for poetry.

The imagery in these new poems had to be sublime, for the poet's mind was stirred by the vast plenitude and fertility of nature shown in the new worlds revealed by the telescope in the heavens and by the microscope in the millions of creatures invisible to the naked eye. The poetic imagination was stirred, too, by the harmony and order existing in these two contrasting worlds and by the exciting prospect of still further discoveries as improvements were made in optical instruments. Josephine Miles used sublime as a descriptive term for all eighteenth-century poetry in her *Eras and Modes in English Poetry* (1957) because 'it is the era's own term, and suggestive even now of the sweeping, lofty, harmonious, emotional concerns which characterized poetic choices in the eighteenth-century mode'. The adjectives here fit scientific poetry even more than that of other subjects, and it is well to see how the poets were aware of it.

Newton demonstrated mathematically what they had long be-lieved, that the celestial bodies, and even comets, moved in orderly orbits. Observation of minute organisms with the help of the microscope showed that well organized worlds existed in a drop of water or in a rotting plum or on the underside of a leaf. All this, added to the study of plants and animals and insects in the visible world, furnished the proof that they had been looking for, that the study of nature revealed the wisdom and power of God. The subjects were lofty and the imagery was sublime.

I. THE AESTHETICS OF SCIENTIFIC POETRY

Science seems to need no justification for its use in poetry when it is well done, yet in the late seventeenth century the best example among the ancients, Lucretius, was constantly under suspicion for his atheistic ideas, and the more recent poetry of Donne, More, and Milton was not classified as scientific. It is not surprising, therefore, that in 1667 when he wrote *The History of the Royal Society* Thomas Sprat should vigorously call attention to the appeal of experimental science to the poetic imagination. Poets should realize, he insisted, 'that their interest is united with that of the Royal Society; and that if they shall decry the promoting of experiments, they will deprive themselves of the most fertil subject of fancy'. Sprat lists 'the works of nature' among those subjects which can furnish imaginative writing with images that are gen-erally known and therefore 'bring a strong, and a sensible im-pression on the mind'. His clearest defense of science as a subject for poetry is his emphatic statement 'that there is in the works of nature an inexhaustible treasure of fancy, and invention, which will be reveal'd proportionably to the increase of their knowledge'.

But the poets paid little heed to Sprat. When they wrote about science it was usually a Latin didactic poem, as in the case of Cowley's *Historia Plantarum*. The suggestion was made again in 1697, specifically for an English 'philosophical poem', when William Molyneux requested John Locke in a letter to persuade Sir Richard Blackmore to write such a poem, and added significantly, '*a natural history of the great and admirable phenomena of the universe* is a subject, I think, may afford sublime thoughts in a poem'.[1]

John Reynolds cited this letter in the preface to his *Death's Vision*, the first long scientific poem of the eighteenth century, and went on to give his own important aesthetic discussion of scientific poetry, the first of the century. Religion has been the subject for 'eminent and lofty poems', and now science should be used in a similar way:

> Will not that by infallible steps lead us up to religion, and to the grand author and object of it? Especially, since old mechanism is discarded, and the new one must needs be resolv'd into the wise and free constitution of an Almighty Agent. Sir Isaac Newton's universal law of gravitation must needs depend upon the arbitrary appointment of a most wise architect. . . . Since then these laws of motion, founded on boundless wisdom, and arbitrary determination, reach to all things we see, and converse with, justly may appeal be made to the *phaenomena* of heaven and earth, for demonstration of divine existence and perfection. . . . Is it not wonder then, that mong the numerous subjects, that are elaborately sung, philosophy in a philosophical age (and so philosophical, that such problems have been resolv'd, and discoveries made, as no ages are known to have been blest with before) shou'd be no more cultivated by the sons of the muses?

Reynolds continued the defense of his own 'philosophical poem' with a good aesthetic discussion of the difficulties involved, of the difficulty of using technical language for such 'stubborn matter', discouraging even to Lucretius but compensated 'by the true poetical genius and wit'. The sublime subject of the creation, its vastness and harmonious laws, had been sung by David, Ovid, Virgil, and England's Cowley. It is now time for English poets, he said, to attempt an answer to the 'mad philosophy' of the Epicureans, which would never have lived so long if Lucretius had not

---

[1] *Some Familiar Letters between Mr. Locke and Several of his Friends* (London, 1708), p. 219.

been so skillful in adorning it. Reynolds claimed no such ambitious design for his own poem but hoped that the 'philosophical poem' requested of Blackmore (*The Creation*, not published until 1712, was evidently then being written) would 'supply one of the desiderata in the learned world'. Reynolds set only a modest hope for his own poem, to arouse veneration for the 'incomparable power and greatness' of God 'by contemplating and rehearsing some of the Creator's works', yet this very design set the pattern for many physico-theological poems of the century.

Other writers of early scientific poems also showed in their prefaces that they were conscious of the problem of whether science should be made into poetry. Blackmore in 1712 was concerned, in his preface to *The Creation*, mainly with refuting atheists, yet he stated plainly that he chose poetry to avoid the 'obscure, dry and disagreeable' manner of those who had written on the subject in prose, and then usually 'in the learned languages'. He knows he has a difficult task, 'to demonstrate the self-existence of an eternal mind from the created and dependent existence of the universe', and so he chooses the harmony of verse because it 'engages many to read and retain what they would neglect, if written in prose'. He has tried, he said, to make the material clear and varied, and the style more pleasing. The modern reader will question his success, but here we are concerned only with his aesthetic purpose, which was to popularize in the manner of Fontenelle's dialogues on the plurality of worlds, 'to bring philosophy out of the secret recesses of the schools, and strip it of its uncouth and mysterious dress, that it may become agreeable, and admitted to a general conversation'.

Later poets continued to cite science as a subject for poetry. In 1721, as we have already seen, Aaron Hill deliberately borrowed images from the new astronomy of Newton to increase the horror of his last judgment. And William Thompson, in the preface to his 1726 paraphrase of Job, defined clearly the role of science in religious poems:

> The Deity and the works of nature seem, of all other subjects, to afford the properest matter for the divine spirit of poetry to exert itself upon. . . . And the reader will be soon convinced, that nothing does with greater force produce this strong and agreeable emotion in us, than the delightful scenes and paintings of nature. . . . The true God is here represented as wielding all the

elements of nature and commanding each part thereof, light and darkness, snow and vapour, wind and storm fulfilling his word.

This is the way the early scientific poets justified their use of science as a subject for poetry. The best summary of this early point of view comes, however, in an obscure occasional poem by Thomas Cooke, 'To Dr. Woodward', showing how scientists like the famous author of *The Natural History of the Earth* could assist 'the poet's great design' by showing the muse how to go with the sun

> And round the globe, in search of knowledge, fly.
> Boldly she wou'd the glorious race pursue,
> And by thy doctrines trace all nature through;
> Whence the loud thunder roar, and zephyrs blow,
> And forked lightnings fright the world below;
> Travel the various seasons of the year;
> Describe the great abyss, that liquid sphere;
> The source of rivers, and whence fountains rise,
> What drains their springs, and what their springs
> supplies;
> Whence plants receive their vegetable birth;
> And whence the dread convulsions of the earth.[2]

Science was recognized, it is now clear, early in the century as a subject for poetry. The poets, justifying their practice by the aesthetic theory revealed in their prefaces, led the way, and it is not surprising that the academic lecturers on poetry followed. Joseph Trapp, for example, lecturing early in the century, was enthusiastic over the possibilities of using poems on natural philosophy as a happy union of poetry and philosophy. Nothing is more suitable to the dignity of a poem, he explained, 'than to celebrate the works of the great creator', and nothing enhanced the variety of a poem more 'than to describe the journies of the heavenly orbs, the rise of thunder, and other meteors, the motion of the earth, and the tides of the sea; the attractive force of the magnet, the impulsive motion of light, and the slower progression of sound; and innumerable other wonders, in the unbounded store of nature'. As examples he quoted Lucretius and Virgil but found no

---

[2] The poem appeared in *Miscellaneous Poems and Translations by Several Hands*, *published by Richard Savage* (London, 1726), pp. 169–72. A note to a translation of Manilius in Cooke, *Original Poems, with Imitations and Translations* (London, 1742), p. 279, explains that he had changed his opinion of Woodward.

modern poem worth mentioning except Buchanan's Latin poem on the sphere: 'But as natural philosophy has, by the help of experiments, been lately brought to much greater perfection than ever; this kind of poetry, no doubt, would have made proportionable advances, if the same age that shew'd a Boyle, a Halley, and a Newton, had produced a Virgil.' [3] Thomas Tickell, on a similar occasion in 1711, saw the possibilities of science as a source of descriptive nature poetry. Whereas the philosophical themes lent themselves to obscurity, he concluded that country scenes and nature combine the advantages of morals, philosophy, and the arts, and that English poets should imitate the georgics, 'endowed by the hand of Nature, the master craftsman, with sweetness and splendour together'. [4]

2. SCIENTIFIC POEMS FROM REYNOLDS TO THOMSON

John Reynolds' *Death's Vision, represented in a Philosophical Sacred Poem*[5] cannot be said to live up to the lofty aesthetic purpose of the preface, yet it is significant as the first scientific poem of the century. There was much science in the verses themselves, a great deal more in the 52 pages of appended notes, and still more in the greatly expanded footnotes of the revised version printed in 1725 under the title of *A View of Death*. Reynolds summarized in verse and prose the scientific knowledge of his day and in his notes cited such authorities as Descartes, Locke, Newton, Huygens, Halley, Boyle, Keill, Cheyne, Derham, Whiston, and Wollaston. The title of the poem is explained by the poet's imagining himself after death looking down from the heavens at created nature with the perspective of an angel. In what may be the first of a series of scientific cosmic voyages in verse, he becomes 'a more than New-

---

[3] Joseph Trapp, *Lectures on Poetry read in the Schools of Natural Philosophy at Oxford*, translated from Latin (London, 1742). The Latin lectures were published 1711–36, this one in 1715.

[4] Published from manuscript and translated in Richard Eustace Tickell, *Thomas Tickell and the Eighteenth Century Poets* (London, 1931), pp. 198 ff.

[5] London, 1709; reprinted 1713 and in an expanded version in 1725 as *A View of Death: or the Soul's Departure from the World*. Collation shows that the 1725 revision enlarged the scientific footnotes considerably but altered the verses only in theological sections. A few more additions were made when the poem was appended to *Memoirs of the Life of the Late Pious and Learned Mr. John Reynolds* (London, 1735). See Fairchild, I, 151–3.

ton' as he watches the movements of planets and comets, and sees
on earth the mysteries of nature:

> Heaven's shops unlock'd, and workhouses I view,
> What cool alembic drops the rain and dew;
> What lathe so turns, what art japans the bow,
> What looms prepare and weave the fleecy snow;
> In what tight mills the icy balls are ground,
> Why small or large made, why white and round;
> This servant, nature, hath no leave to play,
> But sits at restless work, both night and day.

From the vantage of a position on Saturn the poet views the
intricate motions of the solar system, including the four satellites
of Jove and the ring of Saturn. In a kind of Newtonian ecstasy he
sees the celestial harmony as a demonstration of the wisdom of
God:

> Great God! what pow'r, and prudence to the full
> Are scatter'd thro' th'expanded whole!
> Stupendous bulk, and symmetrie,
> Cross motion, and clear harmonie,
> Close union and antipathie,
> Projectile force, and gravitie,
> In such well-pois'd proportions fall,
> As strike this artful mathematic dance of all.
> Come hither, all you atheistic tribe,
> Who this wise scene to senseless cause ascribe,
> Come hither, as e'er long you must, and see
> The radiant demonstrations of the deitie!

This divine harmony is the answer to the skeptical questioning of
providence in the harsh nature found in mountains, hurricanes,
and tropic heat, for 'never was this law of love so well evinced and
establish'd as in the Newtonian philosophy'. The poem abounds
in illustrations from scientific discoveries in astronomy, magnetism, botany, and microscopy, as well as in some problems that
interested scientists, such as the role of underground streams in
the circulation of water, the 'seminal virtues' and capillary growth
of plants, and the Great Chain of Being, where 'in close ascents the
rising orders grow . . . from smallest microscopic species there, /
Of nature's armies the most distant rear, / Up to the frontier squad-
rons of the skies.' Reynolds was consciously following the earlier

poets, for he cited Cowley and George Herbert, but his zest for science was new in poetry. Even though the verses may falter in their attempt to reach the sublime, science has become an integral part of poetry.

In 1712 Sir Richard Blackmore, physician and epic poet, published the first long physico-theological poetical essay, *The Creation: a Philosophical Poem in Seven Books.* The very title suggests a connection with Biblical paraphrases of the account of the creation in Genesis, yet the encyclopedic use of the new science and recent philosophic controversies bears out Blackmore's promise in his preface to bring philosophy out of the schools and make it agreeable to general conversation. He was aware that the subject lent itself to the sublime, for in 1706 in *Advice to the Poets* he appeared to describe the rise of his 'tow'ring muse' to the vast stars in immense space,

> All suns of equal bulk, and equal flame
> With that, which rules the world from whence I came.
> All glorious centers, whose attractive sway
> Revolving moons and wand'ring worlds obey,
> Each is a globe immense, each is a source of day.[6]

Blackmore accomplished what John Reynolds urged English poets to do, to put into verse the wisdom of God in nature as demonstrated by 'natural philosophy' in the discoveries of the new science. He followed the earnest pleas of earlier scientist-theologians, Sprat and Glanvill, Ray and Boyle, to refute atheism by means of scientific examples, 'to demonstrate the existence of a Divine Eternal Mind'. He handled the subject with lyric enthusiasm in other poems besides *The Creation*, for example, in 'A Hymn to the Light of the World' as early as 1703, in 'An Ode to Jehovah, Creator', which is a Pindaric summary of the theological part of *Creation* with added scientific imagery, and in 'An Ode to Jehovah, Immutable, Merciful, and Just', which belongs among the scientific poems on the last judgment with its description of the 'last throws of Nature's agony'. But none of them approaches the encyclopedia of physico-theology that is *The Creation.*[7]

[6] P. 27. An answer to *Advice to the Poets*, entitled *A Panegyrick Epistle . . . to Sir R—— B——* (London, 1706), pp. 3 f., recognizes this new scheme by which Blackmore's muse flies through various worlds, 'Explores new earths, and traverses new skies.'

[7] R. Blackmore, *A Collection of Poems on Various Subjects* (London, 1718), pp. 321–31, 359–69, 387–409.

Except for the specific refutation of religious heresies in Books III–V, *The Creation* is like the many longer poetical essays that reflected science after 1727, yet because it was the earliest of the encyclopedic poems designed to show the wisdom of God through science, it has a certain historical importance that was recognized in its day by numerous reprintings. Its treatment of design in nature as evidence of the attributes of God reaches inspired moments that merit the praise given to it by Dr. Johnson, and yet it is seldom read today and unjustly dismissed by critics along with Blackmore's dismal epics.[8]

Books I and II of *The Creation* contain the heart of the scientific interest, where the poet often approaches the sublime in showing how the glories of sky, sea, and land proclaim 'the power divine, that rais'd the mighty frame'. Order and design in nature demand 'a conscious, wise, reflecting cause':

> And here behold the cause, which God we name,
> The source of beings, and the mind supreme;
> Whose perfect wisdom, and whose prudent care,
> With one confed'rate voice unnumber'd worlds declare.

Pausing for a lengthy refutation of Epicurus' doctrine of creation from the chance concurrence of atoms and Descartes's theory of attraction, the poet parades, in the rest of Book I, the glories of the earth, the uplifted mountains and the abundant growth of valleys, the gems and mineral wealth, underground streams, the lakes and rivers, and the sea with its puzzling phenomena of salt water and lunar tides.

Book II demonstrates God from instances of design in the celestial motions, especially in the solar system. Here the poet first celebrates the power of the sun and shows the usefulness of variations in light and heat, for ice and frost and decay in winter can be as beneficial as growth in summer. He summarizes the attempts of Ptolemy, Copernicus, and Kepler to explain heavenly motions, which in a way are vain because there are still many questions that cannot be answered even about the solar system, and we now know that this is but one of thousands of systems 'perhaps as glorious, and of worlds as full'. The imagination soars in the boundless space where present telescopes do not reach, to still invisible mil-

---

[8] Albert Rosenberg, *Sir Richard Blackmore: a Poet and Physician of the Augustan Age* (Lincoln, Neb., 1953), especially pp. 98–108.

lions of new suns with their own planets, 'lost in the wilds of vast immensity'. The rulers of modern science, 'the masters form'd in Newton's famous school', have shown the orderliness of celestial motion by theories erected 'by mathematic laws', yet 'these sagasious sons of science' wisely attribute the first motion to God. Book II ends with a summary of scientific ideas on the atmosphere and the winds, including the cycle of evaporation and precipitation and the effect of winds on climate, commerce, and disease.

Book III answers the objections of atheists to creation by a wise and beneficent God, and among the atheists he includes the followers of Lucretius and, more recently, Vaninus, Hobbes, and Spinoza. For example, when the atheist says that nature is full of faults, such as ferocious beasts, arid deserts, harsh climate, and deadly plague, the poet asserts that these are mere inequalities on the earth, which is itself an insignificant part of a universal whole. The glorious orbs in the sky outdo the earth in beauty and magnificence, and the people dwelling on them must necessarily excel this 'low world's inhabitants'. Furthermore, what seems harsh in nature has usefulness: mountains are the source of rivers and minerals; storms are useful for commerce and for cleansing the air of noxious vapors; and inequalities of light and heat are necessary for the balance of nature. The design of the creation demands a God who can stand at the helm 'and with a steady, never-erring hand, / Steer all the floating worlds, and their set course command'. All things in nature, the vast and the minute alike, 'are one prodigious aggregated God, / Of whom each sand is part, each stone and clod. / Supream perfections in each insect shine, / Each shrub is sacred, and each weed divine.'

Book IV is a special answer to Epicureans who say that creation arose from the chance concurrence of atoms. The richness of nature and such miracles as subterranean streams, winds, hail, and snow proclaim a guiding mind, a 'wise and sovereign architect' who is necessary to give motion to the numerous worlds after they are created. Book V similarly answers the followers of Aristotle, who declared 'That things, which seem with perfect art contriv'd, / By the resistless force of fate arriv'd.' In both books the monotonous repetition of theological ideas is only occasionally enlivened by rhetorical questions that summarize the new science.

Book VI demonstrates the proof of a deity from the human body, and here Blackmore the physician is on firm ground. Here he explores with considerable accuracy a branch of science that later poets treated in a casual manner. His long medical descriptions summarize contemporary knowledge of anatomy and physiology from the development of the embryo (50 lines) to the fully developed body, with 150 lines on the heart and circulatory system, 125 on the digestive system, and 70 on the nervous system. Even if these verses are dominantly didactic, the poet infuses them with imagination when he surveys 'this field of miracles' that proclaim God, the 'master-strokes in each mechanic part' that medical science cannot explain. Physiology becomes poetry when Blackmore probes the origin and texture of the human body to find 'some first cause, some self-existent mind, / Who form'd, and rules all nature':

> When first the womb did the crude embryo hold,
> What shap'd the parts? what did the limbs unfold? . . .
> Then for the heart the aptest fibres strung?
> And in the breast th'impulsive engine hung?

The theme is that of one of Bentley's sermons in the first series of Boyle Lectures, but the rhetoric is new, the spinning of sinews and the weaving of muscles, 'the purple mazes of the veins' and 'all the'arterial pipes in order laid', and the 'sleeping, unexpanded issue' of the foetus where the 'rumpled animal contains / Organs perplex'd, and clues of twining veins.'

Book VII crowns the glorious parade of created works with 'the mind's extended empire', a summary of early psychology as it produces evidence of the deity from instinct in animals and the reasoning process in man. The whole poem ends with a lyrical paean that becomes a hymn to the Creator like an expanded form of the *Benedicite*: let the glittering stars sing his praise, and the winds, the birds, fishes, and beasts, the noisy waves, the hail and rain, and finally man, 'heav'n's viceroy o'er this world below'.

This poem lacks the majesty of Milton, but it has occasional sublime moments far removed from the pedestrian and long-winded epics on which Blackmore's literary reputation unfortunately seems to be based. Among the long physico-theological poems *The Creation* is in some ways the most complete, for, in addition to using nearly all the topics of interest to later scientific poets, Blackmore added, as his special contribution, the refutation of pagan philosophies and the detailed glorification, in anatomical splendour, of the human body.

Between the publication of Reynolds' *Death's Vision* in 1709 and the poetic enthusiasm with which various writers greeted the Peace of Utrecht in 1713, a great deal of interest in science, especially in the ideas centering around the wisdom of God in nature, had been generated by Shaftesbury, Addison, Lady Chudleigh, and Blackmore. It is not surprising then that several poems published in 1713, inspired by the prospect of Britain's future glory, should also include, even in a casual way, an interest in science. These are the common threads that join four apparently quite different poems, Pope's *Windsor Forest*, Gay's *Rural Sports*, John Hughes's *An Ode to the Creator of the World*, and William Diaper's *Dryades*.[9]

Science is treated similarly in the two poems of Pope and Gay as the gentlemanly pursuit of an amateur naturalist who occasionally indulges in philosophic meditation inspired by the study of nature. Pope had begun his poem on his modern Eden earlier, but when he finished *Windsor Forest* in 1713 he added the paradox of 'order in variety' demonstrated by science and the pleasures of the amateur scientist. His happy man who had retired to the country could now include astronomy and botany among his georgic delights:

> He gathers health from herbs the forest yields,
> And of their fragrant physick spoils the fields:
> With chymic art exalts the min'ral pow'rs,
> And draws the aromatick souls of flow'rs.
> Now marks the course of rolling orbs on high;
> O'er figur'd worlds now travels with his eye. . . .
> Bids his free soul expatiate in the skies,
> Amidst her kindred stars familiar roam,
> Survey the region, and confess her home.

The full title of Gay's poem is significant, *Rural Sports: a Poem Inscribed to Mr. Pope*, for the two friends must have thought of these two poems as companion pieces. Gay seems more apologetic

---

[9] These and other poems published in folio in 1713 are bound together in a British Museum miscellany, 643.l.26. Another 1713 poem that combines the Peace and science, *Vertumnus: an Epistle to Mr. Jacob Bobart*, describes botanical study at Oxford and will be discussed later.

in alluding to science, yet his passage on evening meditation owes enough to the general physico-theology of the *Spectator* to allow such gentlemanly science a place with fishing or hunting among rural pleasures:

> Now night in solemn state begins to rise,
> And twinkling orbs bestrow th'uncloudy skies. ....
> Millions of worlds hang in the spacious air,
> Which round their suns their annual circles steer.
> Sweet contemplation elevates my sense,
> While I survey the works of Providence.
> Oh, could my muse in loftier strains rehearse
> The glorious Author of this universe,
> Who reins the winds, gives the vast ocean bounds,
> And circumscribes the floating worlds their rounds!

The two poets collaborated again in the play *Three Hours After Marriage* where they ridiculed science and especially John Woodward. Gay never wrote seriously about science after 1713, but Pope's ideas were later to triumph in *An Essay on Man*. The two lesser poets meanwhile not only included more science in their 1713 poems but also wrote other poems that must now be considered.

John Hughes tells us, in the introduction to *An Ode to the Creator of the World*, that he was paraphrasing the Greek fragments of Orpheus as an example of 'the praises of the Author of Nature, which is the fittest subject for the sublime way of writing'. Like the Biblical paraphrases of his time, this religious poem is inspired by the developments of science. For example, when unfinished nature was seen in the creation, 'motion took th'establish'd law / To roll the various globes on high', and 'the great inspiring Mind, / That animates and moves this universal frame' fills unmeasured immensity and rules the heavens 'beyond th'untravell'd limits of the sky, / Invisible to mortal eye.' God rules also the meteors, hail, snow, rain, wind, rainbow, lightning, and all the animal world 'from nature's giant race, th'enormous elephant, / Down to the insect worm and creeping ant', from the eagle to smaller birds. His power is seen in the gentle change of landscape with the seasons, in the harshness of earthquake and other natural calamities, and finally in the 'unravell'd clue' of the last judgment 'when weary Nature shall her work give o'er'.

Hughes's *The Ecstacy: an Ode*, was not published until 1720 after his death. He adds to Cowley's ode with the same title 'a short view of the heavens, according to the modern philosophy', where he begs clouds and whirlwinds to raise the poet to the serene realms of eternal light:

> Mount me sublime along the shining way
> Where planets, in pure streams of aether driv'n . . .
> I pass cerulean gulphs, and now behold
> New solid globes their weight, self-balanc'd, bear,
>   Unprop'd amidst the fluid air,
> And, all around the central sun, in circling eddies roll'd.

He pauses in his cosmic voyage to describe the moon, the earth, Mars, Juno and his four moons, Saturn and his ring, and the Milky Way and profuse stars where God has 'laid up his stores for many a sphere / In destin'd worlds, as yet unknown.' As a meteor approaches he recognizes the soul of Newton, 'the great Columbus of the skies', who though not yet dead the poet imagines 'daily travels here / In search of knowledge for mankind below.' The poet begs to be the scientist's companion, straying from orb to orb, looking at 'unnumber'd suns', comets, and the source of light and colors in the sun, and in this way to explore fresh wonders for the imagery of sublime poems in praise of 'the great Maker's pow'r'.[10]

William Diaper showed his interest in science by his translation of Oppian on fishes, and especially by his vivid use of scientific imagery in *Dryades*.[11] In this poem on fairies he describes, with considerable zest, the infinitely varied world of microscopic creatures and adds occasionally that larger world of nature that belongs to the bucolic pleasures of retired country gentlemen.

Diaper anticipated Thomson in the close observation of natural life as the English landscape changes with the seasons and in the philosophic attitude of the happy man in retirement. With almost scientific care he describes the glow-worm, the poisonous aconite and nightshade, the caterpillar changing to a moth, and, of course, all the variety of insect life. He knows that much of the varied

---

[10] *The Ecstacy: an Ode* (London: J. Roberts, 1720), fol. 8 pages; reprinted in John Hughes, *Poems on Several Occasions* (London, 1735), II. 297-307.

[11] *Dryades: or the Nymph's Prophecy* (London, 1713), reprinted with Diaper's other poems in the Muse's Library, 1952.

world of nature will escape him as it did Cowley or even the poet
who knows 'what unnumber'd kinds adorn the field':

> New beauties show themselves to nearer views,
> And themes untouch'd expect the skilful muse;
> The vegetable worlds neglected lie,
> And flow'rs ungather'd fall, and nameless dye.

Poetry has neglected, for example, 'Nature's care' in protecting
birds and beasts by 'kind instinct and unstudy'd art', and it ignores
the strange behavior of the poisonous toad, spider, and speckled
snake, or the prudent ant. Yet Diaper describes these creatures
with a naturalist's care and deplores the fact that poets have not
yet sung the little world revealed by science with the aid of mag-
nifying glasses:

> A thousand kinds unknown in forrests breed,
> And bite the leaves, and notch the growing weed;
> Have each their several laws, and settled states,
> And constant sympathies, and constant hates;
> Their changing forms, no artful verse describes,
> And how fierce war destroys the wand'ring tribes.
> How prudent Nature feeds her various young,
> Has been (if not untold) at least unsung.
> To th'insect race the muse her pain denies,
> While prouder men the little ant despise.
> But tho' the bulky kinds are easy known,
> Yet nature's skill is most in little shown.

The poet revels in the exciting variety that the 'curious searcher'
sees with the borrowed sight of 'wondrous opticks', and as he
goes deeper into this new world of teeming insect life in rotting
plum and leaves of summer plants, he imagines that this world
revealed by such 'strange puny shapes, unknown to vulgar eyes'
may indeed be infinite:

> Men nature in her secret work behold,
> Untwist her fibres, and her coats unfold;
> With pleasure trace the threds of stringy roots,
> The various textures of the ripening fruits;
> And animals, that careless live at ease,
> To whom the leaves are worlds, the drops are seas.
> If to the finish'd whole so little goes,
> How small the parts, that must the whole compose!
> Matter is infinite, and still descends:
> Man cannot know where lessening nature ends.

An interesting digression in Diaper's sublime picture of microscopic life points to a theme that keeps appearing in scientific poems from 1713, the glory of British commerce arising from the Peace of Utrecht. Diaper leaves the changing insect life to glorify the recent peace gained by Queen Anne that will enable British fleets to sail the southern seas and go to harbors unknown before.

Henry Needler might have been a significant scientific poet if he had not died in 1718 at the age of 28. As it was, he anticipated the ideas of Addison and Shaftesbury though his works were not published until 1728. But the prevailing ideas of his day may be seen vividly expressed in his poetry and prose. Recent critics disagree on whether he was a follower of Shaftesbury, Newton, or Henry More,[12] but Needler's poetry is clearly in the current scientific tradition. In his paraphrase of Proverbs VIII, for example, he depicted wisdom presiding over the creation when God 'cast in order ev'ry part' of the universe,

> The spheres, that roll their steady course above,
> Prepar'd, and taught the planets where to move;
> When laws he to the swelling ocean gave,
> And bound in ropes of sand the raging wave.

In his verses on *The Creation* he complimented Blackmore for adding the microcosm of man to the great world of planets and tides described by older poets: the poet, he said, flies from pole to pole,

> Observes the footsteps of a pow'r divine,
> Which in each part of nature's system shine,
> Surveys the wonders of this beauteous frame,
> And sings the sacred source, whence all things came.

The sublime subject of Blackmore's poem inspires 'mighty transports' as he too strays 'thro' radiant worlds . . . wafted from orb to orb' to watch 'the spheres in stated courses roll'. Needler showed that he had the desire to write a scientific poem, to bring to English verse what Orpheus and Musaeus had done before, the sublime ideas of scientific discovery:

[12] See C. A. Moore, 'Shaftesbury and the Ethical Poets in England', *PMLA*, XXXI (1916), 264–325; Herbert Drennon, 'Henry Needler and Shaftesbury', *PMLA*, XLVI (1931), 1095–1106; and Fairchild, I, 254–8.

> Exalted truths in learned verse they told,
> And nature's deepest secrets did unfold:
> How at th'Eternal Mind's omnific call,
> Yon starry arch, and this terrestial ball,
> The briny water, the blazing source of light,
> And the wan empress of the silent night,
> Each in its order rose, and took its place,
> And fill'd with recent forms the vacant space.

Needler's summary of what Blackmore wrote is a little philosophical poem in itself, but the main thing for both poets was that the time had come for the atheist to renounce Lucretius and make him 'yield the field'.

If Needler had not died young, he might well have written the great scientific poem, but even what he wrote shows the most imaginative treatment of science between Blackmore and Thomson. His 'familiar letters' are full of scientific knowledge and interest: a description of a visit to Dr. John Woodward's collection of minerals and fossils; discussions of Newton and Locke, with references to Le Clerc, Hooke, Halley, and other scientists; and praise of the advances in the discoveries of nature made possible by the microscope and the telescope, in a letter inspired by a French study of spermatic worms.[13] The best of Needler's essays, entitled 'On the Beauty of the Universe', gives his aesthetic justification for nature poetry based on science, not only in the celestial universe but also in plants, animals, and even insects, and all to prove the wisdom and goodness of God in creating a world of order and beauty which could not have resulted from 'the lucky concourse of atoms'.

Though Needler did not live to write an extended poem based on this aesthetic principle, he wrote two excellent short ones. 'A Vernal Hymn in Praise of the Creator' gives grateful praise to the 'parent of universal nature' whose divinity can be seen everywhere:

> Each herb the footsteps of thy wisdom bears,
> And ev'ry blade of grass thy pow'r declares! . . .
> At thy command, the starry host, the sun,
> And moon, unerringly their courses run.

---

[13] *The Works of Mr. Henry Needler*, 2nd ed., London, 1728, pp. 77-220, contain the letters, pp. 1-46 poems, and pp. 47-76 essays.

The rain, winds, and underground waters, animal instinct, and human reason also illustrate his theme. Another poem on the same subject was sent in a letter from Portsmouth, August 16, 1711, but in this poem his chief illustration of God's wisdom to refute atheists, after surveying 'this ample scene of nature's various works, / The sky and earth, with all their furniture, / And fair inhabitants', is the human body:

> How can the atheist, whilst himself he views,
> Perusing limb by limb, persist to ask
> Convincing evidence to prove a God?
> Who form'd his body? By what artful hand
> Was the nice fabrick made? Who plac'd the bones
> In such a well-knit frame, and with such skill
> And symmetry contriv'd? Who bade the blood
> Forth-issue from the fountain of the heart . . .?

On through arteries, veins, nerves, and anatomy of the eye he describes 'these great and beauteous works' that could only be produced by an infinite God, 'supremely wise and good'. Surely this ill-fated admirer of Shaftesbury represents the best lyrical summary of the scientific thought of the first quarter of the century. Together he and Blackmore furnish a fitting prelude to Thomson.

3. NEWTON, SYMBOL OF SCIENCE IN EIGHTEENTH-CENTURY POETRY

Sir Isaac Newton, as we have shown, was well known to the world of science before the publication of the *Principia*, and in the early eighteenth century was cited by theologians, essayists, and poets alike as authority for the proof of celestial order. By 1712 Reynolds had already idealized Newton in the first long scientific poem, and Addison and Blackmore had cited his work in their conscious attempts to bring science out of the closet and make it agreeable to ordinary readers. It was quite natural then that the death of Newton in 1727 should not only call forth a number of eulogistic memorial poems but also become a catalytic agent for the composition of a number of long scientific poems that demonstrated the wisdom of God in nature with examples from the new science. These new longer poems were inspired by Newton on celestial order and on light and color, but they took their examples from other branches of science as well, from the world of order seen under the microscope, from the visible creation seen in plants and animals and even in minerals, and from the scientific study of the human body and the human mind. Before analyzing this series of poetical essays that appeared in the decade or so after Newton's death, we need to summarize the considerable research that has gone into depicting the role that Newton played in poetry.

Newton's *Optics*, first published in 1704, had an important impact on later poetry. Its metaphysical significance in the history of ideas and its aesthetic influence on the use of light and color in the imagery of the English poets have been amply demonstrated by Marjorie Nicolson in her *Newton Demands the Muse*. This side of Newton is particularly apparent in the poems of Brooke and Akenside, and the influence on the sharper use of light and color in the descriptive poetry may be seen not only in Thomson's *Seasons* but also in its numerous imitations in the second half of the century. But this is only one side of the story, as I have argued elsewhere,[14] and the poems analyzed in this book are offered as further proof that the English poets who wrote about science in the eighteenth century put greater emphasis on the *Principia* than on the *Optics*. The poets knew, from Derham and other popularizers, that Newton had mathematically demonstrated the order of the universe and calculated the orbits not only of the planets in the solar system but of erring comets as well. They used this idea over and over in numerous variations, not only when they mentioned Newton by name but when, in their illustrations of various branches of science they devoted more space to celestial order— illustrated by gravitation, the precise motions of heavenly bodies, and the effect of the moon on tides—than to the physics of light and color.

The poems themselves will be described in the following chapters but here I would like to show how Newton became the symbol of science that made it possible for the poems to be written and published. We have seen how Newton was praised by Reynolds, Hughes, Blackmore, and other poets, and how his discoveries were used by the theologians and essayists to enlarge the imagination and bolster religious beliefs. We could add specific praise of Newton in later *Spectator* papers as 'the miracle of our present age',

[14] 'Newton Further Demands the Muse', Rice University *Studies in English Literature 1500–1900*, III (1963), 287–306.

'the glory of our own nation', or the genius who can break out of the darkness that surrounds human understanding 'and appear like one of another species'.[15] Instead we will cite only the verses, many from obscure sources, that specifically praise Newton in a short time after his death.

When Thomson in 1727 wrote the first of several eulogies to Newton, *A Poem Sacred to the Memory of Sir Isaac Newton*, his main emphasis was on the *Principia*. The cosmic voyage of Newton after death, quitting this earth 'to mingle with his stars', is a sort of frame for a summary of the scientific achievement of 'our philosophic sun', for the tribute ends with Newton wandering 'thro' those endless worlds, / He here so well described', discovering from the angels what he could not learn here, his soul soaring swiftly 'with the whirling orbs, / Comparing things with things, in rapture lost.' For eighty-four lines the poet traces the secret hand of Providence 'from motion's simple laws' and shows how sun and planets and satellites are bound in their places, the whole celestial universe moving 'in silent harmony' through 'the blended power / Of gravitation and projection'; how the moon by attraction affects the tides; how in the skies distant stars blaze into suns, each the living center 'of an harmonious system' ruled by the power of gravitation; how the comet returns 'through the long eliptic curve'; and how sound flows through the air. Thomson then devotes twenty-nine lines to color and light, 'the refractive law' from the *Optics*.

Two other long memorial poems on Newton show a similar proportion of emphasis on the *Principia*. The poem by Richard Glover printed in Henry Pemberton's 1728 popularization of Newton, in an attempt to summarize Newtonian science in didactic verse, devotes six pages to general topics, notably gravitation and the motion of heavenly bodies, the next two and one-half pages to color and light, a similar amount to sound, and a final three and one-half pages to unsolved problems and other concluding matter. In 1735 Dr. Samuel Bowden printed his neglected tribute, 'A Poem Sacred to the Memory of Sir Isaac Newton', with even less emphasis on the *Optics* than either Thomson or Glover. Bowden begins with general praise of the studious sage

---

[15] *Spectator*, 543, 554, and 635. For this and other praise of Newton before 1727, see Alan D. McKillop, *James Thomson: The Castle of Indolence and other Poems* (Lawrence, Kan., 1961), pp. 128 ff.

> Who to creation's distant regions soar'd,
> And wonders hid from human eyes explor'd;
> Did nature's deep recesses open lay,
> Dispel the gloom, and spread immortal day.

Bowden tried in his couplets to explain gravitation, the balance of empire between two different powers, the 'projectile' and the 'central', governed by mechanical laws. Among Newton's accomplishments, he said, are learning to view a comet without surprise, reforming chronology, and explaining such mysterious phenomena of nature as the changes of the moon by attraction, the effect of the moon on tides, the refraction of light (half a page), and the vibration of sound and light waves.[16]

Before Bowden's tribute had been printed, a number of anonymous eulogies appeared, ephemeral verses with little poetic value but often specific in their description of the *Principia*. The first of them, a contribution to *The London Medley* (1731), is an example of what the ordinary person knew of Newtonian thought:

> Newton arose; shew'd how each planet moved. . . .
> He was the first that could unerring trace
> Each orbit thro' th'immense expanded space:
> He was the first that with unweary'd flight,
> Fathom'd the depth of heav'n, and reach'd the height,
> Where comets thro' the void revolving flow,
> Their course oblique and settled period know;
> Guided by him when we survey the whole,
> Worlds beyond worlds that by him measur'd roll,
> And with the vast idea fill the soul;
> What is this point of earth, this mortal seat,
> How little all appears, and He how great!

The second, a more general summary included in *Stowe . . . Address'd to Mr. Pope* (1732), describes Newton as one 'in whom the heavenly mind / Shines forth distinguish'd and above mankind', and gives him credit for having 'first survey'd / The plan by which the Universe was made: / Saw nature's simple, yet stupendous laws, / And prov'd th'effects, tho' not explain'd the cause.'

In 1733 Queen Caroline set up a grotto in the Royal Hermitage as a sort of scientific hall of fame, in which the busts of Newton,

[16] Samuel Bowden, *Poetical Essays on Several Occasions*, II (London: J. Pemberton, 1735), 1–16.

Locke, Boyle, Wollaston, and Samuel Clarke were placed to remind visitors of the achievements of science and physico-theology.
The grotto received considerable attention in a series of occasional
verses written for a contest sponsored by the *Gentleman's Magazine* in April 1733.[17] The first prize, printed in June, contains only
two lines on Newton:

> Newton the volume of the skie unseals,
> And all th' amazing miracle reveals.

The second and third prizes do not mention Newton by name, but
the fourth praises him particularly for the *Principia*:

> Then Newton, wondrous man! still higher soar'd,
> Describ'd the laws by which the shining orbs,
> That through the boundless void incessant roll,
> Perform their course encircling; how they keep
> One certain track, by bonds invisible
> Confin'd, nor through the liquid aether stray.[18]

The sixth poem repeats the same theme of tracking wandering
planets and the orbits of eccentric comets through boundless
space where

> Millions of worlds possess the vast profound!
> Millions of suns with planets circling round!
> Planets, which secondary planets grace,
> Endless the wonders of th' ethereal space.[19]

The seventh prize has abundant praise for Newton, all because of
his work on gravitation and the removal of errors from previous
astronomical discoveries:

> Newton without a rival reigns alone,
> Prince of the new philosophy, his own.

Not until the eighth prize poem is the theory of colors mentioned,
and even then it is overshadowed by gravitation and the motions
of circling orbs and devious comets. The ninth devotes one

---

[17] *Gentleman's Magazine*, III (1733), 207 f. The grotto was described in verses
reprinted (III, 41) from the *Weekly Miscellany*. The poems were collected in a volume,
The Contest (London, 1733).
[18] *Gentleman's Magazine*, III, 369.
[19] *Gentleman's Magazine*, pp. 429 ff. for prizes 6–9.

quatrain to each sage but 'sagacious Newton' is clearly known for the *Principia*. No. 10 sums up Newton's genius:

> The works of nature, that in embryo lay,
> Dawn into life, and in a flood of day
> Newton's great genius to the world convey.[20]

The contest in the *Gentleman's Magazine* produced no great poetry, but surely it is the *Principia*, not the *Optics*, that here demands the muse.

In 1735 Mrs. Jane Brereton wrote two poems complimentary to Newton, in both of which the chief topic is attraction and the orderly motions of heavenly bodies. One of them, entitled 'Merlin', contrasted the crude science of the magician with that which 'blaz'd on Newton with meridian light', revealing 'attraction's mighty force / And how fierce comets run their stated course.' These new phenomena are

> Surprising scenes! by Heav'n reserv'd in store
> For its own fav'rite Newton to explore.

The other poem is addressed to Queen Caroline 'On the Bustoes in the Royal Hermitage', where she praises Newton for revealing God through order:

> Newton, th' All-wise Creator's works explores,
> Sublimely, on the wings of knowledge, soars;
> Th' establish'd order, of each orb, unfolds,
> And th' omnipresent God, in all, behold :
> If to the dark abyss, or bright abode,
> He points; the view still terminates in God.[21]

The death of Newton gave a fresh impetus to a new aspect of the idea of the limitations of science, the cosmic voyage of the scientist who after death wanders among the stars to learn the secrets of the universe that he vainly sought in this life. Even before 1727 Reynolds and Hughes had shown Newton in cosmic voyages, and the more general idea of the contemplative man finding intellectual enjoyment after death appeared often in poetry as an

---

[20] *Gentleman's Magazine*, p. 541.

[21] Both poems were published in *Merlin: a Poem . . . by a Lady* (London, 1735). Mrs. Cockburn's 'A Poem occasioned by the Busts set up in the Queen's Hermitage', probably written about the same time, was printed in *Poems by Eminent Ladies* (London, 1755), I, 234–8.

offshoot of the classical theme of the 'happy man' inherited from the seventeenth century.[22]

Newton among the stars, learning his physics from the angels, is an alluring picture. Thomson gave the theme new life when he used it as the frame for his praise of Newton, and soon after him others took it up, as in the tributes of Allan Ramsay and Edward Young.[23] In the memorial poems already described, Glover and Bowden combine Newton's *Principia* and the cosmic voyage. Glover hinted that if man could find his way to most distant stars Newton would be found immortal there:

> In each new sphere, each new-appearing sun,
> In furthest regions at the very verge
> Of the wide universe should'st thou be seen.

And Bowden, at the end of his poem, showed Newton after death going through space in triumph, learning more than he could on earth:

> See where he mounts the high, diurnal sphere,
> And leaves a trail of light above the air;
> The stars accost him, as he soars along,
> And souls of wand'ring sages round him throng.
> Mark where he halts on Saturn, tipt with snow,
> And pleas'd surveys his theory below;
> Sees the five moons alternate round him shine,
> Rise by his laws, and by his laws decline,
> Then thro' the void takes his immortal race,
> Amidst the vast infinity of space.

The most vivid example of this idea appeared in 1728 in a poem closely influenced by Thomson, David Mallet's *The Excursion*. The passage appears in Book II, that ecstatic survey of the celestial universe as it reveals God, where Mallet describes the order in the skies, how the huge globes, observing 'one unchanging law,/ Revolve harmonious, world attracting world / With mutual love, and to their central sun / All gravitating.'

The scientific exploration of the universe after death was at times

---

[22] M. S. Rostvig, *The Happy Man*, Vol. II: 1700–1760 (Oslo, 1958), pp. 30–33, 162–170. She quotes an ode by William Hinchcliffe that I have not seen, which 'portrayed the happy life of the dead as one continuous college course in Newtonian physics'.

[23] Both poems are quoted in McKillop, *The Castle of Indolence and Other Poems*, p. 136.

applied to gravitation and motion without specific mention of
Newton. In 1729 Richard Savage in *The Wanderer* applied the idea
to Halley:

> Hence Halley's soul etherial flight essays;
> Instructive there from orb to orb she strays;
> Sees, round new countless suns, new systems roll!
> Sees God in all! and magnifies the whole.

In Richard Gambol's *The Beauties of the Universe* (1732), the de-
parted soul goes on a grand tour of the skies:

> Unbounded in its ken, (from prison free)
> Will clearly view what here we darkly see:
> Those planetary worlds, and thousands more,
> How veil'd from human sight, it shall explore.

Joseph Trapp developed the idea in the first part of his long
lugubrious poem, *Thoughts upon the Four Last Things*, the first two
parts of which, 'Death' and 'Judgment', were published in 1734.
It is fitting that Trapp, who as lecturer on poetry at Oxford had
recommended science as a subject for poetry, should use examples
from science to show the delights of exploring hidden knowledge
after death. The gratification of curiosity becomes one of the chief
delights of the after life in searching out infinite nature and learning the causes of phenomena as the soul wanders through the
'unnumber'd world of stars':

> Sees how barb'd comets shake their fiery hair,
> How planets, hung on nothing, spin in air;
> Of plain effects the latent causes views;
> How hail is moulded, and how rise the dews;
> How blended elements unite in strife,
> And bury'd seeds, by dying, spring to life:
> What paints the tulip, and the blushing rose;
> And from the violet the fresh odor flows:
> How cold congeals, and why ascends the fire;
> Why tides swell high, and less'ning ebbs retire.

The poet continues his scientific journey to the bottom of the
ocean to see coral groves and fish, and into the middle of the earth
to see metals in their birth and the hidden seas and rivers that flow
underground. As a final result he will better see the Creator in all

the universe, and how in Him all things live in nature's vast frame, 'the vilest worm below, the highest saint above'.

In 1733 Pope was clearly influenced by this scientific common-place when in the *Essay on Man* he showed the relative superiority of celestial beings, even in scientific knowledge, by letting them show Newton as we show an ape. Yet Mrs. Brereton was closely following Thomson in *Merlin* when she hailed Newton as heaven's own favorite who was able to achieve what Merlin could never do but who must himself wait for death in order to explore fully the skies:

> With faculties enlarg'd, he's gone to prove
> The laws and motions of yon worlds above;
> And the vast circuits of th' expanse survey,
> View solar systems in the Milky Way.

Except for Thomson and Mallet, the clearest expression of the idea that in the future life we will all grasp what the greatest scientists could not discover on earth is found in the anonymous *A Philosophic Ode on the Sun and the Universe*, published in London in 1750. The poem explains that while the great Kepler discovered the law of the motion of planets, the greater Newton showed that the comets obey one general law and 'first fully illustrated these two laws or theorems'. The poet praises Newton for revealing order in the heavens:

> Newton, immortal Newton rose;
> This mighty frame, its order, laws,
>   His piercing eyes beheld:
> That Sun of Science pour'd his streams,
> All darkness fled before his beams,
>   And Nature stood reveal'd.
> Though Newton's genius cloudless shone,
> Discover'd truths before unknown,
>   By none before believ'd;
> That time will come when such shall know
> Much more than Newton ever knew,
>   Than fancy e'er conceiv'd.[24]

And then in a footnote the author amplifies the idea that the grati-fication of curiosity 'will be one of the pleasures of the bless'd:

[24] P. 15. Fairchild, II, 69, discusses this poem and places its science above its philosophy.

and what an ample field does the universe afford! How many ages would pass in barely informing ourselves of the number of worlds?'

There are numerous other poems in the eighteenth century that reflect the influence of Newton by direct reference or by describing the regular motion of heavenly bodies and the effect of gravitation, especially on tides. These poems will be described in the rest of this book, not with reference to Newton but as they take their place in the larger picture of the influence of science. It should be clear, even without this evidence, that these poets, uninspired as they often were, saw Newton as a symbol of the new science, for he could show the orderliness of planets and stars and the beauty of light and color. To them this was additional proof of what they had believed all along, that the wisdom of God is shown in nature.[25]

[25] A number of poems on Newton, supplementing Nicolson, are cited in my article on Newton, pp. 298–305. Most of them will be discussed in a larger context below.

IV

THE TRIUMPH OF PHYSICO-THEOLOGY: SCIENTIFIC POEMS FROM THOMSON TO YOUNG

THE poems reflecting the influence of science on the imagination began early in England but about 1700 took on a new look. The contrasting worlds revealed by the telescope and microscope, reaching far beyond what man had before been able to discover with the naked eye, had already changed man's thinking about his place in the universe and opened up new vistas of the imagination in literature. Yet the new poetry after 1700 dramatized the new discoveries: Biblical subjects and skeptical poems used new imagery, and the dramatic concept of the Great Chain of Being got new emphasis from the realization that the scale of nature from mite to man now stretched infinitely farther, from the visible mite downward to the millions of smaller creatures living an orderly life in a drop of pond scum, and from man upward to the possible inhabitants of distant stars whose magnitude and orderly motion were revealed only by the telescope and the application of mathematics by a Newton.

The new poetry combined science with religion and philosophy as the prose writers of physico-theology had taught them to do, and in this they were immeasurably helped by the *Spectator* and other popular prose essays. The poetic treatment of this new 'natural philosophy', moreover, covered all phases of the world of nature, mineral, animal, and vegetable, celestial and earthly, human and brute, plant, bird, insect, and microscopic creature, it mattered not. Astronomy was the most popular branch of science at that time, for the sun, moon, and stars had been stock examples of the praise of God's handiwork since Biblical times, and the newer concept of orderly worlds in boundless space had considerable appeal. Yet the less dramatic phases of nature were also included, at least in the longer scientific poems, for the poets saw God in nature in all its manifestations. The choice of examples to illustrate the wisdom of God in nature depended on the poet's knowledge of science and his enthusiasm for the subject. That is why Blackmore devoted an entire book of *The Creation* to human physiology, or Reynolds preferred astronomy, or Diaper microscopic botany.

During the first quarter of the eighteenth century, however, the dramatic popular element in astronomy took stronger hold as Sir Isaac Newton became the symbol of the new science. The death of Newton in 1727 therefore was the excuse not only for several memorial eulogies of the great scientist but also, what is more important for our story, for the greatest flowering of English scientific poetry in the eighteenth century. In less than two decades were published the most influential scientific poem, Thomson's *Seasons*, the most artistic one, Pope's *Essay on Man*, and a number of long serious poetical essays that copiously cited the new discoveries of science to illustrate, in a sort of encyclopedic manner, the wisdom of God in nature. Thomson was the spark for this surge of interest, and Newton was the symbol. When Newton died in 1727, Thomson added to the two parts of *The Seasons* already finished a memorial poem that was to be a prelude to many others. Clearly Thomson then helped to make the death of Newton a kind of aesthetic catalytic agent that called into being the series of long scientific poems that had been germinating for two decades in England. The influence of *The Seasons* and its intrinsic value as a scientific poem together make an extensive analysis of the poem necessary at this point.

I. THOMSON AND HIS CIRCLE

The numerous changes in *The Seasons* from the first publication of *Winter* in 1726 to the final edition in 1746 made the finished product uneven and often contradictory, yet in its final form the poem was not only a significant work but during the eighteenth century a model for all moral-descriptive poems about nature. All the ideas in the poem were present before Thomson, but by 1730 when the four *Seasons* were completed and published together for the first time, it was apparent that something new had been added to English poetry, in the fresh imagery from the English (or rather Scottish) landscape, the pleasantly philosophic tone, the gentle sentiments of humanitarianism, and the exotic quality of scenes from distant lands that recalled the popularity of travel books. Most contemporary readers would have also recognized *The Seasons* as a scientific poem, Thomson's own contribution to the series of physico-theological poetical essays that had begun with Reynolds and Blackmore and were to continue with a glorious succession of poems in the next decade. But it was not a scientific poem to begin with, for the first edition of *Winter* was almost purely a descriptive poem. The descriptive passages throughout the finished poem endeared Thomson to later readers and would themselves be enough to assure him a place in literature, but he was not satisfied with that. He himself insisted, in the preface to the second edition of *Winter* (1726), on the moral qualities: 'I know no subject more elevating, more amusing; more ready to awaken the poetical enthusiasm, the philosophical reflection, and the moral sentiment, than the works of nature.'

Following Shaftesbury Thomson put into *The Seasons* the emotional impact of man in nature; following Newton he was concerned with the important theme of treating nature as a manifestation of the glories of God, using frequently the discoveries of science to illustrate his theme. As *The Seasons* became more general and episodic with constant revision, more passages on science were introduced, giving the poem a more eclectic quality and less unity.[1]

The Seasons is full of a variety of things, and so it cannot be thought of as a scientific poem in the same sense as Blackmore's *Creation* or the later poetical essays. The poet chooses what he wants and in his revisions adds more, skipping with the flimsiest of transitions from one subject to another, from the vivid des-

[1] See A. D. McKillop, *The Background of Thomson's Seasons* (Minneapolis, 1942), and Patricia M. Spacks, *The Varied God: a Critical Study of Thomson's The Seasons* (Berkeley, 1959).

criptions of nature in England's countryside to the exotic fauna and flora of distant lands, from the moralizing on man and beast lost in a snowstorm to the evils of debtor prisons, fox hunting, or robbing of a beehive, from praise of the wisdom of the ancients to glorification of Britain, from primitivism to progress. In this eclectic display of varied interests, popular science naturally appears whenever Thomson is reminded of it, which happened more often in the later revisions as he became more aware of the developments of science. Some of these passages are almost purely topical and didactic summaries in verse of subjects that interested scientists in Thomson's day: the mysterious workings of frost in *Winter*, of the flow of sap in *Spring*, and of underground streams and artesian wells in *Autumn*. The most spectacular display of scientific knowledge is that of natural history in *Spring* with its detailed accounts of plants and birds, and of the contrasting worlds revealed by the telescope and microscope in *Summer*. The more general theme of the divinization of nature, the wisdom of God revealed by science, appears by implication in these passages but more fully in occasional philosophic summaries that may have nothing to do with description of nature. Using Otto Zippel's critical edition of the poem,[2] we can see how the various revisions reflect Thomson's scientific knowledge and the philosophy based upon it.

Winter, the earliest of the four parts, started as the nostalgic description of a young Scotsman in London remembering the snowstorms of his childhood, and the best of it remained in that mood. The turbulence of the winter storm, it is true, impressed him with the hidden powers behind nature:

> Nature! great parent! whose directing hand
> Rolls round the seasons of the changeful year,
> How mighty! how majestick are thy works!
> With what a pleasing dread they swell the soul,
> That sees, astonish'd! and, astonish'd sings!

Yet there is no other indication in the first edition of *Winter* that Thomson had any interest in science or physico-theology. The brief description of frost as 'aethereal nitre' could have come from Philips or Blackmore and the summary of scientific research on frost was not added until 1730. By that time Thomson had

[2] *Palaestra*, LXVI, Berlin, 1908, hereafter referred to as Zippel.

109

written a great deal of scientific poetry, in 1727 *Summer* and
A Poem Sacred to the Memory of Sir Isaac Newton, in 1728 *Spring*,
and in 1730 *Autumn, A Hymn to the Seasons*, and the first collected
edition of *The Seasons*. Yet even with considerable changes *Winter*
remained essentially a descriptive poem, keeping the pictures of
winter in Scotland and adding, mainly in 1744, the harsh primitivism of Lapland, Russia, and the Arctic wasteland, taken from
travel books. The contemplation of God in nature, Thomson's
variation of the retired philosopher as scientist, appears for the
first time in 1730:

> With them would search, if this unbounded frame
> Of nature rose from unproductive night,
> Or sprung eternal from th'eternal Cause,
> Its springs, its laws, its progress and its end.
> Hence larger prospects of the beauteous whole
> Would gradual open on our opening minds;
> And each diffusive harmony unite,
> In full perfection, to th'astonish'd eye.

The rebirth of life in spring, a natural addition to the end of
Winter in the 1730 *Seasons*, brings a clear statement of order in
nature ('the great eternal scheme, involving all') and even then it
quickly gives way to the theme of moral benevolence.

Summer, the second of the *Seasons*, is a scientific poem compared to *Winter*, even in the first edition of 1727. Here he begins
with the order of the celestial universe ('a perfect, world-revolving
Power . . . not eccentric once') and ends with the 'Sole Being
right' revealed by 'those radiant tracts on high'. This world
revealed by the telescope is more scientifically described in
Thomson's poem to Newton written about the same time, but
the mood is declared in a sublime manner at the very outset of
the 1727 *Summer* by a hymn to the sun. Without the sun there
would be no life on earth, no plants on it, no minerals inside it; its
system rolls by its 'secret, strong, attractive force'; its light gives
added beauty in its prismatic colors. Even if men forget to praise
God, all created things would proclaim the 'Almighty Poet' revealed in 'Nature's volume, wide, display'd'. Thomson's sole
delight will be 'some easy passage, raptur'd, to translate'.

Thomson adds little more in the 1727 *Summer* that would have
caught the scientist's eye. He shows his first interest in the exotic
natural history that was to follow in profusion by 1746, green

serpent, savages, and tiger. He describes the comets that frighten the superstitious but appear beautiful to the scientist 'inquisitive to know / The causes and materials, yet unfix'd.' His continuous changes between 1730 and 1744 in two passages directly related to science, however, are worthy of more extended analysis.

The most important of these is the passage on microscopic life transferred from the 1730 *Spring* (136–168) to the 1744 *Summer* and enlarged several times. The 1727 *Summer* hints at the subject in a very broad way by the passage immediately following, which scolds the 'impious railer' for believing that 'creative wisdom' ever worked in vain and concludes that every creature has its place in God's scheme in 'The mighty chain of beings, lessening down / From infinite perfection to the brink / Of dreary nothing, desolate abyss!' In the expanded versions Thomson uses the teeming abundance of microscopic life in water, on leaf and stone, and in rotting fruit to lead up to the chain of being. The complete thought can be seen only from manuscript additions in Thomson's interleaved copy now in the British Museum,[3] most of which were incorporated in the 1744 edition.

> Downward from these what numerous kinds descend,
> Evading even the microscopic eye!
> Full nature swarms with life; one wondrous [*heap*] mass
> Of animals, or atoms organiz'd,
> Waiting the vital breath, when Parent-Heaven
> Shall bid his spirit blow. The hoary fen,
> In putrid streams, emits the living cloud
> Of pestilence. Thro' subterranean cells,
> Where searching sun-beams scarce can find a way,
> Earth animated heaves. The flowery leaf
> Wants not it's soft inhabitants. Secure,
> Within it's winding citadel, the stone
> Holds multitudes. But chief the forest-boughs,
> That dance unnumber'd to the playful breeze,
> The downy orchard, and the melting pulp
> Of mellow fruit the nameless nations feed
> Of evanescent insects. Where the pool
> Stands mantled o'er with green, invisible,
> Amid the floating verdure millions stray.

[3] C 28.e.17, MS. additions to *Spring*, 135 ff., transferred to *Summer* in 1744. See Zippel, *op. cit.*, pp. 81–3.

Each liquid too, whether of acid [*taste*] taint
Or oily smooth, whether severe and harsh
Or rais'd to racy flavour, [*bright*] quick and high,
With various forms abounds, whence is, perhaps,
Deriv'd their various taste. Nor is the stream
Of purest crystal, nor the limpid air,
Tho' one transparent vacancy it seems,
Devoid of life. Even animals subsist
On animals, in infinite descent.
These, more and more, th'inspective glass discerns,
As more it's finer curve collects the rays,
And to the curious gives th'amusing scenes
Of lessening life.

The other passage is part of a long addition in 1744 (*Summer* 1325 ff.) describing first the pleasures of philosophic walks in the fields and woods 'to nature's vast lyceum' and working into one of his favorite themes, 'happy Britannia'. The roll of heroes ends with the scientists, including Bacon, Boyle ('whose pious search / Amid the dark recesses of his works, / The great Creator sought'), and Newton ('pure intelligence, whom God / To mortals lent, to trace his boundless works / From laws sublimely simple'). Between these two sublime passages Thomson throws in a miscellaneous assortment of subjects suggested by heat: farm-yard animals; ways to avoid heat; fertile vegetation and tropical violence as a picture of harsh nature far from the temperate climate of fortunate England (as in *Winter*, these pictures of exotic natural history reflect the science found in travel books); and a tragic story of two lovers in a thunderstorm.

Spring (1728) had little science to begin with: Newton's research in refraction of light, the rise of sap in plants, and that passage on microscopic insects which, as we have seen, was transferred to *Summer* and there enlarged. The burgeoning luxuriance of spring leads the poet quickly, however, from description to philosophy, from glowing colors and lavish fragrance to 'Nature's swift and secret-working hand'. In the midst of profuse description in *Spring* appear phrases like 'Nature's ample lap' and 'the negligence of Nature, wide, and wild'. The listing of many flowers with infinite numbers, smells, and colors in 'endless bloom' is the kind of amateur scientific by-product of a handbook on gardening, yet it leads to adoration:

> Hail, Mighty Being! Universal Soul
> Of heaven and earth! Essential Presence, hail!
> To thee I bend the knee, to Thee my thoughts
> Continual climb, who, with a master-hand
> Hast the great whole into perfection touch'd.

The melody of birds, inspired by the 'spirit of love', suggests much descriptive detail of the working of instinct in mysterious ways that interested the scientists of that day: the building of nests, feeding young, protecting by evasive tactics, and teaching flight, examples of divine wisdom that 'never works in vain'. The mighty breath that infuses love through the breasts of birds is 'Inspiring God! who boundless Spirit all, / And unremitting Energy, pervades, / Subsists, adjusts, and agitates the whole.' Indeed the love of nature in spring induces contentment in men, the serenity of contemplation that leads to rapture at feeling 'the present Deity', for chiefly in spring the gentler side of 'the informing Author' appears in his works. Even though the perfection of 'this complex, amazing scene of things' is concealed from the casual observer, it is harmony in nature 'that inspires this universal smile'.

In *Autumn*, written in 1730 and changed mainly by the addition of travel lore, Thomson digresses on commerce and the evils of hunting and other subjects so freely that he comes to the description of autumn after more than 600 verses. Yet he shows a knowledge of some of the subjects discussed by scientists, such as the migration of swallows and storks, the popular fear of falling meteors, and the robbing of beehives, and he treats with some sublimity the cycle of evaporation, the underground rivers, and the consequent usefulness of gloomy mountains. At the end of *Autumn*, however, he saves for the conclusion of his whole *Seasons*, which began with God, the best summary of the way science reveals God in nature:

> Oh Nature! all-sufficient! over all!
> Enrich me with the knowledge of thy works!
> Snatch me to Heaven; thy rolling wonders there,
> World beyond world, in infinite extent,
> Profusely scatter'd o'er the void immense,
> Shew me; their motions, periods, and their laws
> Give me to scan; thro' the disclosing deep
> Light my blind way: the mineral strata there;

> Thrust, blooming, thence the vegetable world;
> O'er that the rising system, more complex,
> Of animals; and higher still, the mind,
> The varied scene of quick-compounded thought.

The actual conclusion, however, is the *Hymn to the Seasons*, a summary of his physico-theology but done in lyric terms, 'the varied God' filling the 'rolling year'—beauty and tenderness in spring, glory in summer, profuse bounty in autumn, and 'horrible blackness (*majestic darkness* in 1744) on the whirlwind's wing, / Riding sublime' as winter humbles nature with its northern blast. The trite digressions have no place here, and the eclectic combination of science and moral philosophy is blended into the ecstatic hymn that becomes Thomson's contribution to the liturgy, his own *Benedicite*. The 'mysterious round' marks the harmony of nature as a chant of praise, for each of his works is asked to praise the Lord and magnify Him forever: winds, streams, ocean, herbs, fruits, flowers, forests, harvests, stars, sun, hills, rocks, and birds, all join in the great music of praise. The ending of the manuscript version for the 1744 edition fits the note of progress and belief in providence that Thomson wishes to leave with us at the end of *The Seasons*:

> When even at last the solemn mandate comes,
> And my dark flight I wing to future worlds,
> I cheerful will obey, there, with new powers,
> Will rising wonders sing: I cannot go
> Where universal goodness does not reign,
> Sustaining all yon orbs and all their sons,
> From seeming evil still educing good,
> And better thence again, and better still,
> In infinite progression.—But I lose
> Myself in Him, in Light ineffable![4]

Thomson's patron and executor, Lord Lyttelton, did not show, in his published poems, any interest in science, but the additions he presumably composed for *The Seasons* reveal that he too felt deeply on the subject.[5] For example, he expanded the section on

[4] Zippel, *op. cit.*, p. 338. The MS. has three separate writings of most of these lines, but the only variants not recorded by Zippel are: it's awful mandate; winging thro' the dark gulph to other future worlds.

[5] John Mitford's copy of these MS. revisions of Lyttelton is now in the British Museum, C. 134.c.1: Realizing their importance, Zippel collated them with the original copy which was then at Hagley and printed them, pp. xxii–xxxi.

divine philosophy by whom 'conducted, with serene delight I range / O'er Nature's works through all the varied year.' The adoration of the Creator at night, which precedes this passage, reminds him that the stars are not for man alone: 'To various systems of dependent orbs / Bright day, and animating heat they give, / The life-infusing suns of other worlds.' Finally, his expansion of the lines on Boyle and Newton show his great admiration for these English scientists.

When *The Excursion: a Poem in Two Books* was anonymously printed in March 1728, those who knew that the young author, David Mallet, was a good friend of Thomson would have recognized the influence of the 'Seasons' then printed, especially in the first half of Book I, for example:

> Now sacred Morn, ascending, smiles serene
> A dewy radiance, bright'ning o'er the world,
> The western grey of yonder breaking clouds
> Slow-reddens into flame. The parting mists,
> From off the mountain's brow, roll blue away
> In rising waves, and open all his woods.

The changes of the seasons are there, too, and 'Nature's God', and an intensified picture of harsher nature in the devastation of tropical heat or thunderstorm. But about midway in Book I the imagination of the 'excursive traveller' takes over, and 'light fancy speeds along, / Quick as the darted beam, from pole to pole.' The cosmic voyage in the skies, which occupies nearly all of Book II, is not like the *Seasons*. It stems from the philosophical tour of the scientist after death that was already old when Thomson applied it to Newton.

The last half of Book I takes a quick tour of foreign scenes where Nature's harshness abounds, first in the north with its 'white waste of ice' and 'hills of snow . . . in blue, bleak precipices', then in the burning desert contrasted with fair southern scenes 'where all is paradise', and finally in a long and vivid account of a devastating earthquake. Since Thomson added nearly all his accounts of nature in arctic cold and tropical heat to the 1744 edition, and since he touches only lightly on the earthquake in the early versions of *Summer*, we can only conclude that Mallet influenced Thomson, perhaps even more than, as Johnson much later unjustly stated, *The Excursion* was a servile imitation of

The Seasons.[6] Mallet's vivid picture of the volcanic eruption that overwhelmed 'a spacious city . . . in round extent magnificent' covers thirteen pages in the first edition, a truly sublime account of the 'black eruption' with its whirling stones, its 'liquid lake . . . mad-boiling from its lowest cave'. Yet all the horror poured upon guilty and just alike, 'seemingly severe' as it is, asserts divine providence as reason, confused and subdued 'To silence and amazement, with due praise / Acknowledges th'Almighty, and adores / His will unerring, wisest, justest, best.'

Mallet devotes all of Book II to his cosmic voyage, where he makes a rhapsodical description of the celestial universe, which in the manner of Thomson reaches its imaginative height in its tribute to Newton. He mounts quickly to that 'shoreless sea of fluctuating fire' where 'Ten thousand suns blaze forth; each with his train / Of peopled worlds; all beneath the eye, / And sovereign rule of one eternal Lord.' In the solar system he describes the sun with its mysterious spots and in order the planets, Mercury, Venus, 'this speck of earth' and her attendant moon 'whose attractive power / Swells all her seas and oceans into tides', Mars, Jove whose four moons are described at length, and Saturn with his moons and mighty ring. Mallet's use of astronomy in the poem, while not as technical as some didactic poems, is far more than Thomson revealed before 1730. Yet Thomson's poem to Newton was probably in Mallet's mind when he described the harmonious revolutions of these worlds attracting each other 'and to their central sun all gravitating', certainly when he attributed the first knowledge of 'this spring of motion' to 'great Newton! Britain's justest pride, / The boast of human race! whose towering thought, / In her amazing progress unconfin'd, / From truth to truth ascending, gain'd the height / Of science.' If this greatest of scientists, the poet continues, has to wait till death to find out the secrets of nature, how can mortals

> Attempt this blue profundity of heaven,
> Unfathomable, endless of extent!
> Where unknown suns to unknown systems rise,
> Whose numbers who shall tell! stupendous host!

[6] McKillop, *Background*, p. 68, has shown how Mallet's description of comets adding fuel to the dying sun "had in turn a direct influence on the later versions of *Summer*."

> In flaming millions thro' the vacant hung,
> Sun behind sun, with gulphs of sky between,
> Measureless distance, unconceiv'd by thought!

After a long description of comets, quoted by McKillop to show Mallet's influence on Thomson's scientific passage, the poem ends with 'that first Cause, who made, who governs all . . . all-wise, all-good', but not before tribute is paid to the Great Chain of Being, 'sumless orders and degrees' descending by gradual scale from the angels. *The Excursion*, we may conclude, is truly a scientific poem in the sublime manner and far from an imitation of the *Seasons*.[7]

The influence of both Thomson and Mallet can be seen in Richard Savage's 'vision' in couplets, *The Wanderer: a Poem in five Cantos* (1729). Not only are both poets praised in Canto I but the whole scheme is a kind of imaginative excursion that begins with a long and vivid but not too coherent description of winter. Like the contemplative philosopher that Thomson does not add to *Winter* until 1730, Savage's hero studies science to find God, first with astronomy where one can with 'the beams of the far-lengthen'd eye / Measure known stars, and new remoter spy' and imagine an ethereal flight like that of Halley's soul. Then the expedition jumps from one phase of natural history to another, studying in turn medicinal herbs, eagles, fish, shells, and the sand that can be fused into glass. The further wandering is hard to follow through toothache and depressed spirits but becomes coherent in the contemplation of British industry with its technological triumphs made possible by science and of British poetry crowned by Pope. The canto ends on a scientific note when Savage's rhetorical questions imply that his private misery is part of the whole and nature's end still remains the same:

> Shall clouds, but at my welfare's call descend?
> Shall gravity for me her laws suspend?
> For me shall suns their noon-tide course forbear?
> Or motion not subsist to influence air?

In Canto III Savage pictures comets as portentous to the ignorant but to the curious astronomer the opportunity for new knowledge. In Canto IV ominous winter comes in again, a

[7] All quotations are from the first edition, London: J. Walthoe, 1728. Reprinted with changes in Chalmers, XIV, 16–24.

picture that could have come only from travel books: 'a wild expanse of frozen sea,' the crashing of 'vast, floating mountains', bears that 'stalk tenants of the barren space', and barbarous, un-social men. Then follows, in direct contrast, a long idyllic descrip-tion of the summer of temperate England like that of Thomson's recent poem but more sweetly sentimental. As he sees the plants bent with dew, he is reminded of botany, the power of the sun, the rise of sap, the growth of plant life:

> Hail glorious sun! to whose attractive fires,
> The waken'd vegetative life aspires!
> The juices, wrought by thy directive force,
> Thro' plants, and trees, perform their genial course,
> Extend in root, with bark unyielding bind
> The hearted trunk; or weave the branching rind;
> Expand in leaves, in flow'ry blossoms shoot,
> Bleed in rich gums, and swell in ripen'd fruit.

In Canto V, before he gets bogged down in allegory and self-pity, Savage produces some charming passages in the georgic manner associated with Thomson. The realism of landscape appears in many sharp vignettes: minnows darting in the stream where sheep drink; the mixture of yellow, green, and red at sun-set; 'the green grass yellowing into scentful hay'; the many-colored wild flowers lying in confusion between ferns and thistles, 'many half grey with dust'. In other passages scientific touches are thrown in, unconsciously perhaps in the catalogue of English birds, wild flowers, and domestic plants, but certainly with an eye on Newton's *Optics* when he describes the colors of the spectrum 'clear-pointed to the philosophic eye'.[8] And he was thinking of physico-theology when he illustrated the harshness of nature with scenes that 'still prove a God, just, merciful, and wise': the tropical heat that ripens oranges even while it withers plants, or the winds that strip the trees in autumn yet bring 'the milder beauties of a flow'ry spring', or the dread earthquake that destroys and at the same time clears the air of plague and fever. He nods in passing to English scientists in his praise of Mary Wortley Montague, in whose thought Bacon and Newton con-spire. *The Wanderer*, like Mallet's *Excursion*, is an imaginative fantasy, not a scientific poem, but its imagery borrowed from

---

[8] The passage is quoted by Marjorie Nicolson, *Newton demands the Muse*, pp. 25 f.

science and its georgic passages based on landscape description help to redeem what often flounders in the incoherent musings of weak philosophy.[9]

Two long poems published in 1728 show the direct influence of Thomson, both in their blank verse and in their specific tributes to his poem on winter. Samuel Edwards, *The Copernican System: a Poem*, a rambling description of the celestial universe, is didactic in tone without showing much knowledge of astronomy. Its praise of Newton redeems it from obscurity, praise of the *Principia* implied in the comment on direful comets 'threat'ning destruction and the wrecks of worlds' but for the strict bounds set 'when th'Almighty in creating hour / From chaos call'd the glorious universe', and praise direct in asking where were the stars 'when tow'ring Newton's eyes were clos'd in death'.[10]

James Ralph devotes each of the four books of *Night*[11] to a separate season that adds to the picture of the English landscape an account of the changes in nature in foreign countries. He consciously follows Thomson, whom he praises in his preface for his blank verse and for writing on neglected subjects 'as are in themselves truly noble and sublime.' At the same time he anticipates Thomson in treating all the seasons in 'the circling year' and in using the travel books with scientific implications, a theme that Thomson developed fully after 1728. For example, in Book I spring in America, where Ralph had lived, is described in terms of profuse nature, thick forests, and purple blossoms. In Book II summer in England reminds him of the harshness of nature: disease and earthquake in Greece; scorching heat and volcanic eruption in Africa, exotic fruits and disease in the West Indies. In Book III autumn is the month of fruitful harvests for favored England 'secure from rapine, and the waste of arms', far from the devastating eruptions of 'Etna's ever-burning heights'.

In Book IV winter in America, Greenland, and the Baltic countries gives Ralph the opportunity for sublime description that should help to rescue him from the company of Pope's dunces. The madly furious plunge of American rivers leads him

[9] The quotations are from the original edition (London: J. Walthoe, 1729), reprinted in Chalmers, XI, 201–317, and in *The Poems of Richard Savage*, ed. Clarence Tracy (Cambridge, 1962), pp. 94–159.

[10] Cambridge, 1728, 16 pp.

[11] James Ralph, *Night: a Poem in four Books* (Dublin, 1728).

to the wild power of Niagara Falls, probably the first poetic description of that great novelty of nature:

> Thus where, athwart a ridge of broken rocks,
> The rapid, sea-wide Niagara falls,
> With head-long haste it hurries down the steep,
> As from a mountain's brow, and, raving loud,
> For ever thunders in the deeps below;
> A rising mist hangs o'er the frothy gulph,
> And horrid whirlpools rage along the shore,
> All white with boiling foam for many a league.

Again Ralph introduces aspects of winter that Thomson did not introduce into his poem until 1730, the scientific study of astronomy and the arctic frozen north. The first allows him to explore meteors, comets, the solar system, the milky way, and

> To tow'r yet upwards, and be lost amid
> New stars, and suns, and worlds, as yet unknown,
> That fill the boundless space, and prove the pow'r
> Of an Almighty hand, thro' all the heav'nly frame.

The second is a majestic picture, first of Greenland with its cracking icebergs and thrashing whales, then of 'the Baltic main oppress'd with heaps / Of thick-ribb'd ice, and chain'd, from shore, to shore.' This forgotten poem has close affinities with Thomson's *Winter* and *Summer*, Mallet's *Excursion*, and Savage's *Wanderer*. To a contemporary reader, all these poems must have seemed to be from the same general source. The descriptive idea of English seasons is Thomson's, but the harshness of nature in tropic heat and arctic cold is probably Mallet's, developed further in Ralph's *Night* along with the first complete seasons, and intensified by Savage to receive its fullest treatment in the later revisions of Thomson's *Winter* and *Summer*.

2. POETICAL ESSAYS ON THE WISDOM OF GOD IN NATURE, 1727–39

From 1727 for more than a decade a number of miscellaneous lengthy scientific poems appeared. They are miscellaneous in the sense that the scientific phenomena described are taken from all fields of 'natural philosophy', but unified in the sense that each usually has its own moral purpose, chiefly to show the wisdom of God in nature in a general way but sometimes to emphasize divine providence or power or to restrain the pride of man. Many of these long poems bear the subtitle of 'poetical essay', which became the term applied, perhaps under the influence of Pope, to any long discursive poem that united many ideas under a loose general head. I have not seen any contemporary discussion of the genre, and the first definition I know does not appear until 1750 when the author of the anonymous *Poetic Essays, on Nature, Men, and Morals. Essay I to Dr. Askew of Newcastle* described the way in which he filled up the intervals in many fragments on the relation between natural phenomena and human morals 'so as to appear one connected whole, not quite heterogeneous and inconsistent in its parts.' He had put his thoughts into verse, he explained, to give them more life and make them more agreeable, and so 'he presents his piece under the indefinite title of poetic essays'. Perhaps after analyzing several of our essays we can make our own definition.

The first of these antedates the circle of Thomson, Richard Collins, *Nature Display'd* (1727), a pedestrian array in 82 pages of miscellaneous scientific curiosities. Judging by the relative space devoted to various subjects, we may assume that the poem was influenced by Blackmore, for the first 33 pages are given to the human body and its relation to the mind and soul, the next 24 pages to the celestial universe and the meterological phenomena affected by it, and the rest of the book to a description of natural history, minerals, and other terrestrial objects.

An example of Collins' preoccupation with didactic physiology is the following comparatively concise description of the alimentary process:

> Nature stands always ready to receive
> Whate'er, we eating to the stomach give.
> And thence, by the intestines, to the liver,
> She soon conveys, what aliment we give her:
> The succous juices, there, not long have stood,
> 'Ere changing colour, they all turn to blood,
> And mixing with the blood, which there they find,
> Increase the stock; and, soon, improve the kind.

The circulation of the blood and the anatomy of the organs of the senses and their nerves lead to the effect of the physical upon sensation, perception, thought, and ideas in a tedious versifying of Locke.

After about 1,000 lines of this physiological basis of psychology, Collins shows the fitness of God's work by 20 pages of elaborate scientific explanation of the operations of the sun and moon and their effect on the seasons, the circulation of water (the purpose of 'hideous mountains' is to condense vapor and bring rain), refracted light and the motion of planets and comets, the meteorological phenomena of lightning, thunder, snow, hail, and windstorms, and the ebb and flow of tides. He often refers to scientific authorities, three times to Newton.

Without transition the verses shift to earthquakes and volcanos, and then become involved for two pages with the origin of springs and the physical basis for artesian wells before they abruptly change the subject to natural history. The next 13 pages on birds, beasts, fish, and plants show that early in the century science was concerned with the zoology and botany that was to dominate its interest in the second half of the century. In describing animals Collins was most concerned with the wonders of nature, such as oviparous and viviparous birth and the mating and migration of birds as examples of instinct, or with the question of the usefulness of animals, even snakes and insects, to man. In botany he showed more knowledge, though he proposed to summarize only the general characteristics of plants, since even John Ray was unable to classify them properly. He described plants much as a contemporary gardening dictionary might have done, yet he included those wonders that science cannot explain, such as the succession of flowers, the growth of the seed, the fall of leaves, and the sensitiveness of some plants to pressure or heat. After this unusual display of natural history, Collins subsided into three pages on minerals and ended abruptly with the promise of a second essay on social history.

Richard Gambol showed that the wisdom of God in nature is the main theme of his 30-page poem, *The Beauties of the Universe* (1732), both in the preface and in the opening lines:

> When universal nature I survey,
> And mark eternal wisdom's bright display,
> Where all is beauteous, all is wisely wrought,
> Surpassing far the reach of humane thought:

Fully convinc'd, that God in all things shines,
Assenting reason straight my soul inclines
To love, adore, and that great Being praise,
Who did from nothing this fair structure raise.

The illustrations that Gambol used furnish a good example of what scientific ideas were prevalent when Pope was writing his *Essay on Man*. He began with the astronomical universe: the stars, which 'point the hand by which their orbs were slung', are suns around which their planets 'wheel in order as they gravitate', and their orderly movements and attendant satellites stand as 'sure tokens of unerring wisdom's hand'. On earth man, 'a little world in narrow compass wrought', shows God's wisdom not only by the wonderful perfection of the human body but also by 'useful knowledge from reflexion' that enables him to praise the Creator. Among the animal creation the poet elaborated on what interested him personally: feminine beauty, the versatility of the horse, the intelligence of the dog, the great variety of birds ('the meanest songster of the air / Shows wisdom's lib'ral hand, and gracious care'), the revealing metamorphosis of the silkworm, the great display of wisdom and mathematical genius in the bee and spider, the numerous beauties of flowers, and the teeming worlds within worlds seen under the microscope. In the study of these and other parts of the book of nature that lies open to all, man can in one page gain more knowledge 'than all the volumes in the world contain.'

This summary of an obscure physico-theological poetical essay shows that Gambol was repeating, with slight variations, the ideas of divine wisdom and providence revealed in the contrasting universes of telescope and microscope and in the power of instinct in animals. From Thomson he added the georgic description of flowers and fruits and the patriotic theme of Britannia's glory, whose ships made from England's oak sail to scatter terror and still give 'gentle laws in foreign lands'. The 'book of nature' displays God's wonders in profusion, yet never is the picture more full of imagination than in the microscopic world. He depicted the metamorphosis of the gaudy butterfly from 'a despicable worm', quoting Boyle on the admiration aroused by the study of commonly despised creatures through the microscope. He cited Shaftesbury on his 'worlds within worlds, of infinite minuteness . . . pregnant with more wonders than the most discerning sense, joined with the greatest art, or the acutest reason, can penetrate or unfold'. He quoted the inspirer of his poem, his late friend Henry Needler, on the wonderful discoveries 'made by the help of this most noble instrument' enabling us 'to pry into the most secret recesses of nature' until we are assured 'that every corner of nature is stock'd and crowded with infinite numbers of little inhabitants', making us realize that 'this terrestrial globe, which we think so vast, is, in comparison of the boundless extension of the universe, only a little atom, swimming among myriads of others in the liquid aether'. To these tributes to microscopic imagination Gambol added his own picture of plenitude in nature:

> See! here unnumber'd creatures live and move,
> And round in orb with endless labour rove!
> The hardest rocks with teeming life abound,
> Each leaf and flow'r with forms minute is crown'd!
> Drop on thy glass one speck of quick'ning spawn,
> While scaly broods, of life are in the dawn,
> You'll find a flood, and fish in wanton play,
> More faintly moving as it dries away!
> Who thus will the all-wise Creator trace,
> The works of wisdom never can disgrace.[12]

The very rare *Poetical Essays* of Dr. Samuel Bowden[13] contain the usual number of pedestrian translations and occasional verses, but several poems, while not really 'essays', deserve wider recognition. In the opening poem of the first volume (1733), 'The Retreat, or Contemplative Solitude,' in the manner of Thomson describes a 'romantic hill . . . where huge deformed rocks salute the eye', wild birds and flowers and pensive cows, 'their solid necks reclining to the ground'. A cursory history of medicine gives Bowden the opportunity to praise contemporary science in his verses 'On the New Method of Treating Physic, inscribed to Dr. Morgan, on his Philosophical Principles of Medicine'. In medicine, Galen and Sydenham and Morgan followed the 'mechanic reasoning' of the pure scientist:

[12] *The Beauties of the Universe, a Poem by a Gentleman of the Navy* (London: J. Roberts, 1732), pp. 24 f.
[13] *Poetical Essays on Several Occasions* (Vol. I, London, 1733; Vol. II, 1735). The British Museum has the only copy I have found (78.i.30). Fairchild, II, 55–58, mistakenly assumes that they were included in Bowden's 1754 *Poems on Various Subjects*.

> They build on sense, then reason from th'effect,
> On well-establish'd truths their schemes erect;
> By these some new *Phaenomena* explain;
> And light divine in every prospect gain.

Newton formed his 'wondrous plan' on this basis:

> Led by this clue he travel'd o'er the sky,
> And marshal'd all the shining worlds on high,
> Pursu'd the comets, where they farthest run,
> And brought them back obsequious to the sun.

The tribute to Morgan does not obscure, however, the enthusiastic paean to the future of science and especially medicine that now appears prophetic:

> My raptur'd muse sees with prophetic eyes
> New ages roll along, new nations rise;
> Sees physic on mechanic reas'ning climb,
> And raise a structure to the skies sublime;
> Sees sickness fled, health bloom in ev'ry face,
> And age creep on with slow, reluctant pace.

A poem on smallpox and a tribute to the statues of scientists in Queen Caroline's grotto add a scientific flavor to the first volume, while 'On Solitude' lyrically praises God in nature:

> God is the theme of nature's glorious song,
> The stars repeat it as they roll along,
> The vallies echo with the chearful voice
> And in the solemn truth the hills rejoice . . .
> Now on some mountain, tune the muse's lyre,
> While Nature, and its God, each lay inspire.

'Antiquities and Curiosities in Wiltshire and Somerset' is a good combination of topographical poem, georgic, and scientific poem with its pictures of Stonehenge and Roman ruins, savage mountains and noble castles, commercial Bristol and healing Bath, and finally, with John Ray's manual as his guide, the botanical student gathering specimens on the Cheddar cliffs, watching lapwings, falcons, skylarks, and seagulls in flight, and remembering Cowley's Latin verses on plants when 'the fields . . . bloom'd afresh in his botanic strains'.

The second volume begins with his 'Poem Sacred to the Memory of Sir Isaac Newton', which, as we have seen, emphasizes

Newton's banishing conjecture by mechanic reasoning, yet makes it plain that the scientist adores the power of God:

> He sees the chain from heav'n to earth descend,
> And on their latent cause effects depend,
> That unseen Cause which agitates each sphere,
> Pervades the mass, and rules the circling year.

'Recovering from Sickness' describes the marvellous artistry shown by the human body, especially the flow of blood seen under the microscope. 'The Deserts of Devonshire' contrasts the desolate countryside with the heavens studied by the scientists 'who wise nature's laws explore' and watch 'the distant suns on high / Which nightly dart their glories o'er the sky.' 'The Tempest' describes vividly wild 'nature in labor'. 'To a Friend in Wales: Writ in the Spring' gives the gentler side of nature in her universal song 'while birds, plants, beasts in symphony conspire'. The 12-page 'The Earth: a Philosophical Poem' resembles the longer essays but in miniature, since the two phases of nature used to show the glory of God are the ones he knows best, the English landscape ('Where nature blooms in everlasting greens / And sheds around ten thousand charming scenes') and the human body, illustrated by analogy with the earth, the circulation of blood with artesian wells, nerves and bones with rocks and hills, and the hair with forests. Yet he describes with delight the fecundity of the earth, within whose 'womb exhaustless stores lie hid', the plastic energy containing the seeds of varied life from microscopic animals to 'vast Leviathan'.

The next scientific poem to appear was probably Henry Baker's *The Universe: a Poem intended to Restrain the Pride of Man*,[14] though the title would place it among the several answers to Pope's *Essay on Man* published in 1733. Baker was himself a scientist and later wrote several popular books on the microscope, and so it is natural that his main theme of the contrasting worlds of telescope and microscope should be illustrated with the latest discoveries and amplified with scientific footnotes. For example, he illustrates the idea of the earth appearing as a small point in boundless space by referring to Huygens' calculations that the fixed stars are so

---

[14] The poem appeared in London without date but Fairchild, I, 463, dates it 1734. See G. R. Potter, 'Henry Baker, F.R.S.', *Modern Philology*, XXIX (1931–2), 301–21.

far away that it would take a cannonball 700,000 years to reach them. The stars appear more numerous as telescopes improve, and so it is reasonable to believe that there are still more worlds yet undiscovered, which are 'inhabited by those numberless orders of more glorious beings which are betwixt us and the Creator'. He describes the planets and their satellites as well as comets that move 'in determin'd times, through long ellipses'. A sample from this section shows that the verses, while not as scientific as the notes, combine the didactic and the pseudo-sublime:

> Along the sky the sun obliquely rolls,
> Forsakes, by turns, and visits both the poles.
> Diff'rent his track, but constant his career,
> Divides the times, and measures out the year. . . .
> Bring forth thy glasses: clear thy wond'ring eyes:
> Millions beyond the former millions rise:
> Look further:—millions more blaze from remoter skies.

Baker approaches the other end of the Great Chain of Being, the microscopic universe with which he is more familiar, by way of the meteorological phenomena of seasons, wind, dew, and frost. On the earth the power of God is seen in the fertility of seeds ('each myrtle seed includes a thousand groves') and in such larger animals as lion, horse, eagle, peacock, and crocodile. We can learn about God from spider, bee, and ant, but most of all from the myriads of myriads of living creatures that swarm in a space smaller than a grain of sand. Here the notes quote copiously from microscopic science, notably Leuwenhoek, Hooke, and Ray on flies and insects and caterpillars that metamorphose into splendid butterflies. The conclusion is that all creatures, 'or great, or small they be, in water, earth, or air', show God's care, wisdom, and power, and therefore man should forget his pride:

> Alas, what's man, thus insolent and vain?
> One single link of nature's mighty chain.
> Each hated toad, each crawling worm we see,
> Is needful to the whole as well as he.
> Like some grand building in the universe,
> Where ev'ry part is useful in its place.

Henry Brooke's *Universal Beauty* (1735)[15] is perhaps the longest

---

[15] All quotations are from the first edition, published in six separate parts, London: J. Wilcox: 1735; reprinted Chalmers, XVII, 337–65.

and most tedious of these early poetical essays. Ambitious and rhapsodical to the point of becoming often incoherent, it is nevertheless worthy of special analysis for the numerous scientific examples used to illustrate the main theme of the harmony of the universe, from seraph to microscopic creatures, inspired by 'boundless love' that comes from God, who is 'essential truth'. Embellished with numerous repetitious variations, the poem contains a notable array of scientific ideas and, at least in the notes, considerable knowledge of science.

Part I declares the main theme of God's infinite wisdom in the contrasting worlds of telescope and microscope. It begins in the heavens:

> Orb within orb in living circlets turn,
> And central suns thro' ev'ry system burn; . . .
> All, distance due, and beauteous order keep,
> And spinning soft, upon their centers sleep;
> Th'eternal clue the mazy lab'rinth guides,
> While each in his appointed movement glides,
> Transverse, ecliptick, oblique, round they run,
> Like atoms wanton in the morning sun.

The 'universal wedlock' of gravitation that holds the celestial bodies in harmonious motion shows 'the curious texture of Almighty hand', yet this boundless universe 'where countless orbs, thro' countless systems shine' is but a symbol of the variety and plenitude of swarming nature that may also be seen under the microscope,

> Adjusted to the trunk's unwieldy size,
> As nice proboscis of luxurious flys,
> Or azure tribes that o'er the damson bloom,
> And paint the regions of the rip'ning plum.

The poet begs Nature to dispel ignorance and show 'what pow'r, all height of pow'r transcends', to say why the earth does not wander 'vagrant thro' the boundless space', and what its motions are that control the seasons and climate. His questions and explanatory notes show that Brooke was familiar with scientific research, but his concern is to show that the 'infinite wisdom' of God could not make even one error: 'Omniscience here no lower mean admits, / One slip, had maim'd ten thousand, thousand hits.' His examples at the end of Part I of 'the wonderful textures

of the air or atmosphere' show how he can catalogue, in bewildering verses and scientific footnotes, the varied uses of air to prove
that its 'seemingly inconsistent qualities' are suited both to individual interests and 'the entire and uniform weal of the whole'.

Part II continues to describe the air, goes on to light,[16] and
then adds the element of water. Lengthy summaries of scientific
problems include the physics of light, the respiration of aquatic
animals, and the cause of thunderstorms. He introduces a favorite
subject in scientific poems, the circulation of water in nature as
an example of 'the eternal circle and order in all things', from the
ocean by evaporation, to the clouds where condensation brings
it to earth, inside the earth in underground streams, to rills and
rivers and back to ocean again. This order in variety can be seen
throughout nature:

> Nature! bright effluence of the One Supreme!
> O how connected is thy wondrous frame!
> (Thy grand machine, thro' many a wanton maze,
> Steer'd where it winds, and streightning where it strays,
> There most direct, where seeming most inflext;
> Most regular, when seeming most perplext;
> As tho' perfection on disorder hung,
> And perfect order from incaution sprung.)

Variety and order, he said, are knit together 'That Deity,
throughout the world may shine; / And Nature's birth, confess
her Sire Divine.' Here is the crux of Brooke's religious ideas.
Whether he was a deist following Shaftesbury or a Christian
Platonist,[17] Brooke was a sensitive young poet who was well read
in science and tried to use it in a philosophical and religious way.
To him God was the Maker who flies high above his work, the
creation that is infinite 'beyond what Clarks can prove, or New-
tons can explore.' But even though science could not answer
many questions, it was for him the best proof of divine order.

Part III, after a brief survey of subterranean nature, is devoted
to Brooke's favorite study of botany and microscopic life, but
the opening verses serve as an interim variation of the main
theme:

---

[16] The influence of Newton's *Optics* is clear in this section, as Nicolson, *Newton demands the Muse*, pp. 67–69, has shown.

[17] His religious ideas are discussed, with many examples, in Fairchild, I, 475–81. See also H. M. Scurr, *Henry Brooke* (Minneapolis, 1927).

> The One grows sundry by creative pow'r;
> Th' Eternal's found in each revolving hour;
> Th' Immense appears in ev'ry point of space;
> Th' Unchangeable in Nature's varying face;
> Th' Invisible conspicuous to our mind;
> And Deity in ev'ry atom shrin'd.

The poet uses the microscope to see the miracle of the plant germinating within the seed or the circulation of blood in the human body or to search out the 'myriad minim race . . . that mock unseen'. Scientifically he studies the rose:

> Or now we pore with microscopic eye,
> And Nature's intimate contextures spy;
> Her economics, her implicit laws,
> Th' effects how wondrous deep!—how wondrous
>   high the Cause! . . .
> Within, the guests of animalcule race
> Luxuriant, range at large its ample space.

A long botanical passage of more than 300 lines—on germination, flow of sap, luxuriant animal life feeding on plants—is but a prelude to the philosophical message of 'infinity within the sprouting bower' dwelling 'immense within the minim shrine' of the seed. Plant within plant, the process continues:

> In forms complete essentially retain
> The future semen, alimental grain;
> And these again the tree, the trunk, the root,
> The plant, the leaf, the blossom, and the fruit;
> Again the fruit and flower the seed enclose,
> Again the seed perpetuated grows,
> And beauty to perennial ages flows.

The paeans of praise continue in Part IV to the 'Sovereign Geometrician' who created the physical wonders of the animal kingdom in circulatory systems and sensory organs and such moral wonders as the soul of man. Part V returns to the great variety of the microscopic universe and shows how God is seen 'great and conspicuous, in minutest things', and how the great variety in the insect world makes us imagine worlds yet unknown where millions of tiny creatures have organs for procreation, nurture, and metamorphosis, where phenomena are hid 'deep from our search, exalted from our soar'. The end of Part V and all of Part VI illustrate at great length the unexplained wonders of nature, especially in the instinct of birds, bees, spiders, and beavers. The concluding rhapsody makes clear that the idea of providence attributed to nature in Part I ('Nice to a point, each benefit selects; / As prudent, every mischief she rejects') ultimately comes from God, for stars, earth, fish, beasts, worms and birds,

> All, all from thee, Sole Cause Essential! tend,
> Thence flow effusive, thither, cent'ring end;
> The bliss of providential vision share,
> And the least atom claims peculiar care!

Nearly all physico-theological ideas appear in Brooke's poem but the description in Part III of the Great Chain of Being as the climax of God's creative power sums up best his attempt to combine science and philosophy:

> Hence from the seraph's intellectual ray,
> To reason's spark, that gilds our sensual clay;
> To life (scarce conscious) in th'instinctive brute;
> To reptile; plant and vegetating root;
> The features in conspicuous semblance shine,
> And speak, thro' all, *One Parent all Divine*.

If there is any doubt about Brooke's meaning in his effusive verse, it is cleared up by his prose footnote to his hymn to eternal spring in Part V: 'The Deity necessarily inferred from the contemplation of every object, but more especially visible in the animate creation, so infinitely diversified in the several species and kinds of fish, reptiles, quadrupeds, insects, and birds.'

One of the most impressive of the early physico-theological poetical essays is Moses Browne's 'An Essay on the Universe', first published in three books in 1739[18] but composed over the previous 'ten years and longer'. An analysis of the expanded version in four books published in 1752 shows that it contains, in its verses and notes, a compendium of popular science as well as philosophy. In the original preface Browne says that he was led to write the poem 'to give less judicious and considerate

---

[18] Browne, *Poems on Various Subjects* (London: Edward Cave, 1739), pp. 281–390. It appeared in an expanded form in four books as Part I of *The Works and Rest of the Creation* (London, 1752), a long religious poem, Part II of which was called 'Sunday Thoughts'. The 1752 version divides Book I, 'a survey of the terraqueous globe', and expands the scientific sections, especially on the microscope.

persons an easy, and at the same time magnificent, conception of the amazing theory of the universe, improvable to a virtuous and religious end', for, he continues, 'Nature, or creation, is the Book of God'. The poem travels in descriptive glory from praise of the profusion of nature on the earth and in the water and air to the planetary worlds, the sun, and the fixed stars, but over and over it comes back to the 'various reptile race' seen under the microscope.

Book I declares the poet's purpose to lead the ladies, tempted but frightened by science, 'to read deep systems' and range creation from earth 'to stars, and suns of boundless space', rising to worlds yet unseen:

> Hear, how Creative Wisdom first design'd
> This beauteous world, the seat of human kind.
> Orbicular he turn'd the ductile mold,
> And thro' vast space the pondrous wonder roll'd.

His praise of the big things of 'parent earth' leaps around the globe but soon he descends to the countless animalcules visible only under microscopes:

> In one small humid speck, the curious eye
> Can millions of their little forms descry.
> What kingdoms of th'innumerous insect-kind,
> On one small leaf commodious dwelling find! . . .
> O Nature, thy minutest works amaze,
> Pose the close search, and lose our thoughts in praise!

The world of plants contains 'rich funds of inexhaustible delight', and with his eye on herbals or botany texts, he lists by name flowers, medicinal and aromatic herbs, exotic and domestic trees for shade and fruit, and describes some of them in detail. The concluding passages on mountains and waters are less scientific but introduce such popular scientific subjects as underground rivers and new theories of the origin of mountains.

Book II forces many scientific subjects into the loose category named for the two ancient elements of air and fire. Air is necessary for respiration, for disseminating species of plants, for carrying odors and sounds, and best of all for providing a habitat for birds, the domestic lark, pigeon, falcon, and swallow, and the foreign condor, mocking bird, humming bird, and 'the proud guara, gay in tinctur'd blooms'. The poet seems to equate 'ethereal fire' with the original source of heat and light that makes life possible, but in nature it takes for him the form of such phenomena as flame, glow-worm, will-of-the-wisp, aurora borealis, lightning, and that most dread of all fires, the volcano that breeds earthquake and destruction. The idea of the harshness of nature invites the poet to a long moral digression on providence in which he sees the good behind seeming evil, and finally to a very interesting summary of 'philosophy' (experimental science) as a safe guide to virtue and happiness, a form of study full of blameless delights, 'a field of contemplation . . . for ever pleasing, innocent, and new'. In a sort of ecstatic hymn to the microscope and telescope he describes the boundless worlds of the great and small, the teeming abundance of life in nature. By day the amateur scientist can study 'creation's grandest miracles' in the perfect shapes of hidden force 'in animalcules, germs, seeds, and flowers', and by night he can observe the suns, planets, and moons 'with Galileo's far-discovering eyes'.

The last two books of *An Essay on the Universe* contain a scientific explanation of the celestial universe as illustration of the order in nature created by a wise, powerful, and beneficent God. The technical portions are in pedestrian didactic verse, accompanied by copious references to Newton, Halley, Huygens, Keill, Harris (*Astronomical Dialogues*), and other learned men of science, but the philosophical portions are often in the sublime manner and the whole poem ends in a hymn of praise that is a prelude to the liturgical lyrics of Christopher Smart. By the very space devoted to it (913 lines in the 1739 version expanded to 1081 in 1752) Browne showed his interest in astronomy and his delight that the telescope revealed an 'unmeasured universe' to prove by the orderly motion of the spheres that 'nature's wise, harmonious laws' could not, as the 'vain dreamers' who followed Lucretius believed, have sprung 'from weak chance'. Though his main subject here is astronomy, he constantly comes back to the contrasting world of the microscope, a branch of science that was developing so rapidly that one of his longest and best additions to the 1752 version (IV, 306–331) describes the beauty of objects magnified 'many thousand times.' Because this is an important part of a poem that is fairly inaccessible to scholars, I shall quote freely from it.

Book III, on the planets, turns quickly from the praise of

solitude to the nocturnal pleasures of studying 'the upper worlds of light'. Browne pours out technical information profusely in verse and footnotes on Mercury, Venus, Earth, Mars, Jove, and Saturn with their size, distance from the sun, and attendant satellites, but he seems most concerned with the philosophical question, popularized by Fontenelle, of the use of the myriads of worlds only seen by the 'optic christal' and the countless others waiting to be discovered in 'uncompass'd space'. For the planets he cites scientific evidence to show that these worlds might be inhabited

> With creatures, suited to their various seat,
> Intense degrees of cold or heat to bear,
> Of light, or gloom, a pleasing, proper share,
> To them agreeable, by nature blest,
> Painful, howe'er, imagin'd to the rest.

The moon, which seems obvious but is least known because of its 'strange phenomena', offers special problems, particularly to those rash voyagers who have contemplated trips to the moon but forget that the earth's attraction that 'checks her centrifugal force / Wou'd fast withhold thy strange, eccentric course.' These too ambitious men would do better to explore the polar tracts or better still, the mind of man or study astronomy ('Heav'n's ample volume studious to peruse') and contemplate its lessons: the relativity of time shown by comparing the revolutions of the planets around the sun; the nature of the inhabitants of these other worlds; and finally, the realization that there is 'one Deity, one Sole Creating Cause'. Book III ends with a hymn to astronomy, 'science heavenly-born', that puzzled the ancients, 'vain Epicurus, and his frantic class', until Copernicus 'the true planetary system taught'. Improved by Tycho, Hevelius, Flamsteed, Halley, Galileo, Cassini, and Huygens, astronomy developed rapidly until Kepler showed the way to Newtonian order, when he saw

> Th'elliptic motion, nature's plainest law,
> That universal acts thro' every part:
> This laid the basis of Newtonian art.
> Newton! vast mind! whose piercing pow'rs apply'd
> The secret cause of motion first descry'd;
> Found gravitation was the primal spring,
> That wheel'd the planets round their central king.

Book IV describes first the sun, deceptively small to our eyes, but actually

> So large, ten million earths like ours below
> Wou'd but suffice his equal'd mass to show.
> So distant, eighty million miles wou'd fail,
> Vast sum! to count a full proportion'd tale.

The 'prolific light and heat' dispensed by this seemingly exhaustless 'orb of fire' refresh mankind, darkened only occasionally by the mysterious spots recently discovered. The poet then describes the fixed stars whose staggering number and distances overwhelm the imagination as the 'boundless scene breaks on the mind'. In his verses Browne reaches the sublime while his notes summarize the recent calculations of astronomical research. For example, Sirius, 'the only measur'd star we know', is nearest of the fixed stars to earth, yet Huygens' calculation of '27,664 times the sun's distance from us' is more 'than mind can soar'. To try to imagine the stretching universe beyond Sirius is indeed a 'perplexing thought':

> Farther from this, than this from earth is plac'd,
> Th'ethereal regions with new orbs are grac'd;
> Farther than those from this, fresh numbers still
> The depths of lost infinity may fill. . . .
> What can they be? (thus self-illustrious shown)
> What, less than suns? resembling each our own.

The philosophic and religious implications are also staggering, since even the 'elating pride' of man cannot believe they were created in vain; at least the poet's questions suggest that 'heav'n meant their systems as compleat as ours' and that the 2000 stars in Orion 'discernible to aided sight' are but a small sample of innumerable others that now elude us, each perhaps a system with satellites, each inhabitable:

> Have each (a sovereign in his system's bound)
> Their lighted earths, and moons, revolving round,
> Inhabitable all? their plants and flow'rs?
> Their insects, animals, and reasoning pow'rs?

Browne then tackles the puzzling philosophical problems inspired by recent observations of comets and of the appearance and disappearance of stars, but takes refuge in the statement:

'Omnific God! . . . To trace thy works all man's ideas fail.' Yet he is convinced that the Epicureans, 'worse patrons of absurd misrule', have only to see how the beautiful precision of a gnat or butterfly's down degrade human skill and prove God's wisdom:

> If lesser proofs such demonstrations show,
> What may th'unmeasur'd universe bestow?
> Think, cou'd blind chance, dead, unexisting name,
> Produce such order, so complete a frame?

At this point Browne added to the 1752 version a passage on the Great Chain of Being as further proof of sublime wisdom where the vast plan absorbs varied interests in one view, acting 'by parts, subservient to the whole'. The poem then concludes with 'a hymn of praise to the tremendous and adorable Deity', Browne's ecstatic version of the *Benedicite* (sun, stars, moon, 'ye comets! that in long ellipses stray', winds, meteors, frosts, seasons, plants, insects, birds, brutes, fishes, man, and angel choirs, praise ye the Lord), his own song of David:

> Praise him, each creature, plenitude, and space;
> Things of inanimate and living race!
> From the terrestrial to the starry pole,
> Praise him his works, and thou, my prostrate soul![19]

With Browne the parade of encyclopedic physico-theological poetical essays ends. Beginning with Thomson the poets delighted in using the exciting discoveries of the new science to proclaim the wisdom, power, and benevolence of God in nature. They explored the contrasting worlds revealed by the telescope and microscope with voluminous zeal and often with a poetic fervor that reached the sublime. At the same time they added nature in other scientific aspects, minerals, animals, plants, the changes of the seasons, the circulation of water in underground streams. The Psalmist had said that the earth was the Lord's and the fullness thereof, and Virgil was a useful model for combining science and georgic descriptiveness. Thomson led the way, though Bowden and Baker and Browne knew more science and Brooke

[19] Among Browne's shorter scientific poems, the most interesting is 'To her Majesty on her Grotto', where he praises Newton for his laws of motion: 'Amazing artist! whose discerning eyes /Search'd the vast systems of th'illumin'd skies, / Taught what first laws the circling orbs obey, /And first describ'd the comet's devious way.'

was more metaphysical. Thomson had an appeal to other poets in his combination of nature description with science and religious contemplation, and with the popular interest in the study of natural history during the second half of the century Thomson became the model for scientific poetry.

Meanwhile other poets were using science of one sort or another for various purposes. Many moral poems followed the lead of Pope's *Essay on Man*, and in the early 1740's this effective use of scientific illustration and imagery reached a new plateau of accomplishment in Young and Akenside. After 1740 the encyclopedic type of scientific poem, except for occasional exceptions, gave way to shorter poems, frequently in the lyric manner made famous by Christopher Smart. We now turn to these new developments, first to Pope and the moral poems that used science.

V

THE NEW SCIENCE IN MORAL POEMS

SCIENTIFIC discovery dominated the ideas and imagery of the series of poetical essays from Thomson to Moses Browne that I have described as the triumph of physico-theology. Encyclopedic in their treatment of science, they roamed from Newtonian astronomy to the latest microscopic research, and their subjects included whatever science the poets knew best. To them nature in all its aspects revealed the wisdom of God in the creation, insects, microscopic creatures, and flowers as well as the human body or the motions of heavenly bodies. To this extent these dominantly scientific poems were also moral poems, for they had the same purpose as the Boyle lectures, to refute atheism with science. Yet there were other moral poems that used scientific imagery and ideas to bolster their verse discussions on many philosophical problems, such as harmony, happiness, immortality, providence, contemplation, or the problems of man. The dramatic discoveries of the new science, Newtonian or botanical or microscopic or what not, were a part of everyday thought, and the imagery borrowed from this science helped to put new life into many a dull subject. Not all such poems were dull: in a way the story begins with an exciting poem that set the pattern for moral poems with scientific interest, Pope's *Essay on Man*.

In February 1733 the first epistle of the *Essay on Man* appeared anonymously, with a subtitle ('Of the Nature and State of Man, with Respect to the Universe') that showed immediately that it was in the scientific tradition of the earlier physico-theological poems. By the time the four parts of the poem had been separately published, the *Essay on Man* was recognized as the work of Pope, much to the chagrin of some who had hailed its religious soundness. To relate it to the influence of science, the complete poem is best understood as one of the series of poetical essays that used science to portray God in nature, Pope's own personal and rhetorically effective version of this old subject. The importance of the poet and the poem warrant a close analysis of the science in the *Essay on Man* to show that, though it is another scientific poem, it is the best of the whole tradition. Pope may have known less science than Baker or Browne but in his concise and imaginative verses he was better able than all others to put into poetry what scientific writers of all kinds had been often saying but were never able to express so well.

The first half of the *Essay on Man* is really Pope's scientific poem, for in the first two epistles the main theme is paradoxical man in his relation to the paradox in nature that he visualizes as 'a mighty maze, but not without a plan'. This theme is developed in terms of two closely related ideas that are found in many scientific writers: (1) order in nature as shown in the heavens by Newton's laws and on earth by the microscope and the observation of the world around us, and (2) providence which reconciles the partial ills of harsh nature with the general good. Closely tied to the development of these main themes are several metaphors and commonplace illustrations from science, such as the Great Chain of Being, instinct in animals, the confused disorder of nature in the last judgment, and the limitations of science. These ideas are not treated separately but tied in with the whole picture of paradoxical man, 'the glory, jest, and riddle of the world', on the one hand the crowning example of God's wisdom in the creation, and on the other hand a miserable failure full of presumptuous pride. Yet in the overall picture man's time is but 'a moment, and a point his space', for man is part of the perfect order of the 'vast chain of being' extending from God to 'Natures ethereal, human, angel, man, / Beast, bird, fish, insect, what no eye can see, / No glass can reach; from infinite to thee; / From thee to nothing.' For this reason man must submit to Providence and look for the general good behind the seeming error in nature such as earthquake and tempest, realizing that 'The gen'ral order, since the whole began, / Is kept in nature, and is kept in man.' Let us illustrate this masterful use of scientific metaphors in the first two epistles.

The idea of providence, as it developed in the early eighteenth century, assumed that evil was necessary to fill out the divine scheme and that imperfections were therefore a vital part of the chain of being. In this poem Pope repeated common examples of harsh and violent nature—earthquake, storm, plague, and tropical heat—to illustrate his own version of providence, the optimism that Basil Willey calls 'cosmic Toryism':[1]

> But errs not Nature from this gracious end,
> From burning suns when livid deaths descend,
> When earthquakes swallow, or when tempests sweep
> Towns to one grave, whole nations to the deep?
> 'No' ('tis replied) 'the first Almighty Cause
> Acts not by partial, but by general laws.'

Twice again in the *Essay on Man* Pope used the same idea of harsh nature as metaphors, once to compare the evils of nature with the evils in man that result in tyrants like a Borgia or a Cataline, and again in a picture of that lawless confusion of planets and suns when orderly orbits break and worlds are wrecked, the same disorder that appears as the main theme of many contemporary judgment-day poems:

> Let earth unbalanc'd from her orbit fly,
> Planets and suns run lawless through the sky;
> Let ruling angels from their spheres be hurl'd,
> Being on being wreck'd, and world on world;
> Heaven's whole foundations to their centre nod,
> And Nature tremble to the throne of God.

But all evils, including the harshnesses of nature, are not only consistent with divine wisdom but also a necessary part of God's infinite goodness:

---

[1] Basil Willey, *The Eighteenth Century Background* (London, 1940), pp. 43–56, shows how this idea can reach the high mood of stoic endurance in Spinoza or Leibniz, but more often stood in the early eighteenth century for the complacency of a conservative generation, a gospel of acceptance of the *status quo* that gave way later in the century to a more dynamic doctrine of progress and perfectibility.

All Nature is but Art, unknown to thee;
All chance direction, which thou canst not see;
All discord, harmony not understood;
All partial evil, universal good.

If there is any doubt as to Pope's belief in God's wisdom in the creation, it is removed by the rhapsody near the end of Epistle I, the finest lyric expression of this physico-theological theme in the century:

All are but parts of one stupendous whole,
Whose body Nature is, and God the soul;
That, chang'd thro' all, and yet in all the same;
Great in the earth, as in th'ethereal frame,
Warms in the sun, refreshes in the breeze,
Glows in the stars, and blossoms in the trees,
Lives thro' all life, extends thro' all extent,
Spreads undivided, operates unspent. . . .
To him no high, no low, no great, no small;
He fills, he bounds, connects, and equals all.

There are in the *Essay on Man* still other metaphors taken from science. A very familiar one is the instinct of animals that is analogous to reason in man. Pope used as examples of instinct the same bee and spider and asked the same questions that the skeptic philosophers like Prior's Solomon had asked, to show the limitations of science. Furthermore, Pope saw a relativity of instinct, a variation in sensual and mental powers according to the place in the Chain of Being. This relativity could be used to show Providence: note the metaphors of the fly's microscopic eye and man being spared from dying 'of a rose in aromatic pain' or being stunned by the music of the spheres. The poem goes on to show how the variation in sensual perception ascends 'from the green myriads in the peopled grass', with extremes of sight, smell, and sound illustrated by metaphors from natural history. Animal instinct, so keen in the spider and bee, can vary too, from swine to half-reasoning elephant. Yet instinct and reason, Pope argued, though very near each other, are forever separate, and it is because of 'this just gradation' that some animals are subject to others and all of them to man.

In the use of metaphors from astronomy Pope differs from other scientific poets, for though he can see the sublime in the 'worlds unnumber'd' his subject is man and our duty is to trace

God only in our own world. Nevertheless his very impatience with the arguments of order in a stretching celestial universe shows his awareness of the plurality of worlds and their inhabitants, as well as his uncanny skill in saying concisely what other scientific poets verbosely amplified:

> He who through vast immensity can pierce,
> See worlds on worlds compose one universe,
> Observe how system into system runs,
> What other planets circle other suns,
> What varied being peoples every star,
> May tell why Heaven has made us as we are.

Again in Epistle II he ridicules the scientists who can explain the universe but cannot know themselves, and this time it is definitely in terms of Newton, indicated not only by the allusions to Newton's writings—the *Principia* and *The Chronology of Ancient Kingdoms Amended*—but also by reference to recent poems on Newton's cosmic voyage after death. It is difficult to reconcile these lines with Pope in another context, 'God said, Let Newton be, and there was light', but a reading of the entire passage shows that Newton was being praised as the best of futile scientists:

> Go, wondrous creature! mount where science guides;
> Go, measure earth, weigh air, and state the tides;
> Instruct the planets in what orbs to run,
> Correct old time, and regulate the sun. . . .
> Go, teach Eternal Wisdom how to rule—
>   Then drop into thyself, and be a fool!
>   Superior beings, when of late they saw
> A mortal man unfold all Nature's law,
> Admir'd such wisdom in an earthly shape,
> And show'd a Newton as we show an ape.
>   Could he, whose rules the rapid comet bind,
> Describe or fix one movement of his mind?
> Who saw its fires here rise, and there descend,
> Explain his own beginning or his end?

In the last two epistles Pope continued to use the metaphors of science to illustrate his moral ideas. At the beginning of Epistle III the chain of love pressing 'to one centre still, the *gen'ral good*' goes from lifeless matter ('single atoms each to other tend, / Attract, attracted to the next in place') to vegetable life, to beast and man, in a chain whose end is unknown. The lark, linnet, steed, steer, and hog are all examples of the care that Nature takes for her children, yet tyranny prevails in nature, the falcon over the dove, the jay over the gilded insect, and the hawk over the nightingale, reminding man that though he 'feasts the animal', he too must perish when his feast is over. Man alone has reason to predict his end, but in animals God sets the proper bounds of bliss. From his knowledge of natural history Pope adds to the common examples of instinct:

> Who taught the nations of the field and wood
> To shun their poison, and to chuse their food?
> Prescient, the tydes or tempests to withstand,
> Build on the wave, or arch beneath the sand?
> Who made the spider parallels design,
> Sure as De-Moivre, without rule or line?
> Who bid the stork, Columbus-like, explore
> Heav'ns not his own, and worlds unknown before?

The moral lesson is important to Pope as mutual happiness is tied to the Chain of Being:

> So from the first, Eternal Order ran,
> And creature link'd to creature, man to man.
> What'ere of life all-quickening aether keeps,
> Or breathes thro' air, or shoots beneath the deeps,
> Or pours profuse on earth; one nature feeds
> The vital flame, and swells the genial seeds.

When Pope allows 'the voice of nature' to tell man in the beginning of civilization to copy instinct and learn from creatures how to organize society and government, he takes his examples, as did Prior before him, from the naturalists. Finally, in Epistle IV as the theme of happiness becomes dominant, the scientific metaphors decrease, yet the oldest metaphor of all, the Platonic Chain of Being, is used again for the crowning argument that happiness comes through virtue, regardless of wealth or learning, if man seeks God through nature:

> Slave to no sect, who takes no private road,
> But looks thro' Nature up to Nature's God,
> Pursues that chain which links th' immense design,
> Joyns heav'n, and earth, and mortal, and divine.

143

From this analysis it should be clear that the *Essay on Man*, though it may not be thought of as a scientific poem, is made more vivid by reference to recent scientific discoveries and by repetition of the very ideas and illustrations already common in physico-theological writings. The science is old but the poetry is unparalleled imaginative discourse, the best example in the century of the rhetoric of science. For this reason it set the pattern for scientific imagery in other moral poems, at least two of which were answers to it.

In 1733 after the first epistle was printed but before the whole poem was finished, Bezaleel Morrice published, also anonymously, *An Essay on the Universe: a Poem*, which enthusiastically attempted to trace God in those 'worlds unnumber'd' where Pope had said it was not man's business to trace him. He was impressed by Pope's performance, for in the prefatory verses he called him 'auspicious bard' whose 'muse, sublime, significant and clear, / At once informs the soul, and charms the ear.' Morrice was concerned, however, that man recognize God's omnipotence in the entire creation, for among the stars scarcely visible to the searching eye 'Millions of worlds he fram'd, and rules them all, / Millions! ev'n more magnificent than this!" Matter is inexhaustible and the plenitude of nature stretches endlessly to things yet uncreated ('motion ready to prepare / Things yet unmade, and made, to furnish more'). This plan involving boundless care may seem like 'some well-fram'd mechanical design', but the active Creator Morrice depicts leaves no place for the materialist's often-quoted metaphor of the clockwork that runs the universe. Harmonious order reigns in a universe where the process of creation goes on, where 'suns and worlds may perish and renew'.

Pope's idea of a benevolent providence was attacked by a later answer, William Ayre's *Truth: a Counterpart to Mr. Pope's Essay on Man* (1739). Ayre's repudiation of benevolence, similar to Voltaire's later indignation at the Lisbon earthquake, is matched in vigor only by his defense of Newton:

> What greater paradox in words can be!
> Than what I see, is not the thing I see;
> That groans, and shrieks, and screams, and dying cries,
> Are, mix'd with something else, great harmonies;
> That all the monstrous crimes, which men commit,
> Are universal order, just and fit;

> That earthquakes, whirlwinds, deluges, and flames,
> All, all are order under other names.

The influence of Pope on moral poems appears in a number of poems published or written in the 1730's on a variety of subjects. The first poem of Joseph Trapp's *Thoughts upon the Four Last Things* (1734), already described, includes a comprehensive cosmic voyage through all nature consciously designed to refute the atheist who chooses the 'somewhat milder name' of deist. He was concerned that some believed God had set up a clockwork to run nature, and concluded that the materialist who believes that the universe is 'some curious, delicate machine' that might stop or fly to pieces has accused God of a folly that 'no mortal fool e'er reach'd'. The idea of order was in the air, and Pope's use of science to illustrate order was turned to other purposes. Isaac Hawkins Browne used it for aesthetics in his youthful *On Design and Beauty* (1734):

> The love of order, (sure) from Nature springs,
> Our taste adapted to the frame of things:
> Nature the pow'rs of harmony displays,
> And truth and order animate the mass.
> Who that this ample theatre beholds,
> Where fair proportion all her charms unfolds;
> This sun, and these the stars that roll above,
> Measuring alternate seasons as they move;
> Who, but admires a fabric so compleat;
> And from admiring, aims to imitate.

Thomas Catesby, Lord Paget, used it to contrast with the pride of man in his popular poem, *An Essay on Human Life* (1735):

> Look o'er the wide creation, see how all
> Its several parts obey the Master's call:
> The earth how fertile, and how rich the sea,
> In various salts, for Nature's chimistry;
> How air digests, what burning suns exhale,
> And dews, and snows, and rains, by turns prevail.
> Beasts, birds, and reptiles, see 'em all conspire,
> To act whate'er their sev'ral states require.[2]

The idea of scientific order, used by Blackmore to refute the

[2] London: Fletcher Gyles, 1735. Two more editions appeared in 1736. The second edition has a preface on the history and usefulness of scientific poetry.

Epicurean doctrine of creation by chance, is renewed in several moral poems of this period. It is implied in the title of Bevill Higgons, *A Poem in Nature: In Imitation of Lucretius* (1736), where the argument is illustrated by his personal interests in Newton's laws of motion and in mountains, those 'heaps of ruins' that nevertheless provide underground streams, rainfall, minerals, peculiar animals and plants, and political boundaries. It is much more scientifically and lyrically presented in Matthew Tomlinson's poem with an unlikely title, *The Trinity*, published in 1750 but written at Cambridge in 1726. Following the Boyle lecture of Samuel Clarke, who united 'Locke's strong sense and Newton's piercing wit', Tomlinson begs the 'vain atheist' to view in 'the large distant spaces of the skies' the sun and millions of remote worlds, 'resistless proofs of an almighty skill'. The studious with their telescopes can see how 'these well-pois'd planets roll', and with regular motion mark the limits of days, years, and seasons: ' 'Tis not by chance; these motions speak aloud, / The wise, th'unerring conduct of a God.' No one can explain 'exclusive of a God' the cause of storm, thunder, lightning, comets, and the perfection of the varied earth where the Creator is seen in 'each herb, each weed, each insect, ev'ry clod'. Newton only partly explains 'why thus the sea resistless ebbs and flows', for his stated laws show that 'the moon's the instrument, but God's the cause'. This obscure poem thus becomes a good example of how, even before Thomson, a student poet was using science to prove the 'rich perfections' of an orderly universe.

Order throughout all nature is lyrically expressed in the anonymous *Order: a Poem* (1737), not only in 'the beauteous order of the sky' where the planets 'advance harmoniously' around the sun and the moon 'obeys the earth, and guides the swelling main', but also on the earth where all things animate and inanimate 'in order all pursue the ends assigned', especially in nature's own cycles:

> Rains feed the earth, nor does the earth deny
> To send 'em back in vapours to the sky;
> Seas fill the springs, the springs again repay
> Their grateful tribute to the flowing sea;
> Night follows day, seasons the year divide
> 'Twixt winter's nakedness and summer's pride.

Yet in most of the moral poems Newton is the symbol of order in nature, the 'harmony of motion' used, for example, by Thomas Hobson in *Christianity the Light of the Moral World*, a poem written in 1737 and published in 1745. Here Newton is honored for having aided the moral poet not only with his *Principia* ('unbroken laws of kind attraction') but also with his *Optics*, where he shows the 'seven-fold light' of the sun as the source of color and the plastic warmth that brings to life plants and insects. Yet when man 'the outward animal machine' made up of complex springs and tubes, explains harmony in the moral world, his mind 'gives the little system laws, / And, self-dependent, regulates the whole, / As Newton's sun the erring planets guides.' In this moral world science can only describe the effects, not the causes of light and magnetism: 'The deep, mysterious cause a Newton shuns. / These far evade the microscopic eye / Of all-exploring reason, unperceiv'd.'

Pope set the pattern for aesthetic expression in most of these moral poems but Shaftesbury often furnished the inspiration. This is apparent in the ambitious poem of John Gilbert Cooper, *The Power of Harmony* (1745), where the poet uses as emblems of divine order not only the majestic fields, woods, streams, valleys, and rocks, but also the humbler rose, violet, moss, dove, lark, and 'all the brute creation'. Though he quotes Shaftesbury, Cooper follows Thomson more closely, as he contemplates nature's harmony in blank-verse descriptions of 'created worlds' whose various motions correspond 'to one harmonious plan', of animals 'from the large / Unwieldy elephant, to th'unseen mote', and of the birds and flowers that adorn the English countryside. He even follows Thomson in parading the inequalities of nature that become reconciled by Providence, from the spring flowers of peaceful England to shaggy rock, barren heath, violent storm, tropical desert, and winter desolation. Nature, he concludes, has formed 'One plan entire: and made each sep'rate scene / Co-op'-rate with the general force of all / In that harmonious contrast.' This long moral poem contrasts with the *Hymn to God* (1746), where the same theme is treated in lyric Pindarics that sing the praise of God in terms of elephant, rhinoceros, and rolling worlds.

Perhaps the most complete picture of the use of science in a moral poem of this period is Samuel Boyse's *The Deity* (1739), which Fielding quoted and praised in *Tom Jones*. This ill-fated poet, for whom Dr. Johnson collected sixpences, shows how scientific discovery reveals in turn each of the attributes of God, though not as lyrically as in Christopher Smart's later Seaton poems. Omnipresence is illustrated throughout nature from the systems of unnumbered worlds to the weak embryo; wisdom in the harmony of the solar system, the changes of tides and seasons, and the gradations in 'the chain of animated beings'; providence in God's care despite the seeming harshness of storm and earthquake; goodness in the bountiful variety of fertile nature; glory in birds, flowers, and stars unknown even to Newton; and omnipotence in big and little alike, planets, elephant, ant, and the teeming life in a rotting plum.[3] With a bow to Shaftesbury Boyse enlivened moral poetry with scientific imagery, but the ideas are closer to Thomson, especially in the poetic summary of the wisdom of God revealed by science that he put into a shorter poem, 'Wisdom':

> See, how associate round their central sun,
> Their faithful rings the circling planets run;
> Still equi-distant, never yet too near,
> Exactly tracing their appointed sphere.
> Mark how the moon our flying orb pursues,
>   While from the sun her monthly light renews;
> Breathes her wide influence on the world below,
> And bids the tides alternate ebb and flow.
> View how in course the constant seasons rise,
> Deform the earth, or beautify the skies:
> First spring advancing, with her flow'ry train,
> Next summer's hand that spreads the sylvan scene,
> Then autumn with her yellow harvests crown'd,
> And trembling winter close the annual round.
> The vegetable tribes observant trace,
> From the tall cedar to the creeping grass:
> The chain of animated beings scale,
> From the small reptile to th'enormous whale;
> From the strong eagle stooping from the skies,
> To the low insect that escapes the eyes![4]

[3] *Deity: a Poem* (London: J. Roberts, 1739), reprinted Chalmers XIV, 545–52. Fielding first praised it in *The Champion* for 12 Feb. 1740.

[4] S. Boyse, *Translations and Poems Written on Several Occasions* (London, 1738), pp. 73–82, 137–153. The same theme was in two earlier poems that Boyse wrote to commemorate visits to two country estates, *Nature* in 1732 for Dalkeith, and *Retirement* for Yester.

The theme that is most prominent in these moral poems is that of order in the universe that reveals the wisdom of God in nature. This is often closely tied with the idea of a benevolent God whose providence reconciles the harshness of nature by showing that the seeming ill is a necessary part of the general good. This theme is the subject of separate poems in the second half of the century, provoked perhaps by the earthquakes that shook England in 1750 and destroyed Lisbon in 1755, but these poems on providence will be treated later. Among the old ideas from the seventeenth century that received new emphasis from science was that of the happy man, as in Pomfret's *Choice*, who enjoys studious contemplation as part of the golden mean. In Pope's *Windsor Forest*, Gay's *Rural Sports*, and other early poems of country life, the happy man in retirement continued to pursue scientific study and contemplate in nature the wisdom of the Creator. In several later poems besides Thomson's *Winter* this became the main theme.

In *Retirement: a Divine Soliloquy* (1722) the poet goes to the country to explore 'the origin of nature and her laws', not only in the celestial universe where millions of millions of curious springs 'speak aloud, as clocks that cannot err, / The wisdom of the great Artificer', but also in the little world where 'filthy slime such pretty insects yields'. He studies the physics of sap in plants ('Small veins, like pipes, in ev'ry part being laid / Thro' which the vital juice is still convey'd'). He contemplates the favorite puzzles in science regarding flowers, fish, minerals, fossils, underground streams, and stars.

In *Of Active and Retired Life* (1735) William Melmoth uses retirement to show how science and moral philosophy combine. The scientist shows physical harmony ('Newton's mighty genius soar'd / And all creation's wondrous range explor'd, / Far as th' Almighty stretch'd his utmost line, / He pierc'd in thought and grasp'd th' entire design') and the moralist follows the lead of Shaftesbury to 'the nice concord of a well-tun'd mind' by using the scientific analogy, 'Systems to poise and spheres to regulate, / To teach the secret well-adapted force / That steers of countless orbs th'unvaried course.'

An anonymous poem, *Solitude: an Irregular Ode inscribed to a Friend* (1738) also contemplates God 'in unknown tracts / Where spheres pursue their circling rings' as well as in the metamorphoses of insects. We study science in what the senses show us but only contemplation can show 'their cause and workings'. James Grainger believes, however, that in retirement man should study science in the seasons, storms, comets, and planets, but after contemplating the meaning of nature ('To one great end, the general good, conspire, / From matter, brute, to man, to seraph, fire') he should as a social animal return to humanity.[5] This is, of course, what Pope was trying to emphasize, and this is the conclusion of Mark Akenside's *Pleasures of the Imagination*, by far the most important moral poem of the century to combine aesthetics and science with some of the moral themes we have been discussing.

When *The Pleasures of the Imagination: a Poem in Three Books* was first published anonymously in 1744, poem and notes alike showed that the poet was aware of what science could contribute to the poetic imagination.[6] The flame of genius and poetic inspiration comes chiefly, Akenside said, from the contemplation of nature, particularly those manifestations of the divine mind in the sun and moon and motions of the planets, in the alternations of light and dark, warm and cold, sun and rain, 'And clear autumnal skies and vernal show'rs, / And all the fair variety of things.' But not to all is this wealth revealed alike: some study astronomy, some botany, and some 'temper'd with a purer flame' meditate on philosophical problems:

> To these the sire omnipotent unfolds
> The world's harmonious volume, there to read
> The transcript of himself. On every part
> They trace the bright impression of his hand.

Man is especially blest with a striving spirit that searches out the sublime, flies through the air to pursue the whirlwind and lightning, and with the astronomer hovers round the sun, watches

---

[5] 'Solitude: an Ode', in Dodsley's Miscellany (1760), IV, 233–43. An American poem, *Philosophic Solitude: or the Choice of a Rural Life* (New York, 1747), written by 'a gentleman educated at Yale College', who was later identified as William Lipscomb, Governor of New Jersey, shows the same theme transplanted. With his telescope he pursued 'the planets whirling thro' the sky' and thought of 'immortal Newton' who rode on the sun 'And scann'd th'unfathomable works of God.!' /Who bound the silver planets to their spheres, /And trac'd th'elliptic curve of blazing stars!'

[6] My analysis is restricted to the 1744 version printed by R. Dodsley. The numerous changes in the revised version elaborate the metaphysics and take away much of the freshness and imagery of the original poem, especially in the portions dealing with nature and science. Both versions are reprinted in Chalmers, XIV, 59–97.

the 'reluctant planets' bent to the sun's gravity, follows the swift course of 'devious comets', and finally loses himself in the thought of stars in outer space whose light has traveled 6,000 years and still not reached the earth.

In an excellent passage near the end of Book I (438–566), Akenside agreed with Pope that all the study of nature is of importance only as it is revealed to the mind of man, which contains in itself 'the living fountains . . . of beauteous and sublime'. In the successive steps by which he arrived at this summit, however, the poet painted a loving picture of what the scientific study of shells, plant nutrition, animal life and heavenly bodies can lend to the imagination. Yet this is all vain unless it helps man. The profoundest study of the secrets of nature in the dark depths of earth and sea, tracing 'the forms / Of atoms moving with incessant change / Their elemental round', or observing 'the energy of life' kindling the seeds of being, all this scientific study is dull if it does not reach the heart, is useless if it does not aid the 'creative wisdom' through which man learns the truth.

In Book II Akenside showed that any distrust of science he might have was purely relative. In one of the best early tributes to science (97–135), he argued that the rainbow becomes more pleasing because science has revealed it as sunlight broken into many colors, and that other branches of science yield pure delight as well as instruction in 'wisdom's artful aim':

> Speak, ye, the pure delight, whose favour'd steps
> The lamp of science through the jealous maze
> Of nature guides, when haply you reveal
> Her secret honours: whether in the sky,
> The beauteous laws of light, the central pow'rs
> That wheel the pensile planets round the year;
> Whether in wonders of the rowling deep,
> Or smiling fruits of pleasure-pregnant earth,
> Or fine-adjusted springs of life and sense,
> Ye scan the counsels of their author's hand.

There is little opportunity in the rest of the poem to glorify science, but the theme of the wisdom of God shown through science continues throughout the poem as one of the main inspirations of poetic imagination. For example, in Book II, the poet describes the Great Chain of Being and uses a vivid metaphor from scientific laws to show how God is the center of all life:

His parent-hand with ever-new increase
Of happiness and virtue has adorn'd
The vast harmonious frame: his parent-hand,
From the mute shell-fish gasping on the shore,
To men, to angels, to celestial minds,
For ever leads the generations on
To higher scenes of being; while supply'd
From day to day by his inlivening breath,
Inferior orders in succession rise
To fill the void below. As flame ascends,
As bodies to their proper center move,
As the poiz'd ocean to th'attracting moon
Obedient swells, and every headlong stream
Devolves its winding waters to the main;
So all things which have life aspire to God,
The sun of being, boundless, unimpair'd,
Center of souls!

And in the final summary in Book III of the blessings that imagination imparts to 'the well-tun'd heart . . . favour'd of heaven',
the varied blessings enjoyed include a substantial amount of
nature, whether in his examples from the tempestuous storms of
Shakespeare and gentler landscape of Waller or in his own Thomsonian description of rural England. The conclusion serves as a
reminder, however, that the most important gift of imagination
is to learn from nature to understand God, to behold and love

What he beholds and loves, the general orb
Of life and being; to be great like him,
Beneficent and active. Thus the men
Whom nature's works can charm, with God himself
Hold converse; grow familiar day by day,
With his conceptions; act upon his plan;
And form to his, the relish of their souls.

An obscure poem, the anonymous *Poetic Essays on Nature, Men,
and Morals. Essay I to Dr. Askew of Newcastle* (1750), comes to the
same conclusion but by a more conventional process. The poet
describes the discoveries of Newton and medical science to
vindicate providence and demonstrate 'an entire system' that is
orderly and good. Only in man is evil found, for perfect harmony
in nature keeps each planet attracted to its sun:

> And what in this one system you explore,
> Conclude, adjusts and orders millions more;
> One pow'r, one principle, unmix'd, unchang'd,
> That formed each orb, proportion'd and arrang'd,
> Reaching, pervading ev'ry distant ball,
> Eternal, claims the aggregate of all.

The moral is clear, that man must learn from the book of nature, which is 'the work of God, a fair original'. The inspiration comes from simpler things of natural history as well as from astronomy, 'nature's whole stock that pours on ev'ry sense', yet it is foolish to study science without applying it to morals: 'To me, in vain ten thousand systems roll, / If no fixt purpose regulates my soul.'[7]

By far the most significant moral-scientific poem after the *Essay on Man* is Edward Young's *Night Thoughts*, published as nine separate poems between 1742 and 1745. The tedious rhetoric of this lengthy epic of melancholy is considerably enlivened, after the fourth book, by scientific imagery, and at the end the reader who has persevered is inclined to agree with the selective praise of Johnson: 'The power is in the whole; and in the whole there is a magnificence like that ascribed to Chinese plantation, the magnificence of vast extent and endless diversity.' When we remember that Young had used science very effectively in his early poems on the last judgment and on Job, we are surprised to find no scientific imagery until Night IV when, having finished the personal laments that occasioned the writing of the poem, he embarked on his more universal consolation of philosophy. Even this first brief exploring of scientific discovery in Night IV (1743) is designed to show that the whole splendid creation revealed by science is but a poor prelude to the 'great First-Last' whose 'nod is nature's birth'. The glory of the day with sun and roaring winds and thunder, and the glory of the night unfolding unnumbered worlds to view, though they declare the wisdom of God in their praise, are yet but 'a meer effluvium of his majesty'. He sums it up with ecstatic exclamation and rhetorical question:

> Down to the center should I send my thought,
> Thro' beds of glittering ore, and glowing gems,
> Their beggar'd blaze, wants lustre for my lay;

[7] Newcastle and London, 1750. An excellent Hayman-Grignion engraving on the title page portrays a philosopher and a poet studying nature together. Another anonymous poem, *Nature, a Poem* (1747), follows Pope closely in the ideas of order and providence, with considerable illustration from science.

Goes out in darkness: If, on tow'ring wing,
I send it thro' the boundless vault of stars;
The stars, tho' rich, what dross their gold to thee,
Great! Good! Wise! Wonderful! Eternal King?

And yet this rhetorical maze of Christian metaphysics would
have been poorer but for the occasional scientific imagery that
lightens the tedious repetitions of lugubrious melancholy. In
Night VI, for example, Young describes the puny earth which
man's soul quits as 'this small nest, / Stuck in a corner of the
universe, / Wrapt up in fleecy cloud, and fine-spun air.' He follows with his version of the cosmic voyage after death when man
gains full knowledge, not only of the moral world but also of the
material one which we have in life seen in fragments,

Unbroken, now, illustrious, and entire,
Its ample sphere, its universal frame,
In full dimensions, swells to the survey. . . .
How shall the stranger man's illumin'd eye,
In the vast ocean of unbounded space,
Behold an infinite of floating worlds
Divide the crystal waves of ether pure,
In endless voyage, without port? The least
Of these disseminated orbs, how great?

The 'stupendous whole' also includes the 'divine fecundity' of
'those twinkling multitudes of little life' seen under the microscope:

Who tost this mass of wonders from his hand,
A specimen, an earnest of his power?
'Tis, to that glory, whence all glory flows,
As the mead's meanest flowret to the sun,
Which gave it birth. But what, this sun of heaven?

The perennial theme of immortality is illustrated near the end of
the same book by the cycle of change in nature:

Look Nature through, 'tis revolution all.
All change, no death. Day follows night; and night
The dying day; stars, rise, and set, and rise;
Earth takes th'example. See, the summer gay,
With her green chaplet, and ambrosial flow'rs,
Droops into pallid autumn; winter grey

> Horrid with frost, and turbulent with storm,
> Blows autumn, and his golden fruits away,
> Then melts into the spring; soft spring, with breath
> Favonian, from warm chambers of the south,
> Recalls the first. All to reflourish, fades.
> As in a wheel, all sinks, to reascend,
> Emblems of man, who passes, not expires.

Here he makes a passing bow to Thomson, and then to praise of man with that scientific knowledge and technological skill which brings seas, winds, and planets into his service, levels mountains, and builds great cities. 'Britannia's voice! that awes the world to peace' tames the ocean, and science explores the secrets of nature:

> Earth's disembowel'd! measur'd are the skies!
> Stars are detected in their deep recess!
> Creation widens! vanquish'd Nature yields!
> Her secrets are extorted! Art prevails!
> What monuments of genius, spirit, pow'r!

When Young wants to emphasize the importance of one immortal soul in Night VII, he uses the image of the expansiveness of the celestial universe:

> Behold this midnight glory; worlds, on worlds!
> Amazing pomp! Redouble this amaze ;
> Ten thousand add; add twice ten thousand more;
> Then weigh the whole; one soul outweighs them all.

He returns to this idea later in the same book when he begs the sceptic to read the 'whole volume' of God and see the relative importance of earth 'to yon boundless orbs' and of them in turn to man, for man can still imagine further worlds, make 'new creations' in his 'capacious thought'. Pope seems to be much in Young's mind here as in the memorial verses, like a funeral paean, at the beginning of Night VII.

Readers familiar with Young's earlier *Poem on the Last Day*, which had been reprinted many times by 1745, would not be surprised at the vigor of the judgment-day passage in Night IX:

> See all the formidable sons of fire,
> Eruptions, earthquakes, comets, lightnings, play
> Their various engines; all at once disgorge
> Their blazing magazines.

This vivid scene, 'the last in nature's course', portrays every mountain outburning Vesuvius, rocks melting, stars rushing as 'final ruin fiercely drives / Her ploughshare o'er creation.' The scientific metaphor of the reversal of nature's order can be seen again in phrases like 'all Nature struggling in the pangs of death' and 'her strong convulsions . . . her final groan'. Again Young, later in the same book, uses the common scientific examples of things in the material world to show that partial evils in nature are universal good in the scheme of providence. The summary is amazingly concise for Young:

> The winter is as needful as the spring;
> The thunder, as the sun; a stagnate mass
> Of vapours breeds a pestilential air;
> No more propitious the Favonian breeze
> To Nature's health, than purifying storms;
> The dread volcano ministers to good,
> Its smothered flames might undermine the world;
> Loud Aetnas fulminate in love to man;
> Comets good omens are, when duly scann'd;
> And, in their use, eclipses learn to shine.

The scientific imagery piles up in this long final book of *Night Thoughts* as Young makes his 'moral survey of the nocturnal heavens' a fitting setting for 'The Consolation' as man approaches God.

> Thou stranger to the world! thy tour begin;
> Thy tour through Nature's universal orb:
> Nature delineates her whole chart at large,
> On soaring souls, that sail among the spheres.

Man's soul will blossom there among the tens of thousands of stars, above the atmosphere whose 'intestine wars' bring rain and hail and snow, thunder and lightning, above the tempests and 'far-travell'd comets calculated blaze'. In 'Nature's system of divinity' every student of the night can read not only the existence of God but also of other beings above man, 'natives of aether'. He can also see omnipotence rushing from 'That infinite of space, / With infinite of lucid orbs replete' and the emblem of benevolence in the 'mutual amity' of each system's planets. But these are merely images that the reason of man creates for those who, 'weak of wing, on planets perch'd' are concerned only with the material world, with thought that 'dwarfs the whole, / And makes an universe an orrery.' Science, the study of nature, must help us from material to metaphysical until we learn to view the skies as 'the garden of the Deity, / Blossom'd with stars', where the soul finds moral food. Wisdom can find astronomy useful as it marks

> The mathematic glories of the skies:
> In number, weight, and measure, all ordain'd. . . .
> Tho' splendid all, no splendor void of use;
> Use rivals beauty; art contends with pow'r;
> No wanton waste, amid effuse expence;
> The great Oeconomist adjusting all
> To prudent pomp, magnificently wise.

There are many other scientific passages in this long final book[8] but none more sympathetic to 'the subtil sage' who with his lifted tube 'to celestial lengthens human sight' than the cosmic voyage he himself takes 'in contemplation's rapid car' from the diminished earth. He pauses at every planet to 'ask for Him, who gives their orbs to roll', until from Saturn's ring, 'in which, of earths an army might be lost', he takes his bolder flight with a comet amid the stars, 'a wilderness of wonders burning round; / Where larger suns inhabit larger spheres', where he stands 'on Nature's Alps' and sees 'a thousand firmaments beneath'. The astronomical metaphor becomes indeed sublime when he yearns for metaphysical knowledge:

> O for a telescope his throne to reach!
> Tell me, ye learn'd on earth! or blest above!
> Ye searching, ye Newtonian, Angels! tell
> Where, your great Master's orb? His planets where?

Anything would be anticlimax in *Night Thoughts* after the New-tonian angels, who show that Young's early interest in science has come in again at the very end. This sublime moment when he recalls Newton almost repays the tedious reading of thousands of sentimental verses of philosophic melancholy.

Young's *Night Thoughts* may seem tedious to us but the melancholy meditation must have been highly acceptable at the time,

---

[8] All quotations are from the original editions that were printed as nine separate poems, in royal quarto, between 1742 and 1745. I was 30 pages and the average of II–VIII was about 53, but IX is 119 pages long.

for there were numerous reprintings during the century and at least two contemporary replies in verse. The first was the anonymous *The Vindication: or Day-Thoughts on Wisdom and Goodness* (1753), which takes Young to task for neglecting to use more science to bolster moral teaching. The author explains that his reply was made unnecessary by Night IX, yet the fact that he published it shows that scientific imagery is a commonplace of moral poems in the 1750's, for he sees the goodness of God in the orderly motions of heavenly bodies, even eccentric comets, that never 'rush forth against each other, to destroy the whole'. In 1754 Henry Jones added to his other scientific poems *The Relief: or Day Thoughts: a Poem Occasioned by the Complaint, or Night Thoughts*, in which he attempts to supply the scientific imagery that he felt was missing in Young: 'See nature, in her various stile, express / The thankful tribute of incessant praise, / From lifeless matter, to the sprouting blade / Of humble grass, upon the liv'ry'd lawn; / From trodden daisies, to the plant of Jove.'

Three poems that treat the theme of immortality with the help of science may have been suggested by *Night Thoughts*. Thomas Cooke's *Immortality Reveal'd* (1745) shows how science can achieve surprising moral truths by observing the secrets of nature:

> That things surprizing might be done, 'tis own'd,
> By those, who nature's depths unwearied sound,
> Who trace her in her mazes, and descry
> Those secrets, which escape th'incurious eye:
> Great are her hidden pow'rs, when art directs,
> Compounds, or severs them, to work effects.

In 1754 Isaac Hawkins Browne wrote in Latin a poem on the immortality of the soul, popular enough to be translated in six English versions, that praised Bacon, Newton, and others of 'that exalted tribe, the sons of science' who 'unlock great nature's secret springs' and with their restless minds collect 'the parts of truth that scatter'd lie'. Of the three Thomas Denton uses science with the greatest poetic effect, however, in his *Immortality: or the Consolation of Human Life, a Monody* (1754), where the metamorphosis of the beautiful moth from 'the slow reptile grov'ling o'er the green' becomes a symbol of man's ascent from 'plant-like foetus' to godlike knowledge after death. He developed also the metaphor from Thomson of nature's cycle in the seasons, for the revival of life in spring reminds us of human life after death that enables deathless Newton to 'measure time and space'.

Pope set the pattern for moral poems with scientific themes, and Young showed that the new imagery could be used effectively in religious poems. One more poem will illustrate this freedom of scientific commonplaces in a most unlikely subject, Aaron Hill's *Free Thoughts upon Faith: or the Religion of Reason, a Poem* (1746). Hill cites astronomy to confute proud and presumptuous man, developing Pope's theme in Youngian blank verse that achieves a sublime quality before he ends his scientific examples with natural history that anticipates the lyrical quality of Smart. How dare proud men, 'o'er weening, mole-blind, furrowers of dark earth', think they deserve God's whole care when they are inhabitants of 'this dim ball, / That, day by day, rolls round its eyeless bulk, / To beg light's needful alms, from one, kind sun— / While tracts, superior to conception's bound, / Sees suns, in millions, o'er new worlds, pour blaze— / Yet, reach but confines of new suns—and die!' Even on the earth, the glory of God is seen in fertile nature, whether in the harshness of Columbia's tropical heat or Zembla's ice-bound wastes or in the variety of animal and vegetable life around us. Here a lyrical enthusiasm like that of Smart foretells the future dominance of natural history in scientific poetry. Plant life abounds in the variety of trees, herbs, grains, and flowers. Birds of every sort and color fly on the downs along the seacliffs. The creatures that swim in the sea are infinite in numbers and 'still more infinite, their shapes, / Bulks, movements!—Swift, slow, timid, fierce, horn'd, barb'd, / Coatless, finn'd, scaly, shell'd, wing'd, motionless.' And at the lowest end of the scale of nature countless microscopic 'unresembling sons of endless change' are to be found in 'each puny drop, with varied states— / Each leaf, with new-shap'd nations.' With this moral poem that looks back to Thomson, Pope, and Young, and forward to Smart, we are ready to describe the transition period.

VI

THE TRANSITION: 1750-1770

By 1750 science had achieved a rhetoric of its own in English poetry. Lofty subjects led to sublime treatment when the exciting discoveries of the natural sciences in many fields prodded the imagination. This new rhetoric prodded pedestrian poets like Blackmore to add an occasional sublimity to their persuasiveness. Newton became a poetic symbol of the ability of science to persuade with convincing proof of divine order, and his death was a signal for a series of poetical essays combining natural science and natural religion. For a moment the new fervor touched the best poet of the age, and Pope left his dunces and little men to write his own version of physico-theology, his own 'essay' on the relation of man to the universe and to God. When other moral essays followed, the varying ideas of Young and Akenside and a number of lesser poets showed that science could be used to bolster moral teaching in many ways, that science had indeed achieved a persuasiveness that marked its new rhetoric.

From the middle of the century the picture becomes less clear as science begins to show itself in a number of miscellaneous ways. In poetry, for example, a new lyric element that had been fostered earlier by the women poets influenced by Thomson begins to take strong hold, and at the same time new moral subjects find a place for scientific illustration. Science itself became more the pursuit of ordinary people as the new classification scheme of Linnaeus in natural history made the world around them—plants, birds and various animal life—more understandable. Astronomy and the study of the microscope continued to be used as the subject of poetry but with less frequency and less fervor. The great world of the contrasting telescopic and microscopic universes shrank into a more familiar and intimate world where birds and flowers gradually replaced the more sublime imagery of earlier science. With the growing popularity of scientific study, the appearance of didactic poems on scientific subjects naturally became more frequent. Let us see then if we can find a common denominator for this transition period, by considering in turn the lyric, moral, and didactic poems.

I. THE LYRIC ELEMENT IN SCIENTIFIC POEMS

In the early eighteenth century the combination of science and theology naturally produced long poems of a discursive nature, but even then the lyric impulse was often dominant and sometimes expressed itself in the shorter introspective poems that we call lyric. Among the best examples of this tendency before 1750 were the women poets, the 'blooming, studious band' described by John Duncombe in *The Feminiad* (1754) as attracting attention 'with various arts', some tuneful, some moral, and others contemplative, ranging 'the heav'ns with philosophic eye'. Of this band Catherine Cockburn, 'philosopher, divine, and poet join'd', can be omitted because few of her poems have survived, but four others left a lyric impression on the scientific poetry before 1750.

Mrs. Elizabeth Rowe (1674–1737), the earliest of them all, continued the Biblical tradition with lyrics on the creation and the last judgment, yet the scientific examples she used to show the divine wisdom in nature emphasize the intimate things of rural England. It is no wonder that she singles out Thomson for special praise for the delight he showed in rural pleasures, for she herself uses the carnation, rose, and purple amaranth with 'ten thousand od'rous flow'rs of various hue' to praise 'the mighty Maker of the universe', whose divine order and plenitude are seen in nature:

> Millions of footed creatures range the woods,
> Millions with fins divide the crystal floods;
> Millions besides, with wanton liberty,
> On painted wings rise singing to the sky.

Lyrically she reads the name of God on every spire of grass and in the fragrant blossom of pink, jessamine, and purple rose. When she traces 'the first almighty cause' (in the fortieth of the blank-verse 'divine soliloquies'), she looks first among the things she knows best on earth—streams, lakes, meadows, valleys, rocks, groves, and song of birds—before she turns to the skies where God shows his control of stars, wind, lightning, and tides.[1]

Elizabeth Carter is the most learned of the band. In 1739, at the age of twenty-two, she made two translations that reflect her scholarly interest in science, one of Crousaz's criticism of the *Essay on Man*, the other of Algarotti's *Newtonianism for the Ladies*. Her interest in astronomy appears, not only in the popularization of Newton but also in her preface to the translation of Crousaz. The telescope shows us suns beyond computation and beyond them 'it is very probable that an unbounded immensity is still filled with creatures, for the wisdom and power of God are absolutely infinite'. Life is too short to master science but she will try with enthusiasm to understand the natural world around us: 'In proportion as my taste for the knowledge of nature grows strong and advances, it seems to me that our earth contains wonders enough to take up whole lives infinitely longer than mine.' Her devotion to science appears in many poems but perhaps most lyrically in these lines on order in the skies:

> He saw while matter yet a chaos lay:
> The shapeless chaos own'd his potent sway.
> His single fiat form'd the amazing whole,
> And taught the new-born planets where to roll:
> With wise direction curv'd their steady course,
> Imprest the central and projectile force,
> Lest in one mass their orbs confus'd should run,
> Drawn by th' attractive virtue of the sun,
> Or quit the harmonious round, and wildly stray,
> Beyond the limits of his genial ray.[2]

Among the followers of Thomson before 1750 were two obscure women poets who loved the gentler aspects of science and displayed in their short descriptive lyrics a sharp observation of

---

[1] *The Miscellaneous Works in Prose and Verse of Mrs. Elizabeth Rowe* (2 vols., London, 1739).

[2] *Poems on Several Occasions* (London, 1762), pp. 5–7. See also 'Ode to Wisdom' and 'Written at Midnight in a Thunderstorm'.

natural history. Mary Masters echoed Thomson in a number of her poems collected in 1733. Her description of rural landscape is particularly good in 'A Journey from Otley to Wakefield', with pictures of the wide heath, where the prickly furze pleases with its ten thousand golden blooms and its grateful scent, and where the skylark prolongs his notes as he towers high in the air ('Tho' lost to view, his melody we hear, / Like magick sounds it strikes the wond'ring ear'). She shares with us the varied shades of green in the fields along the Whorf River, the nostalgia of narrow lanes, the warbling notes of some linnets and the falling note of answer, the fruitful fields, and finally the more orderly landscape near town.[3]

Mary Leapor (1722-46) wrote a number of nature poems that have been forgotten. At times she timidly asks questions raised by 'Newton's art' about the sun, moon, stars, and 'Saturn's frozen clime', but she seems more at home when she describes the infinite 'worlds in miniature' under the microscope, where a leaf may show little forests, a dewdrop may be like a mighty ocean with creatures playing like whales, and an acorn reveals the future oak in its kernel: 'All matter lives, and shews its Maker's power / There's not a seed but what contains a flower.' From the huge whale to the senseless oyster we can follow the gradations of nature 'through her mazy way, / From the mute insect to the fount of day', but to do so would take more learning than she had, and even 'grave-fac'd wisdom may itself be wrong'. This young woman who died at twenty-four knew better how to describe the seasons and list their birds and flowers. She even adds her own realistic pictures to Thomson's winter scenes: the silent linnet skulking to his hawthorn; the mournful lark and finch; the seas of mud after snow and cold rain; the wretched country woman with her nose dripping into the pail as she stalks from cow to cow, her garments trickling, her 'wet locks all twisted in a string'.[4]

In a way the lyrics of these four women poets grew out of the philosophical scientific essay, and the connecting link is the influence of Thomson. There are indeed lyric touches in many longer poems, sometimes in surprising places. We have already

[3] Mary Masters, *Poems on Several Occasions* (London, 1733), pp. 140-4. The British Museum copy was a gift from the author to Mrs. Carter. The poems in her *Familiar Letters and Poems* (London, 1755) have no scientific interest except for the paraphrase of Psalm 104.

[4] Mary Leapor, *Poems upon Several Occasions* (London, 1748), pp. 196-200, 256-8.

seen an example in the conclusion of Henry Jones's poem, 'An Essay on the Weakness of Human Knowledge', where a moral theme becomes a lyrical prophecy of Blake: 'The smallest worm insults the sage's hand; / All Gresham's vanquish'd by a grain of sand.' An even better example is Christopher Smart, who started writing scientific poems for a prize contest, moral essays on the attributes of God, but as he wrote fervor took hold and science became lyrical. For a lyrical summary of what the physico-theological poets had been trying to say, there is no better example than this versatile and gifted poet who, like Thomas Gray, might have been one of England's best poets if his talents had not been dissipated. Attracted to the subject of physico-theology by the prospect of the prize set up by Thomas Seaton in 1750 for the best poem on the 'attributes of the Supreme Being', Smart won the contest for the first four years and again for 1755. These five poems are a fresh approach to an old subject. Taken together they show what good lyrical poetry can be made from the ideas and imagery of science.

The first poem of the group, *On the Eternity of the Supreme Being* (1750), emphasizes the creation and the last judgment, which are themselves mere episodes in the everlasting existence of the wondrous Being whose great name every atom of nature contains in undeciphered characters. The sun and moon and the stars that are 'million leagues and million still remote' will perish when nature dissolves, but God and the soul of mankind will survive.

On the Immensity of the Supreme Being (1751) is an inspired version of how nature with ten thousand tongues praises God with her morning song. The mind loses its way searching out the immensity of God, whether in the sky where the planets go harmoniously round the sun and comets dart through infinite space to their distant goal and brighter suns have their own planets and satellites, or in the sea with its coral gardens and whales, or inside the earth with its rich jewels, minerals, and hidden streams, or on the earth with its varied beauty that defies human art.

On the Omniscience of the Supreme Being (1752) is mainly a glorification of reason in man and instinct in animals, a favorite theme in physico-theology, with a digression on the vanity of the scientist who studies to investigate the powers 'Of plants medicinal, the earth, the air, / And the dark regions of the fossil world' but grows old without more knowledge than comes from building 'baseless fabric from conjecture'. The secret power of instinct that guides the magpie and bluejay to avoid poisonous fruits defies the 'proud reas'ner, philosophic man', and the migration of swallows shows a skill in navigation that Newton, 'illustrious name, irrefragable proof / Of man's vast genius', sought in vain. The ant defies the astronomer and the economist, and the bee outdoes the most learned chemists and political thinkers. The old ideas take on a fresh lyrical quality in Smart's lines on the creation, where the knowledge of Newton pales in comparison with the science of God:

> Yet what wert thou [Newton] to him, who knew his
>   works,
> Before creation form'd them, long before
> He measur'd in the hollow of his hand
> Th' exulting ocean, and the highest heav'ns
> He comprehended with a span, and weigh'd
> The mighty mountains in his golden scales:
> Who shone supreme, who was himself the light,
> E'er yet Refraction learn'd her skill to paint,
> And bend athwart the clouds her beauteous bow.

On the Power of the Supreme Being (1753) describes the sublime majesty of the terrifying aspects of nature, the 'fire-fraught wombs / Of fell volcanoes, whirlwinds, hurricanes, / And boiling billows.' The power of God is seen in magnetic attraction and the shock from an electric spark, a power that defies the research of the natural philosophers:

> By his omnipotence, Philosophy
> Slowly her thoughts inadequate revolves,
> And stands, with all his circling wonders round her,
> Like heavy Saturn in th'etherial space
> Begirt with an inexplicable ring.

On the Goodness of the Supreme Being (1755), the last of Smart's five Seaton poems, sums up in lyrical praise of God all the others and prepares the way for his two great poems, *A Song to David* and *Jubilate Agno*. Here Smart begins with praise of David, 'Israel's sweet psalmist', who gave voice and sound to hail and snow, the inspiration of his own desire to glorify the liturgy of the Church of England. In this poem Smart sings like David the praises of the 'immense Creator, whose all-pow'rful hand /

Fram'd universal Being.' In lyrical ecstasy he thanks God for the tokens of his power and goodness in nature, for the sun that paints the east and shows the color in garnet, lily, tulip, auricula, peacock, and pansy, for the sweet music of blackbird, thrush, woodlark, and robin, even for the 'coarse ruttling' cries of the ravens in the greenwood. He summons the far corners of the world to bring exotic nature to praise the Creator, elephants and spices from Araby, camels and lions from Africa, pomegranates and pineapples from India.

In 1756 Smart wrote his 'Hymn to the Supreme Being' in the mood of the Psalms and in 1763 published that restrained and beautifully modulated lyric summary of the praise of God in nature, *A Song to David*. Here the psalmist 'with harp of high majestic tone' sings of God, angels, man, 'the world—the clust'ring spheres he made', the vegetable kingdom yielding blossom, fruit, and gums, the birds like quail, cock, raven, swan, and jay, the fish and shells in the deep, the beasts like beaver, tiger, coney, and goat, and the gems like jasper and topaz. The adoration section resembles the *Benedicite* of the Prayer Book but with Smart's own array of examples from the science and travel books he had been reading: polyanthus, almond, humming bird, ounce, pheasant, ermine, sable, swordfish, ostrich, gier-eagle, whale, bullfinch, sugar-cane, cocoanut and many others. The native and the exotic crowd together to adore the Creator, the damson and the pineapple as well as the squirrel and robin, the English countryside blending with the natural history of Tahiti and the West Indies. The contrasting worlds of telescope and microscope are blended in lyric simplicity:

> For ADORATION, in the skies,
> The Lord's philosopher espies
>   The Dog, the Ram, and Rose;
> The planet's ring, Orion's sword;
> Nor is his greatness less ador'd
>   In the vile worm that glows.

All this is but itself a prelude to the ecstatic marathon of madness, science, adoration, and autobiography that was only recently discovered and published, first as *Rejoice in the Lamb* and later with Smart's Latin title as *Jubilate Agno*. Here all the patriarchs, including the three Hebrew children of the *Benedicite*, joined with

166

hundreds of others, friends and strangers alike, come with a prodigious parade of beasts and birds and fish and insects and plants to rejoice in the Lamb of God, the beetle and the butterfly along with the baboon and the camelopard. This strange medley of science and fiction glorifies the earlier paraphrases of the Anglican Book of Common Prayer and at the same time looks forward to the use of natural history by many lesser poets. The poem assumes an importance, therefore, that warrants a brief analysis.

Jubilate Agno apparently attempts to adapt the antiphonal responses of Hebrew poetry to English. The balancing pairs of lines, designed to be chanted by two choirs, may be illustrated from the beginning of Fragment B 1:

> Let Elizur rejoice with the Partridge, who is a prisoner of state
> and is proud of his keepers.
> For I am not without authority in my jeopardy, which I derive
> inevitably from the glory of the name of the Lord.

There is a general consistency in the pairs, for in the surviving fragments the 'Let' lines are impersonal variations of the exhortation to individuals to worship the Creator with some creature from nature, whereas the 'For' lines are personal and often autobiographical. The 'Let' lines contain most of the scientific allusions, for each introduces a new animal, bird, plant, or mineral, at first from the Bible and then in profusion from his reading of natural history books. In Fragment A, for example, Smart tries to match Biblical persons with Biblical animals, but after about 50 lines begins to bring in names from his own observation and from books, native and exotic alike, with no respect to any seeming order except that nine out of the last ten are songbirds found in England. In Fragment B 295 creatures, mainly birds, continue the ingenious parade of natural history, a multiplication of scientific allusion that must have reached enormous proportions in the 475 'Let' lines that have been lost. Fragment C contains 162 plants commonly found in herbals or gardening dictionaries, and Fragment D a miscellaneous array of 237 natural objects, precious stones followed by a random assortment of birds, fish, plants, quadrupeds, and serpents. There is very little system at first, and none at the end, for poetic deterioration seems to have taken place as the poem progressed. Apparently, *Jubilate Agno* is a medley of science and liturgy that began with poetic fervor and feeling but ended in compulsive therapy to relieve mental oppression. With its passionate intensity and lyrical genius, however, the poem serves as a fitting climax to the work of a fine poet who is only now being properly recognized, whose lifelong desire to improve the Church service resulted in the best combination of science and lyric beauty in the eighteenth century.[5]

2. MORAL-SCIENTIFIC POEMS AFTER YOUNG

The dividing line is not always clear between lyric poems with a moral purpose like those of Smart and the discursive moral poems whose scientific imagery often gave them a lyric quality. It becomes increasingly clear, however, that after Young scientific illustrations were commonplaces in moral poetry on a variety of subjects. The miscellaneous character of this transition period will appear as we analyze some of these moral-scientific poems, but a pattern can be seen in the two prevailing subjects that appear, often in the same poems. One is the theme of providence, a dominant offshoot of the idea of order which was the subject of most of the earlier moral poems. The other is the quiet contemplation of rural nature in England as the main scientific illustration of divine wisdom, and here the growing popular interest in the study of natural history combines with the steady interest in Thomson's *Seasons* in a sort of crescendo that culminates in the romantic poetry of the next century. Thomson's influence in a more direct way will be treated in a later chapter, but here it seems best to show the miscellaneous character of the transition period by watching the Thomson pattern emerge from its blending with other moral poems.

Let us begin with Benjamin Stillingfleet who combined the old and the new, the old in the few poems that he published, the new in his study of Linnaeus that might have made him a pioneer in natural history. He is best known for the blue stockings that he wore to the meetings of learned ladies at Elizabeth Montagu's London house, yet his pioneer publication in 1762 of three calendars of flowers set the example for hundreds of devoted amateur naturalists like Thomas Gray and Gilbert White of Selborne. Like

---

[5] Quotations from Smart's poetry are from the Muses Library, the most nearly complete edition: *The Collected Poems of Christopher Smart*, ed. by Norman Callan (2 vols., London, 1949). See Chapter II, note 10.

White he wrote what he observed, but his papers on natural history did not contain the literary quality of White's letters to Pennant. Two of his poems have considerable scientific interest. One is on an old theme, scientific proof of order in nature: all things in the Chain of Being—plants, animals, minerals, sea, and 'rolling spheres', as well as minute things like moss, shell, and insect—are 'design'd for some great end' and hold an important rank in God's plan, 'a rank, which lost / Would break the chain, and leave behind a gap / Which nature's self would rue.' The other poem, *Some Thoughts Occasioned by the Late Earthquakes* (1750) is a timely comment on the two earthquakes that disturbed England, an instance of nature's harshness that seldom touched England. The rhetorical questions in this poem imply that Stillingfleet, like those other English poets who wrote about the Lisbon disaster in 1755, believed that God's providence had not been disproved but that this seeming evil in nature was merely a warning:

> Would he who fram'd this mighty mass of things;
> Who clothes it all in beauty; makes it move
> With harmony; and every part adjusts
> With nicest order: Can we think, that he
> Would leave this wond'rous subterranean power
> To act at random?[6]

Whatever the reason, four long poetical essays between 1759 and 1771 develop the idea of providence with many rhetorical variations of the usual scientific evidence. William Kenrick, in *Epistles Philosophical and Moral* (1759), treats providence with other moral themes in eight knotty epistles. The overall view is developed in II to show that nature does not stray 'Where order still from order flows, / And never interruption knows; / Capricious but to mortal sense, / The harmony of providence.' In V the limitations of science are described: vainly we try to scale the heavens, facing the sun like an eagle, when we should be content to trace in nature 'the lines, the shadow, of his face'. The problem of nature's evils is expressed more explicitly in VI, where the poet insists that providence cannot be blamed for earthquakes, tidal

---

[6] This poem and other writings published in *Miscellaneous Tracts on Natural History* (London, 1762) were reprinted in the second volume of William Coxe, *Literary Life and Select Works of Benjamin Stillingfleet* (London, 1811).

waves, comets, and polar horrors if no one is there to feel them: 'Let Malstrooms roar, and Heclas blaze / Where fools nor cowards stand to gaze: / Let islands drown; let mountains melt; These are no evils till they're felt.' Like a complex engine whose parts move in many directions, providence must be looked at from the overall point of view: 'the sev'ral springs of providence, / In concert, at their maker's will, / Their ends harmoniously fulfil.' The last epistle concludes that human genius, which reaches its heights in Plato, Locke, and Newton, has enabled us, through the study of nature and contemplation, to raise our thoughts to God, 'Taught us to beat the wilds of space / And worlds on worlds in ether trace; / Planets and suns unknown explore, / And hence their maker, God, adore.'

The main theme of John Duncan's *An Essay on Happiness, in Four Books* (1762) is that true happiness comes from benevolence and that good is produced from evil by providence. Duncan, in his lengthy blank-verse moralizing, considerably enlarged in the 1772 edition, presents scientific evidence for order and benevolence in the physical universe. He sets the tone with his definitions of nature, first in a prose note as 'the regular and established order of things . . . by which the universe is govern'd', then rhetorically in verse:

> When the Great Parent's all-enliv'ning smile
> First beam'd forth Nature, o'er unnumber'd worlds
> He fix'd in laws impartially benign
> Her delegated sway. Th'Eternal Word
> At one collective glance the various births
> Of space and time concent'ring, view'd and bless'd
> The beauteous whole, pronouncing all in all
> Completely happy, as completely good.

Such reminiscences of Thomson pile up as the poet calls on 'countless worlds, in full harmonious choir' to praise the bounteous God who created them 'from the gloom of unessential night', as he finds divine joy in the returning seasons unmarred by 'scorching summer blaze' or 'deep-ribb'd ice', and as he pictures the effect of simple nature on a sensitive man: 'Nor peep'd a lowly violet, nor blaz'd / A star sublime, but on the open heart / Of man impress'd its portion of delight.'

It is only through the mind of man penetrating the secrets of nature that we can discover these laws of order, and here Duncan looks back to Pope and Akenside and forward to Shelley and Wordsworth. Only superior man (in the preface to the 1772 edition he makes it clear that this means 'Newton, the most pious and most enlightened of all philosophers') has the ability to 'trace his gracious laws, / The mystic springs that hold this goodly frame / In order, founded on attractive love.' He borrows a metaphor from natural history to explain the achievement of rational man through science, springing aloft to explore the laws of heaven like

> Yon sprightly lark, that wakes the meek-ey'd morn
> Springs from the fresh-turn'd furrow, 'mid the clouds. . . .
> Shrill-warbling, hears his new-enamour'd mate,
> That wanton flutters o'er the blooming thorn,
> Charm with alluring and responsive trill.

From the senses fed by nature's beauty in linnet, woodbine, and spring flowers, the imagination develops, 'views forth-issuing from the formless void / Unnumber'd worlds', but the final step belongs to reason to trace 'The shadow of his footsteps, whom nor heav'n, / Nor all creation's vast circumf'rence holds.'

John Ogilvie's *Providence: an Allegorical Poem in Three Books* (1764) uses the more conventional metaphors from science to argue for the good that arises from the seeming evils of nature. Catastrophic winds, rainstorms, and earthquakes bring benefits to man. Without earthquakes, for example, there would be no pleasing variety in nature like the Scottish Highlands, rough rocks in romantic wilderness, 'the mountains piled / Sublime in horrid grandeur to the sky / That shrouds their misty brow, where nature sits / In rude magnificence.' Even volcanoes are useful because they give vent to destructive forces that would be more disastrous to the populous plains. 'The mighty chain of things' is used as an argument for providence: we cannot see everything, the inhabitants of other worlds for example, but we can reason by analogy from what we see in nature 'from sensitive to animal; from brute, / To human', from the sensitive plant to 'the small shell but just impregn'd with life'.

In 1771 a long and significant physico-theological poem by William Hayward Roberts was published as three separate poetical essays on the existence, attributes and providence of God. The influence of science appears dramatically in Part I, *A Poetical Essay on the Existence of God*, where Newton, 'pride of Britannia's isle', is the symbol of science that shows the sublime aspects of nature to be the work of the 'Great Architect' whose creative word called harmonious order from a vast and shapeless chaos. Like earlier poets he bids the sceptic look up to find 'what hidden power / Wheels the bright planets round their central orb.' In Part II Roberts sums up all the attributes of God in the harmony of nature:

> His wonders who shall tell? His hand supports
> The golden chain, that links a thousand worlds.
> His undivided essence fills the realms
> Of time, and boundless space: his eye surveys
> Effects far distant, ere their causes rise.

The new science of psychology appears here too: the mind of man is a wonderful thing, where the senses convey images, the judgment sorts them, and the memory stores them to be brought forth on fit occasion. The description of this favorite theme of Wordsworth shows that the ideas of Hartley were already of interest to poets: 'Hence the sweet scenes of innocence and youth, / Renew'd by recollection, please again.' The third poem, *A Poetical Essay on the Providence of God*, introduces the mechanical philosophy that most moral poets had refused to recognize. There are, he explains, two schools of thought on God's care of the universe: (1) that God created the universe and set it in motion without interfering with the machine; (2) that 'every wheel / Whose motion speeds thro' space this vast machine, / Is still adjusted, as occasion calls, / By God's directing hand.' In either case God's care is conspicuous, for if one orb should deviate from its proper path, the world, though now bound by gravity, would burst and the resulting dissolution would be like that of the judgment day: the sun would disappear, the planets melt in fire, life on earth cease, and the seas freeze. Roberts finds providence also in other parts of nature: the return of spring after harsh winter, the instinct of animals, and the orderliness to be observed in millions of insects and other little things that go unnoticed but nevertheless fill out the great design in this world of plenitude.[7]

---

[7] All three parts were printed together in Roberts, *Poems: a New Edition*, London 1776. Other moral-scientific poems of the period, mostly on order in nature, include three published in 1763, *Hymn to the Power of Harmony*, John Hey's *The Redemption: a Poetical Essay*, and John Langhorne's *The Enlargement of the Mind, Epistle I*, and in 1773 Richard Graves's *The Love of Order*.

3. THE IMAGE OF THOMSON EMERGES

The influence of Thomson on descriptive poetry with a scientific and religious cast began before he died in 1748, but the first memorial poem[8] emphasizes the phrases from *The Seasons* that became a sort of refrain in the scientific-descriptive poems of the rest of the century. 'Lavish Nature's gifts' enabled Thomson to 'display the rolling year', from spring that 'blooms in her rich array, and shoots profuse / Her vegetable store', to summer that feels 'ripening nature' and bursts with thunderstorms, to autumn fruitful and 'arrayed in yellow pomp', to roaring winter. Most of all the poet's boundless genius to range through 'widening nature' is best expressed in contemplation of God 'who bids our solar year / Revolve, and seasons steer their varied course, / And moves, directs, and agitates the whole.' This image of Thomson comes very clear in later poems, but in this third quarter of the century it emerges in many forms, in nature descriptions of topo-graphical poems and in the rural pleasures arising from the study of natural history, in moral poems and in lyrics of many kinds. The varied tone can best be seen in the very influential *Meditations and Contemplations* of James Hervey, written in prose in 1747, whose very popularity inspired in the next decade a poetic version 'after the manner of Dr. Young' by Thomas Newcomb.

There is a great deal of Thomson in Hervey, especially in the combination of natural science and natural religion, a point that has been so well illustrated by Alan McKillop[9] that we can con-centrate on the scientific verse of Newcomb's adaptations. We can leave 'Meditations among the Tombs' to the graveyard school except for the scientific theme of the last judgment with its repe-tition of the dissolving of nature 'that sinks creation into dust'. Newcomb's 'reflections on a flower-garden', however, look like another version of *The Seasons*, where spring flowers are described in profusion while the lark 'and all the choir / Of feather'd min-strels join their grateful songs / To celebrate their great creator's praise.' Divine power is seen in the red lightning and the loud tempests which spend

[8] *Musidorus: a Poem Sacred to the Memory of Mr. James Thomson* (London, nd.).

[9] 'Nature and Science in the Works of James Hervey', Texas *Studies in English*, XXVIII (1949), 124–38. My quotations are from the two-volume edition of New-comb (London, 1764), which contains (I, 85–159) a revised version of the *Contem-plations on a Flower-garden* (London, 1757).

Their madding fury through the ample space
Stretch'd out above; where worlds unnumber'd roll
Each above each, in beauteous order rang'd!
How great the skill! how infinite the power
Of that creative hand, which spread so wide
The ample dome where stars and planets blaze!

Numerous descriptive passages unroll the progress of the seasons
in the garden and touch on scientific themes: the botanical listing
of plants and trees, the circulation of water, distilling of dew, and
sap of plants. For example, the power of rising sap to produce
beauty may be seen in nature's process: the moisture from earth
and air, 'Passing through curious strainers, and dispos'd / In
ranges of pellucid tubes', concealed from view 'creeps along the
fibres' of moss or lofty cedars, 'in circulating channels . . . pervades each leaf' until it appears in hepatica, poppy, mulberry, or
quince. The richness of blossoms, in wood or field or garden,
reads like a generous selection from a botanical handbook, too
copious for quotation. But it is not all descriptive, for the spiritual
message returns regularly and the revolving seasons reflect the
wisdom of God.

In 'A Descant upon Creation' the science of botany changes to
the universal theme of earlier poems, particularly Thomson's
'Hymn to the Seasons'. The Newtonian 'sacred song' reappears in
the 'radiant heavens . . . beneath whose height / And ample circle
worlds unnumber'd roll', in comets returning from their 'long
excursions', in planets 'who guide the varying seasons', in the sun,
'vast inexhausted fount' of light and heat, in thunder and lightning, in 'frowning winter clouds', in rainbow and hurricane, in
the harshness of Libyan desert and Russian sea, in ocean, mountain, forest, and meadow, in mines and fountains, in birds, animals,
insects, and trees. Let all his works praise his name, 'earth with
heaven in joyous hymns uniting!' With such a belated *Benedicite* it
is no wonder that Hervey, with or without the blank verse of
Newcomb, was influential.

'Contemplations on the Night', like those on the tombs, is more
like Young than Thomson, even when the poet occasionally
pauses on a scientific theme, such as the effect of dew on the sap
of plants or the dissolution of nature at the last judgment. On the
other hand, 'Contemplations on the Starry Heavens' returns to

Newtonian science, not only the solar system but the stretching universe:

> Nor barely is each star a world, it glows
> The centre of some other system, spread
> With magnificence how great above the skies!
> By other globes attended, rolling round
> The parent star, and lighted by its beams.

These are 'sketches only of almighty power', and so our wonder is aroused by the sublime idea of boundless 'empires of the sky' until imagination is lost in trying to conceive immense creation where even the loss of the sun itself would scarce be owned by that great eye

> Which takes in all creation at one view.
> A world extinguish'd seems to him no more
> Than a sand lost upon the ocean's shores;
> Nor would a thousand orbs, if vanish'd, leave
> A blank in those proud works his voice has fram'd.

With all the vast number of systems, each with its planets rapidly circling the central sun, 'none mistake their way, the road assign'd, / As on they fly along the trackless path', for their rotations proceed 'in one eternal harmony', constant to that order established in the beginning. This astronomical rhapsody concludes with quoting Addison's famous hymn, beginning 'The spacious firmament on high'.

Hervey and Newcomb conclude their physico-theological 'meditations' with 'A Winter Piece', which is perhaps closest of all to Thomson. The theme is that of Thomson and Shelley but by no means limited to them: the leafless trees, the silent birds, the stormy air, the fertilizing snow, all are but vivid reminders that nature will be renewed in spring and that for man there will be a life after death 'Where storms shall beat, and winters pierce no more, / But one eternal spring for ever bloom'.[10]

After the concentration of science and religion in Hervey and Newcomb, the miscellaneous influence of Thomson in several poets of the period seems diffuse indeed yet certainly indicative of the gradual recognition of rural scenery and natural history in

---

[10] Hervey's prose version appears much more scientific than Newcomb's verse because of the many documented footnotes, but Newcomb includes so much scientific material that his work may be considered as a major scientific poem.

poetry. Francis Fawkes, best known for his translations of Halley and Smart from Latin, uses much georgic description in his early topographical poem, *Branham Park* (1745), and reflects Thomson's ideas in his 1754 odes to each of the seasons. His most notable contribution might have been a revival of the Middle Scots poet of realistic nature, Gavin Douglas, but this medieval poetry on the seasons got no farther than the reprinting of the original with modern versions and explanatory notes, *A Description of May* (1752) and *A Description of Winter* (1754).

Soame Jenyns, besides translating Browne's scientific poem on the immortality of the soul and a didactic poem on the *camera obscura*, used natural history, especially of microscopic animals, in various kinds of poems published anonymously in 1752 as *Poems by....* 'An Essay on Virtue', for example, varies the old theme of divine benevolence shown by science:

> Thousands of suns beyond each other blaze,
> Orbs roll o'er orbs, and glow with mutual rays;
> Each is a world, where form'd with wondrous art
> Unnumber'd species live thro' every part:
> In ev'ry tract of ocean, earth, and skies,
> Myriads of creatures still successive rise;
> Scarce buds a leaf, or springs the vilest weed,
> But little flocks upon its verdure feed;
> Nor fruit our palate courts, or flow'rs our smell,
> But on its fragrant bosom nations dwell,
> All form'd with proper faculties to share
> The daily bounties of their Maker's care.

When he sends 'a present of shells and stones design'd for a grotto' to a lady, Jenyns makes sure that she does not miss the message that to such 'philosophic eyes' as hers 'each grain of sand, or humblest weed' appears beautiful, and nature in her lowest forms can entertain and instruct.

Nature description and religious sentiment combine about mid-century in the poems of Thomas Blacklock, a follower of Thomson who described rural England with remarkable fidelity for a man blind from infancy. The influence of *The Seasons* can be seen in the most comprehensive of his poems on natural religion, 'A Soliloquy', where he laments not being able to see 'the seasons, in majestic order', yet describes with understanding the progressive beauty of the seasons and the Newtonian universe as well.

His chain of being, extending from telescopic to microscopic worlds, revives an old metaphor: 'From rolling worlds descends thy gen'rous care, / To insect crouds that 'scape the nicest eye'.[11]

An obscure poet from Essex, Edward Stephens, imitated Thomson in many of his descriptive, scientific, and religious lyrics. 'Nature Admired' reflects scientific questions on the sun's 'vital heat' and the vine's 'strength'ning juice'. A lyrical paraphrase of the creation, 'On Creation and Providence', describes the usual examples from astronomy and natural history and goes on to the cycles in nature best revealed in the rural beauty of the 'revolving seasons'. Closer in sentiment and verse form to Thomson is 'Universal Praise', a parade of all the manifestations of 'Nature's God' beginning with 'Ye twinkling fires, / Ye other suns, and moons, and systems fair'. 'The Birth-Day, a Pastoral' turns to georgic, as in this picture of the skylark:

> Thrills her glad notes, still soaring as she sings;
> Now pois'd, she flutters in her much-lov'd skies,
> She drops adown and in the furrow lies.
> Thus to her Parent-God all Nature pays
> The morning tribute of a chearful praise.[12]

The spirit of Thomson can be seen in the rural scenes of John Cunningham's lyrics, beginning with 'Day: A Pastoral' in 1761, but the style is languid in his miscellaneous lyrics, pastorals, and fables. An occasional piece of realism enlivens the bucolic scenes, like the cattle at noon standing in water or a speckled trout rising as blue mists creep over a lake at evening, and the poetic imagery suggests a familiarity with natural history, even in the creatures of the fables, such as owl, thrush, linnet, magpie, and the splendid butterfly that reminds the ant that she was once 'the reptile you spurn'd and despis'd'.[13]

The conscious influence of Thomson may be seen in the varied writings of John Langhorne. It is present even in the youthful 'Studley Park' with its rural scenery, its address to varied nature,

[11] *Poems by Mr. Blacklock* (2nd ed., London, 1756). Joseph Spence's critical essay catalogues numerous examples of a scientific description of natural history.

[12] Edward Stephens, *Poems on Various Subjects* (London, 1759), and *The Birth-Day, a Pastoral, with Other Poems* (Ipswich, 1765).

[13] *Day, and Other Pastoral Pieces* (Edinburgh, 1761); enlarged in *Poems, chiefly Pastoral* (Newcastle, 1766; 2d ed. rev., 1771).

all-bounteous and profuse, its parade of spring flowers, and its
retired gentleman-scientist

> Who nobly dares with philosophic eye,
> Through full creation's boundless orbs to fly;
> Pleas'd in their well-form'd systems still to find
> The matchless wisdom of th'immortal mind.
> Still charm'd, in Nature's various plan, to trace
> His boundless love and all-supporting grace.

It is more conscious in *Genius and Valour: a Scotch Pastoral* (1763)
in the nature images and the parade of the seasons to mourn the
Scottish Thomson, 'child of nature'. The interest in natural history continues in the long moral poem, *The Enlargement of the
Mind* (1763–65), and in the sentimental moralizing of *The Fables
of Flora* (1771).[14]

The new look in scientific poems is reflected in a long moral
poem on an aesthetic subject in Henry James Pye's *Beauty: a
Poetical Essay in Three Parts* (1766). Part I discusses beauty in
nature in the manner of Thomson, rejecting Versailles for forest
and meadow or even the wilder mountains and swamps or 'where
the congregated waters sweep / With foaming lapse, down
Niagara's steep'. Best of all is the gentle British landscape with
its green hill, thick woods, and flowers changing with the seasons.
There is much Thomson and little science, yet a feeling tribute
comes in Part III when he uses scientists to illustrate moral beauty:
these 'sages, who creation's depths explore, / And hang incessant
o'er the pleasing lore' are always busy, 'rushing forward, urg'd
by force divine, / See distant suns on distant systems shine', yet
all the vast Newtonian universe is to him of little value compared
to man. Pye's topographical poem, *Farringdon Hill* (1774), has a
descriptive introduction describing the changes of the seasons but
his only mention of 'pensive Thomson' is a mild protest against
angling. His shorter poems are full of imagery from science, and
his later moral poem, *The Progress of Refinement* (1783), pays a
compliment to Newton, 'whose immortal force / Pursued coy
Nature to her inmost source'.[15]

The medley of natural history and natural religion described in

[14] All poems reprinted in Chalmers, XVI, 407–75.
[15] The second edition of *Faringdon Hill: a Poem in two Books* (Oxford, 1778) contains all the shorter poems. Another topographical poem, Richard Jago's *Edge-Hill*
(1767), contains considerable science of a didactic nature.

the poems of this transition period, except for the unique contribution of Smart, stems from the influence of Thomson's *Seasons*,
an increasing wave of imitation that will be described in a later
chapter as a prelude to Wordsworth. There were other verses,
mainly didactic and satirical, but they are best treated as separate
phenomena off the main beat of scientific poetry. Even the
scientific poems of this transition period are seldom good poetry,
for the sublime imagery stemming from scientific discovery in the
telescopic and microscopic universes had lost its fervor, and most
writers had not yet learned to make natural history into poetry.

Meanwhile the best writers studied science but disdained it as
literature. Thomas Gray studied Linnaeus avidly and added copiously to his science notebooks but wrote what little poetry he
cared to write on other subjects. Samuel Johnson liked chemistry
and added much science to the 'philosophic words' of his dictionary, but in his essays and criticism he seldom showed more than a
passing interest in the subject. The four *Rambler* papers that comment on science (82, 83, 177, 199), for example, consist mainly of
conventional satire on the virtuoso.

Oliver Goldsmith, in need of money in his later years, summarized popular knowledge of natural history in his *History of
Earth and Animated Nature* (1774), yet he knew little science and
his only attempt to put science into poetry, the picture of harsh
nature in *The Deserted Village*, is a miserable failure. Thomas Chatterton tried to take advantage of the contemporary interest in
science to publish a few occasional poems on the subject. They are
of a pattern with his Rowley poems in that both followed a fashion
of the moment in order to gain attention, but they are different in
their inferior quality. 'The Copernican System' (*Town and Country
Magazine*, December, 1769) is a juvenile summary of general
knowledge, and 'Epistle to the Reverend Mr. Catcott' is a curious
mixture of serious questions on the religious implications of
science and playful satire on Catcott's showing the ladies his fossil
collection and his model for explaining artesian wells.[16] Except
for his tragic place in the history of English poetry, Chatterton's
scientific verse would be ignored today.

The picture was soon to change. Cowper and Blake, though

[16] *The Works of Thomas Chatterton* (London, 1803), I, 50, 93. See E. W. H. Meyer-
stein, *A Life of Thomas Chatterton* (London, 1930), especially pp. 305, 310 (treatise
on the deluge).

each protested in different keys the materialistic arrogance of science, were soon to write good poetry that reflected their interest in the world of physical nature revealed by science. And scores of lesser writers, inspired by Thomson and taking their cue from the literary quality of Gilbert White's observations of natural history in the village of Selborne, wrote feelingly and well about new examples of divine wisdom and goodness, birds and flowers and the other creatures of rural England.

VII

NATURAL HISTORY IN
ENGLISH POETRY, 1760–1800

A<small>FTER</small> 1760 natural history became, as we have seen, the favorite branch of scientific study for poets and other amateurs, young and old, male and female. The new classification scheme of Linnaeus encouraged the Englishman's love of plants and flowers, beasts and birds, and as a result the description of rural scenery in English georgic poetry took on a scientific flavor. In a way the transition was easy, for James Thomson was the favorite poet of these amateur naturalists, and the editors of *The Seasons* emphasized nature description as Thomson's strong point. Numerous books on botany made it easy to catalogue flowers in profuse detail, and dictionaries of natural history supplied easily accessible material from which to choose examples of other phases of natural history as proof of God's wisdom in nature.

The aesthetic interest in natural history as a subject for poetry was greatly encouraged by the rapid development of the art of color engraving. From about 1760 and into the next century many books on various branches of natural history were illustrated by beautiful prints, the best of them professionally hand colored but often sold in black and white to be colored by the owners. These books ranged from the simplicity of *Rousseau's Ladies' Botany* to the elaborate birds of Audubon or the ornate and expensive flowers of Thornton's *Temple of Flora*. This glorious episode in the history of art is well known, but it must be kept in mind as part of the same aesthetic interest in natural history that is reflected in the poetry we are about to describe. Back of the imitations of Thomson and the didactic verses of Erasmus Darwin lie the exquisite flower prints of Curtis and Redouté. And back of the contemplation of birdsong in Cowper lies the interest in birds reflected in the caging of wild songbirds[1] and the painting of birds in nature done in hundreds of color prints before Audubon. The beauty of these engravings of flowers and birds is so apparent that it is easy to see why the study of botany and ornithology became more fashionable than zoology or entomology or any other branch of natural history, and why the long lists of flowers and birds reflect the dominant scientific interests of poets in the second half of the century. Whatever the reason, natural history became the chief source of poetic imagery both in descriptive georgics reminiscent of Thomson and in longer philosophical poems. The first significant aesthetic statement of this new use of science in poetry was Dr. John Aikin's *An Essay on the Application of Natural History to Poetry* (1777).

I. THE AESTHETICS OF NATURAL HISTORY IN POETRY

Aikin put into words for the first time what English poets had been showing for many years, that natural history was a fitting subject for poetry and that a knowledge of science was helpful for 'attaining the highest beauties of descriptive poetry'. If poets are to avoid the perpetual repetition of the same images, let them seek novelty where it is most abundant, in 'the grand and beautiful objects which nature every where profusely throws around us'. Aikin recognized the popularity of Thomson's *Seasons* by citing it as the source of 'the greatest variety of genuine observations in natural history'. In 1778 he amplified his criticism of Thomson in his introduction to a new illustrated edition of *The Seasons*. He praised the poem first for description, calling it the model 'whence our modern descriptive poets have derived that more elegant and correct style of painting natural objects which distinguishes them from their immediate predecessors'. Yet we must recognize,

---

[1] For the changes in sentiment about caged birds in this period, see my article, 'The Captive Linnet', *Philological Quarterly*, XXXIII (1954), 330–7.

Aikin goes on to say, that precept is as important as description, that the sublime in Thomson comes from the synthesizing of 'natural philosophy' rather than from the observation of 'natural history'. Thomson, he concludes, 'certainly remains unrivalled in the list of descriptive poets', but the religious element in *The Seasons* is more elevated than the descriptive or sentimental, for 'the genuine philosopher, while he surveys the grand and beautiful objects every where surrounding him, will be prompted to lift his eye to the great cause of all these wonders'.[2]

The criticism of Thomson by Aikin and others in this period takes on significance in the light of the great vogue of *The Seasons* and the frequent conscious imitation of Thomson in the description of nature and the use of rural scenery as a source of religious philosophy. The earliest criticism of Thomson is in the verse imitations themselves. In 1751 W. H. Draper in *The Morning's Walk* laments Thomson's untimely death and speaks of his 'descriptive muse' who

> Rang'd Nature thro', and like great Milton search'd
> In all her boundless vast;—lo! thus he paints
> The summer's blaze, and bids frail man awake
> To chant Creation's praise, and Nature's God.

The anonymous *Muse's Recreation* (1762) includes specific praise of Thomson with the message that the changing seasons bring of birds and flowers by day and contemplation of nature's infinitude by night. The author of *On Beneficence* (1764) calls him 'great parent of descriptive verse' and invokes his aid in the description of the seasons, especially winter. James Grainger in *Beauty: a Poem* (1766) links Thomson with Shakespeare and Milton as the poet of nature: 'Let raptur'd fancy feel the circling year / Roll o'er our heads, and mark the changing scences / Of nature, drest in his immortal lays, / Who sang the Seasons.' William Hawkins, who omitted Thomson in his 1758 *Essay on Genius*, praised him in his 1781 revision among those poets who with science try to penetrate farther into the secrets of nature: 'strong description animates his line'.

---

[2] For a fuller analysis of Aikin's criticism of Thomson and Cowper, see my article in *Journal of Aesthetics and Art Criticism*, XXI (1963), 439–43. Since this was written, Ralph Cohen has published an exhaustive study of criticism on *The Seasons* in his *The Art of Discrimination: Thomson's The Seasons and the Language of Criticism* (Berkeley, 1964).

Three editors of Thomson seem to be impressed also by his sentiment and religious philosophy. George Wright, whose new edition of *The Seasons* about 1770 contained engravings, memoir, critical notes, and a topical index, emphasized tenderness of heart and praised religious passages as 'sublime and beautiful'. Percival Stockdale, who edited Thomson in 1793, cited 'the oracles of celestial truth' and the 'splendid volume of divinity' that Thomson saw in the whole system of creation. Robert Heron appended a long 'Critical Essay on the Seasons' to his 1794 edition, in which he comes to no real conclusion but after analyzing each section of the work as descriptive poetry thinks it 'Thomson's first praise, that he has known so well to unite poetry with devotion'.

The most complete critical analysis of *The Seasons* is John More's book-length study of the poem, *Strictures, Critical and Sentimental, on Thomson's Seasons* (1777). The main part of the book is devoted to showing how Thomson, 'in this country at least . . . the father of descriptive poetry', gives pleasure by his accurate observation of nature, by recalling to memory what we ourselves have seen. The poet's ability 'to present the world with a graphical map of the year, to which there is no parallel, in this, or perhaps any other language' may be due, he feels, to the fact that he 'had his birth and education among the bleak and desert wilds of North Britain'. As a painter of external nature, Thomson preserves inviolate the three indispensable rules of landscape painting: unity of subject, minute fidelity of detail, and a 'coloring from nature' that comes from God in nature. The poem is universally popular in town and country, among young and old alike: 'I have found it in the hands of shepherds, in the remotest solitudes, who never saw another book, save their Bible; and heard some of its finest passages repeated by clowns.' More recalls various objections to the poem and tries to answer them: harshness, want of simplicity, inversion and elaborate style, incautious use of technical scientific terms, and improper management of figurative language. Yet Thomson was accurate: 'Few professed naturalists have studied and traced the various energies and effects of vegetation with more attention and success than he did. . . . In him the love of nature was literally a source of science.' And he found physico-theology a source for the sublime.

Brief as it is, Johnson in his *Lives of the Poets* wrote perhaps the best criticism of *The Seasons*. He praised Thomson for originality arising from poetic understanding that includes realistic detail and philosophic contemplation. He called him 'man of genius' with a discriminating eye for everything in nature and in life that appeals to the imagination, 'and with a mind that at once comprehends the vast and attends to the minute'. In his praise Johnson lingers more on the philosophical, 'the whole magnificence of Nature' in the 'descriptions of extended scenes', yet the part played by the naturalist, he feels, is important, for it is science that helps the poet 'to recollect and to combine, to range his discoveries and to amplify the sphere of his contemplation'.

To the critics of the late eighteenth century *The Seasons* was admired for its pleasing combination of description and philosophy, and the many poems written in imitation show both qualities. Yet Thomson is most often cited as descriptive poet who skillfully assembles in verse those details of natural history that the Englishman knows and loves, the kind of thing that Gilbert White was to do in prose in 1788. Another indication of Thomson's realism, the faithful depicting of the rural scenery of his native Scotland, emphasized by More and later by David Stuart, Earl of Buchan,[3] was a patriotic addition that Robert Burns epitomized in his 1790 memorial verses ending 'While Scotia with exulting tear / Proclaims that Thomson was her son.' Realistic nature description is certainly what many minor poets saw in Thomson. Since it is easier to imitate than his religious philosophizing, and since its attention to details of natural history was in line with the amateur scientific pursuits of many Englishmen, the poets of the time described the rural scenery of Britain with fervor. They varied the topography and the lists of flowers and birds from their science books, but their eye was on Thomson, as we shall see from a sampling of their work.

2. THE INFLUENCE OF THOMSON

A catalogue of the poems that imitate Thomson in the late eighteenth century would be dull and would serve little purpose. We

---

[3] *Essays on the Life and Writings of Fletcher of Saltoun and the Poet Thomson* (London, 1792), pp. 175–280, contains criticism of Thomson and several Scottish tributes, including the letter of Burns with verses.

have already noted a number of poems that from the death of Thomson praised his descriptive powers or showed his influence by a combination of rural description, religious philosophy, sentiment, the theme of the changing seasons, and the use of blank verse. The Thomson touch is not always apparent at first sight. John Huddlestone Wynne's *The Four Seasons, a Poem* (1773), for example, has very little of Thomson, while Robert Colvill's *On the Winter Solstice* (1765), even in its loose Pindaric stanzas, readily shows the conscious imitation of Thomson. This poem turns from the realism of the hushed Scottish winter to the wild harshness of winter storms in Zembla, Norway, Finland, Lapland, and Russia. The pleasures of contemplation in winter lead the mind to explore with science how God rules 'the attracted planets' and those stars 'beyond the glare of Mars, or Saturn's radiant throne'. Whether we dare 'with bold Newton's line' to adjust time and space, or visit snowy Lapland, or enjoy local description, we are aware that Thomson is not far off.

The poems of John Scott of Amwell show a clear influence of Thomson that was later borne out by his essay on *The Seasons*. This critical essay, intended for publication before his death in 1783, is the climax of Scott's lifelong interest in Thomson. Illustrated with numerous quotations, the work notes the defects of bombast and obscurity as well as the beauties shown in close observation and forcible description, especially in the 'lofty strain . . . describing the grand phaenomena of nature'. Let us see how Scott's poems follow the descriptive excellence that he recognizes in *The Seasons*.[4]

As early as 1760 Scott's *Four Elegies: Descriptive and Moral* are in the Thomson manner as they describe the seasons in a pleasing combination of georgic description and scientific moral. The idea of divine order in nature is lightly touched on as the 'wide-extended heav'n with stars emblaz'd' show that man in comparison is 'a point, an atom in the field of space', but the moral themes are heavily accentuated in the natural history of the English seasons, in the jubilant flowers and insects of spring, the oppressive hot weather of summer, and the harshness of winter:

---

[4] *The Poetical Works of John Scott* (London, 1782) contain poems that had already appeared separately. On Thomson, see Scott, *Critical Essays on Some of the Poems of Several English Poets* (London, 1785), pp. 295–386, and the prefatory life of Scott.

> The sun far southward bends his annual way,
> The bleak north-east wind lays the forest bare,
> The fruit ungather'd quits the naked spray,
> And dreary winter reigns o'er earth and air.

Scott continues the georgic parade of the English seasons with more scientific exactness in the 1782 *Amaboean Eclogues*, especially in 'Rural Scenery' where flowers, trees, and even weeds are visually described in verse and identified with Linnaean botany in the notes. The catalogue of spring flowers is in the new manner, but it is the color and profusion of summer species that excite his botanical skill, beginning with crimson poppies in the grain:

> There scabious blue, and purple knapweed rise,
> And weld and yarrow show their various dyes.
> In shady lanes red foxglove bells appear,
> And golden spikes the downy mulleins rear;
> Th'inclosure ditch luxuriant mallows hide,
> And branchy succory crowds the pathway side.

Scott's mingling of georgic and science makes for a loving description of the plants in his garden at Amwell that Johnson called 'Fairy Hall' when he visited it in 1773. In the epistle, 'Winter Amusements in the Country', Scott looks back to Thomson and forward to Cowper in his simple pictures from the English countryside. The botanic touch is in the catalogue of evergreens in the garden and of the exotic plants from Africa and India in the greenhouse. The description of a walk combines natural history with rural scenery: the yellow of prickly furze shows on the steep slopes, the robin looks for insects in the gray moss, the green woodpecker (identified with the aid of Pennant's *British Zoology*) flies with shrill cry and dips his noisy bill into a dry branch, the hare 'starts rustling from the brake, / And gaudy jays incessant clamour make.' In the open he sees a muddy stream, edged with yellow reeds, flowing through russet pastures, and beyond the dark woods a church tower. In the long evenings, like Thomson, he reads history and travel and studies the wonders of nature with the help of some of the popular mechanical models:

> The sun's vast system in a model shows;
> Bids the clear lens new forms to sight expose;
> Constructs machines, whose wond'rous powers declare
> Th'effects of light, and properties of air;

With whirling globes excites electric fires,
And all their force and all their use inquires.
O Nature! how immense thy secret store,
Beyond what ev'n a Priestley can explore.

Yet Scott's scientific interests center in natural history, whether in his own garden or on botanical expeditions with a friend, eager to identify plants in Linnaeus by tracing 'the marks minute . . . whence he his nice distinctions drew', or in his picture of the young artist in foreign lands painting nature 'through beasts, and birds, and insects, fruit, and flow'rs, / In shape and colour all distinct from ours.' He added Linnaean natural history to Thomson's mixture of science with philosophy and description.

The religious side of Thomson can be seen more emphatically in other poems, where the idea of the wisdom of God in nature is stressed in rural scenery though still with an occasional glance at the Newtonian heavens. In 1764, for example, Percival Stockdale in his *Poetical Address to the Supreme Being* wishes to retire 'from a jarring world' and think about the power of God in the ocean's roar but comes at last to lectures from meadow and 'tuneful grove'. The best illustration of this serious side of Thomson is perhaps an obscure long blank-verse poem with a suggestive title, James Foot's *Penseroso, or the Pensive Philosopher in his Solitudes: a Poem in Six Books* (1771). Book I introduces the old theme through the scientific study of the celestial universe and its effect upon the earth, especially in the changing seasons with their apt illustrations of God's 'vast design'. In Book II the teeming luxuriance of summer is used as a prelude to that other wisdom of God which finds good in seeming evil, in the harshness of storm and plague and Lisbon earthquake. God's management demands continuous care, however, and Foot makes it clear that he does not subscribe to the new mechanical philosophy, for it is as hard

> To check the planetary orbs which roll
> Down the dread steep of heav'n, and bring them back,
> From the long journey or of months or years,
> Punctual at stated times, as 'twas at first
> To round them into form, and push them forth
> Pompous along th'interminable void.

God may be seen 'in things minute, / As in the most stupendous works of heav'n', in sun or glowworm, stormy sea or purling rill, moss or oak. In Book III dark winter leads to a long meditation on death and immortality, in which the only scientific reminiscence is in a sublime picture of the last judgment when 'nature sinks convuls'd, the world destroy'd'. In Book IV flowering spring depicted in Thomsonian splendor leads to the superiority of the Christian religion over superstition, nowhere better shown than in man's observing nature and explaining phenomena through science. The imagination lags at the thought of other systems beyond our solar universe and yet the scientist continues to explore space and conquer seas and mountains by his technology:

> He mounts the poles, and with the splendid train
> Of planets travels, traverses the fields
> Of boundless space, and tells how comets speed
> Excursive to the frontier bounds of heav'n.

In the last two books Foot left science, yet as a whole his *Penseroso* is a forgotten philosophic poem that combines Thomsonian science and description.

Several shorter poems by Edmund Rack in 1775 portray the seasons and English landscape in the manner of Thomson. Taken with a later prose 'Essay on the Pleasure and Improvement arising from studying the Works of Nature', they show how a keen interest in science can use natural history with philosophic insight to reinforce other scientific evidence of the wisdom of God.[5] Two poems in particular seem to stem directly from Thomson. 'To Spring' is full of catalogues of spring flowers and scientific accounts of 'nature's propelling power' on plant growth ('The late stagnated sap, now rarify'd / Bursts from its inmost channels, and protrudes / The swelling buds, soft leaves, and pregnant flow'rs'), on minerals and gems in the earth, and on coral and shells in the ocean. The awakening of nature in spring conveys the mind from effects to causes until 'the intellectual eye, enraptur'd soars' above the stars to God. 'Winter: a Poem' has many Thomson touches besides the title: the red-breast and pensive cattle, the sleeping sap, and 'nature's grand design' in the circling seasons. Short poems on spring, summer, night, and a thunderstorm show readers that the new nature description is modelled on Thomson, but two philosophical poems develop

---

[5] *Poems on Several Subjects*, London, 1775. The essay is in *Essays, Letter, and Poems* (Bath, 1781), pp. 225–35.

old ideas with originality. 'The Cell of Contemplation: A Vision' is an allegory of scientific study in 'Cam's delightful grove', overhead the sight of stars, planets, and two comets moving eccentric 'through boundless regions of unmeasur'd space', and on the walls a picture of creation like Milton's but with a botanic slant. 'On the Divine Wisdom' approaches the sublime in the invocation of the creative power that designed the immense plan of nature: with ecstasy he views light

> Dart, and illume, with instantaneous beams,
> Creation's boundless circuit! Wide extends
> Th'amazing prospect! Worlds, succeeding worlds,
> Swarm, through the regions of immensity,
> To nature's utmost bounds; while central suns,
> Fix'd in eternal orbits, beam forth day
> With undiminish'd lustre!

A few more examples will show how the conscious influence of Thomson extends to the end of the century. James Hurdis showed it in *The Village Curate* (1788) by his blank-verse georgics on the changing seasons, his catalogues of English flowers and birds, his tribute to Newton (whose 'quick and piercing eye' penetrates 'the dark abode of clouded mystery'), and his contemplation of God in the book of nature ('Not a tree, / A plant, a leaf, a blossom, but contains / A folio volume'). George Wright, who edited *The Seasons* and quoted them extensively in his *Retired Pleasures* (1787), freely acknowledged his paraphrase of Thomson in *The Rural Christian* (1794) on the seasons and the wisdom of God seen in trees, birds, and flowers. William Gill Wheatcroft in *The Powers of Fancy: a Poem* (1790) praised Thomson's painting of nature 'in stile sublime, yet flowing soft and free' and added a number of scenes from rural England and foreign countries that remind us of Thomson.[6]

Scores of other poems show a casual influence of Thomson in their nature description that frequently touches on natural history. Such were the lyrics of Michael Bruce and John Logan published in 1782. In 1789 Philip B. Homer's *Anthologia; or a Collection of*

[6] Other poems containing specific criticism of Thomson are: 'On the Cultivation of Taste', *A Collection of Original Poems by the Rev. Mr. Blacklock and other Scotch Gentlemen* (Edinburgh, 1760), I, 27 ff.; James De la Cour, *A Prospect of Poetry* (5th ed., London, 1770); *The Poet: a Poem* (London, 1773); W. H. Roberts, *A Poetical Epistle to Christopher Anstey* (London, 1773); Michael Woodhull, *Ode to the Muses* (Oxford, 1790); and W. L. Brown, *An Essay on Sensibility* (London, 1791).

Flowers, in Blank Verse combined botany and sentiment, Thomas S. Dupuis' *Misecllaneous Poems* described winter, and John Rannie's *Poems* revealed a homesick boy in London remembering the Scottish countryside with keen observation. Among the women poets Anna Seward wrote with enthusiasm of birds, flowers, the seasons, and the wild scenery of the Lakes, while Susanna Blamire described in dialect the flowers of Cumberland and Hannah Cowley concentrated on rough mountain scenery. William L. Bowles, H. F. Cary, and Thomas Russell put into the new sonnet form some of Thomson's science and nature description. In a succession of topographical poems touches of Thomson can be seen in miscellaneous places, in older poems like Henry Jones's *Vectis* (1766) and Richard Jago's *Edge-Hill* (1767) as well as in two poems that appeared in 1788, *Lewesdon Hill* and Thomas Whalley's *Mont Blanc*. Compared with these poems, there is more of Thomson in Bowles's *Monody, written at Matlock* (1791) and the undated *Killarney: a Poem*, more physico-theology in Joseph Cottle's *Malvern Hills*, (1798), and more general scientific interest in Thomas Maurice's *Grove-Hill, a Descriptive Poem* (1799).[7]

Toward the end of the century landscape description as a subject for poetry becomes dominant as the interest in science decreases. Yet the clear influence of Thomson is apparent in Thomas Gisborne's *Walks in a Forest* (1794), not only in the subtitle, 'poems descriptive of scenery and incidents characteristic of a forest, at different seasons of the year', but also in the blank-verse nature description and the interest in science. In date and subject, this late imitation of *The Seasons* makes a fitting transition to the romantic poets.

Gisborne in this poem uses the flowers, birds, and animals that would be found in books on natural history and identifies them by Linnaean names and references to scientific authorities. For example, among the spring flowers in the forest he describes with fair botanical knowledge the primrose, pikewort, arum ('that in a mantling hood conceals her purple club'), anemone, wood spurge, harebell, and dog's violet. The wood sorrel (*oxalis acetosa*)

---

[7] Casual influence of Thomson's *Seasons* can also be seen in the poems of William Woty, William Thompson, Thomas Brerewood, William Collier, William Ashburnham, Richard Cumberland, and John Gerrard, as well as in *An Essay on Friendship* (1767), *Poems by Susanna* (1789), and John Gisborne's *The Vales of Wever: a Loco-descriptive Poem* (1797).

is scientifically described in a prose note but the verse tells how she hangs her cups,

> Ere their frail form and streaky veins decay,
> O'er her pale verdure, then with shortening stems
> Beneath the closing leaves her seeds withdraws.

The religious message derived from natural history speaks of the variety of plant life and the way that the plants proclaim the power of God and fulfil

> The ends of their creation. Kindred plans
> Speak the same Author. Mark the varied dower
> Of talents given to man. These trace the laws
> That bind the planets to their orbs, and heave
> The billowy tide.

The sixth and concluding walk, 'Winter. Frost', is closest to Thomson, in the English woods, in the frozen polar region, and in the final message: 'Say, is not Nature's ample tome display'd, / Even to the careless wanderer in the field, / With moral purpose?' The moral purpose is little different from the scientific poems on the telescope and microscope at the beginning of the century, but the illustrations of God's wisdom in nature have changed to plants and birds.

3. EXOTIC BOTANY AND SIR JOSEPH BANKS

About 1760 the older interest in travel books and the newer study of Linnaean natural history converged in poetic description of the fauna and flora of foreign lands, especially exotic plants and trees. This is not surprising when we remember that plants had been imported for more than a century from America, Asia, Africa, and, more recently, the South Seas to supply the Apothecaries' Garden at Chelsea, the university botanic gardens at Oxford and Cambridge, and various private collections. At first the natural history of foreign regions was introduced casually into poems on other subjects. John Armstrong used such exotic fruits as the orange, melon, cocoanut, and pineapple in *The Art of Preserving Health* (1744) to illustrate the extremes of cold and heat in diet. John Dyer described various foreign products in *The Fleece* (1757) as a contrast to the superior products of England.

Several descriptive poems centering in the West Indies illustrate the new interest in exotic natural history and, incidentally, show how easy it is to introduce imitation of Thomson's *Seasons* into strange setting. Indeed the first of these poems, Nathaniel Weeks's *Barbados: a Poem* (1754), by its blank verse and critical preface on descriptive poetry, suggests Thomson transferred to America, yet the exotic touch lies in the emphasis on tropical natural history. He describes the medicinal qualities of the pomegranate and the humming-bird's 'fine glossy hue' and 'small, round, close-compacted nest', but in general he seems more epicure than scientist.

The best known and longest of these scientific poems on the West Indies, James Grainger's *Sugar Cane* (1764), abounds in useful information in the verses as well as in prose notes and a long index of exotic natural history. The four long books are filled with strange plants and animals, and the impression of profuse tropical vegetation is not lost in the poor blank verse. Mosquitos, sandflies, cockroaches, rats, alligators, and carrion birds are balanced by colorful humming-birds, exciting flowers, and delicious creatures from the sea.

The luxuriance of tropic vegetation continues as the main theme of Nathaniel Tucker's *The Bermudian* (1774) and of two poems published in 1777, the anonymous *Jamaica* and J. Singleton's *A Description of the West Indies: a Poem in Four Books*. A frankly scientific poem, George Heriot's *A Descriptive Poem, Written in the West Indies, 1781, Humbly Inscribed to the Royal Society*, deserves more notice. In this warm climate 'vegetation's ever active power' promotes not only profuse growth but also putrefaction from the 'sulphureous, septic particles' that float in the air and bring on fever. A sample of the exotic natural history will show the appeal of books like this: among trees, cotton-tree, cabbage-tree, various palms, and plantain; among birds, humming-birds, king of the woods, parakeet, mocking-bird, woodpecker, flamingo, pelican, man o' war, and booby; among quadrupeds, antelope, peccary, opossum, armadillo, and alligator; among annoying creatures, scorpion, centipede, millipede, tarantula, sawfly, mosquitos, chigoe, various ants, a multitude of microscopic creatures, and a great variety of snakes; and among plants a profusion of wild and domestic species. 'How wondrous then,' the poet concludes, 'the works of nature! how, in ev'ry clime, / Adapted with the most harmonious skill!'

The natural history of distant lands interested English readers, yet exotic plants furnished a ready and dramatic means for them to realize more fully than ever the profuse variety of nature. Immense hothouses built at great expense allowed the English amateur botanist to see the great riches of foreign plants, and Kew Garden became the most readily available collection. Two poems on Kew describe its botanic riches, both domestic and exotic. George Ritso's *Kew Gardens* (1763) adds many flowers and fruits from Asia, Africa, America, and Europe to the plants of England and the captive birds that still sing freely in their 'wise built citadel'. Henry Jones's *Kew Garden* (1767) describes rhododendron, mountain laurel, pimento, banana, sugar-cane that 'fills the coffers of the public weal', coffee, cape jessamine, coronilla, magnolia, diosmo, azalea, camphire, and many other exotic plants that excite interest, not only for their strangeness but also for what they can teach us of 'the principles of vegetating life'.

In the latter part of the century scientific interest in exotic botany merged with popular interest in the noble savage of the South Seas through the accounts of the ambitious expeditions of Sir Joseph Banks. The travels, the scientific discoveries, and the satirical jibes at Banks and through him at science attracted a great deal of attention. The deluge of satirical verse is a late revival of the satire on science that flourished from 1660 to 1740. The serious side was neglected in poetry but can be seen in *Otaheite: a Poem* (1774):

> Much of their search through nature's boundless reign
> The sons of science ask, nor ask in vain.
> From all the vegetable world unfolds,
> All that air or deepest ocean holds,
> Their treasures with collected spoils are stor'd,
> Tribes yet unknown, and wonders unexplor'd . . .
> Thus toils the sage whose penetrating view
> Dares nature to her utmost depths pursue.

The prolific satire on Banks begins in 1773 after his return from a three-year voyage to the South Seas on the *Endeavour* with Captain James Cook.[8] On September 20, 1773, appeared *An Epistle from Oberea, Queen of Otaheite, to Joseph Banks, Esq. Translated by T. Q. X*

---

[8] H. C. Cameron, *Sir Joseph Banks, the Autocrat of the Philosophers* (London, 1952), pp. 243–51, discusses the satire briefly in a chapter on the detractors, especially Peter Pindar and James Gillray.

Esq. Professor of the Otaheite Language in Dublin, twitting Banks in humorous couplets for his amorous adventures. On December 20 an answer appeared in the same vein, *An Epistle from Mr. Banks, Voyager, Monster-Hunter, and Amoroso, to Oberea, Queen of Otaheite.* The baiting of Banks turns to satire on science in an imaginary letter written in 1775 from Omai, the Tahitian who had been brought to England in 1773, *An Historic Epistle, from Omiah, to the Queen of Otaheite; being his Remarks on the English Nation.* This remarkable but forgotten satire in the manner of Goldsmith's *Citizen of the World* devotes three of its 44 pages to ridicule of the Royal Society and its current experiments, as for example:

> Here virtuosi dwell, who strangely wise,
> Are learn'd in maggots, and can nick-name flies;
> Whose skill detects a mite from mouldy cheese,
> Traces his nerves, and even counts his fleas.
> This wond'rous race still pry, in nature's spite,
> Through all her secrets, and transactions write;
> How fiery dames, when drams with age combine,
> Belch, and explode like vapours in a mine . . .
> How Zoöphyte plants with animals unite,
> Where corals copulate, and spunges bite . . .
> All things they prove, and calculations bring,
> How many geese are bred in Saturn's ring;
> How soon a snipe in Mercury would roast,
> And how the sun-beams should prepare the toast.
> They'd set the Thames on fire, to clear a doubt,
> How many days 'twould take in burning out.

This work is dedicated to Banks, who is pointed out to Omai as a scientist who 'traces organs of a sex in weeds' and sends expeditions roaming the world for monsters. It pokes fun at the great chemist Joseph Priestley who 'bottles air without the help of corks' and at Daniel Solander who teaches Banks to classify 'shells, fossils, maggots, butterflies, and grass'.

In 1788 John Wolcot (Peter Pindar) began his long series of satires on scientists and Banks in particular with *Peter's Prophecy, or the President and the Poet, or an Important Epistle to Sir J. Banks, on the Approaching Election of a President of the Royal Society.* An engraving in the original edition shows four men at a table eating snakes, frogs, alligators, and a walrus head with tusks, while on the walls hang mounted birds, animals, and monstrosities. In the verses Peter attacks Banks for daring to take the seat of Newton because of his collecting curiosities, financing expeditions, and hiring Jonas Dryander to write his books.

Peter's Prophecy is a vigorous attack on scientists, ridiculing the Royal Society because it sought to make Banks its president. Since it is probably the best example of its kind in this period, this work deserves special attention. Peter Pindar begins with the humorous suggestion that Banks go back to his 'flow'r amours' in the country and learn

> How gnats can make a cuckold of a fig.
> Form fly clubs, shell clubs, weed clubs, if you please,
> And proudly reign the President of *these*.
> Go, and with periwinkle wisdom charm;
> With loves of lobsters, oysters, crabs, alarm.

The King cannot help him here, though he has done everything to please him

> And though with many a wren you make him blest,
> And many a tomtit's egg and tomtit's nest;
> And many a monkey stuff'd to make him grin,
> And many a flea and beetle on a pin;
> And promise (to cajole the royal mind)
> To make his butcher member, and his hind.

The world says Banks has forced his way in, that Dryander writes his books, that he makes every trifle-hunter who brings in a beetle's wing Fellow, that he is a moth-hunter, 'A hunter of the meanest reptile breed, / A f——l that crosses oceans for a weed!' The Royal Society invites birds-nest hunters, 'Idiots who specks on eggs devoutly ken, / And furbish up a folio on a wren.' The rubberneck rustics still point out Banks as the man who sailed round the world with Captain Cook, and the King still whispers to him at court:

> What's new, Sir Joseph? what, what's new found out?
> What's the society, what, what about?
> Any more monsters, lizard, monkey, rat,
> Egg, weed, mouse, butterfly, pig, what, what, what?

At this point the activities of the Royal Society come in for ridicule. It is an old maid's idle recreation to look for specks on eggs, 'Or gaudy colours of a butterfly, / Or new-found fibre of some grassy blade.' The astronomer Herschel owes more to his good glass and to Mudge than to his head. John Hunter regales the house with fish intrigues, 'the tender history of cooing whales', and produces a 'wondrous *cock-hen bird*'. Daines Barrington 'from old urns to crotchets leaps, / Delights in music, and at concerts sleeps.' And Banks himself, when he protests that he has collected uncommon creatures from distant parts, answers:

> The beautiful deformities of nature:
> Birds without heads, and tails, and wings, and legs,
> Tremendous Cyclop pigs, and speckled eggs,
> Snails from Japan, and wasps, and Indian Jays,
> Command attention and excite our praise.

In 1788 Peter Pindar also published *Sir Joseph Banks and the Emperor of Morocco*, verses on a scientist in search of a rare butterfly. 'The Virtuoso's Prayer' in the preface asks God to send for his museum such items as monsters with legs where legs were never seen, reptiles with heads and eyes in their tails, and butterflies without heads. The next year *Subjects for Painters* continued the attack in 'Sir J. Banks and the Thieftakers'. As Banks, 'Whose wisdom, weed and insect hunter sings', sets out on a botanical expedition, a rival group attacks him and searching him find a motley assortment of specimens in his handkerchief, 'frogs and toads of various shape, / Dock, daisy, nettletop, and dandelion.'

In 1790 Peter Pindar returned vigorously to his attack on Banks with *A Benevolent Epistle to Sylvanus Urban* and *Sir Joseph Banks and the Boiled Fleas* in the same volume. The satire on Banks is incidental to the first poem, where he is hailed as the king of butterflies who made 'a fly-club of a great and fam'd society',

> Who scorning suns and moons, with happier eyes,
> Beholds from dunghill's purple Emp'rors rise;
> More blest on this our earth a frog to see,
> To find a cockleshell and boil a flea,
> Than dwell in yonder skies, with glory crown'd,
> Where frogs, nor fleas, nor cockleshells abound,
> More blest to work a bat's than angel's wing;
> To hear a grasshopper than seraph sing;
> More ples'd to view (if rumour justly paints)
> The tails of tadpoles than the heads of saints;
> And hear (to fame if credence may be giv'n)
> One humming bird than all the host of heav'n.

The second poem describes how Banks announced that he would prove that fleas were lobsters by having Dryander collect 1500 fleas and boil them so they would turn red like lobsters. The verses depict Banks as the queen bee of the Royal Society sending his subjects east and west to collect the best flowers and weeds, seeking novelty 'in mosses, fleas, or cockleshells, or flies.'

In his prolific and inept fooleries Peter Pindar seldom missed an opportunity to ridicule Sir Joseph, but the Royal Society and scientists in general came in for their share of satire. In *The Lousiad*, for example, Banks receives gratefully from George III 'the world of little' that he puts into the journals of the Royal Society to amuse us all, 'flies, grasshoppers, grubs, cobwebs, cuckoo spittle'. Among the 'Subjects for Painters' is a devastating picture of the Royal Society,

> Where fair Philosophy, the heav'nly dame,
> By barb'rous usage cover'd deep with shame,
> No longer shows her exil'd face;
> Where *cent. per cent.* in value rise,
> Toads, tadpoles, grasshoppers, and flies.

The Solomon of this 'fam'd place' is Sir Joseph, swollen by the flatteries of parasitical guests, throwing away a waste of learning and 'proving his superior classic taste, / By swallowing the *sumen* of a pig.' Ridicule of the virtuoso-collector appears also in 'A Lyric Epistle to Sir William Hamilton' where classical 'sauce-pans, lamps, and candlesticks, and kettles' and antiquarian 'dish-clouts, dripping-pans, and spits' mingle incongruously with Banks's wingless moth and headless flea.[9]

There was other satire on science in this period but none so colorful as this flurry of verses on Banks. The general picture of a bemuddled scientist busying himself with a varied assortment of impractical experiments appears in two pieces by Francis Garden, Lord Gardenstone, and with them the spirit of Swift's Lagado comes to life again. The first appears in 'Peculiar Disadvantages of a Modern Poet', where he describes the difficulty of a versifier keeping up with scholarship, now that science is so complex:

[9] Among other works by Peter Pindar in which Banks appears are 'A Complimentary Epistle to James Bruce, Esq., the Abyssinian Traveler' (1769, containing much ridicule of scientific marvels described in travel books), 'A Poetical Epistle to Benjamin Count Rumford', 'An Ode to the Livery of London', 'The Royal Tour', 'A Poetical Epistle to a Falling Minister', and 'Pindariana'.

> But now, the properties of putrid air,
> Some pointers itch, the genius of a hare,
> A rusty coin, a cockle-shell, a mite,
> Provoke the sage to wonder and to write.
> While some with air balloons amuse the mob,
> Some sail in search of rushes round the globe,
> Compute both age, and tonnage of the earth,
> What tadpole cholic gave your foetus birth,
> Teach cannoneers to level, and to load,
> Observe a planet, or dissect a toad;
> Tell the velocities of sound and light,
> Or preach that fractur'd limbs are firm and right.

In a more serious satire, 'On the Diversities of Life', Garden puts the quandaries of the scientist between the sycophant wine-merchant and the pedantic philologist:

> One cloud of sages pore under the sky,
> Others engrave the features of a fly;
> While mad to know what never can be known,
> In metaphysics some their senses drown.
> The chemist feels a just and curious passion,
> But botanizing now seems most in fashion;
> And yet it's votaries make wond'rous din,
> On many topics dearly worth a pin.
> For though our oak our just attention claim,
> Does every pigmy plant deserve the same?
> To squander pages on some useless weed,
> Is but a very silly task indeed;
> Their language too, at which all mankind stares,
> No mortal tongue articulates but theirs.[10]

Science has developed with great strides since Swift and Pope ridiculed the poor experimenter. The satire of Peter Pindar and Francis Garden continues their theme but not with their universal application. The result is topical and enthusiastic, but lacking in literary quality.

[10] *Miscellanies in Prose and Verse . . . by the Hon. Lord Gardenstone* (Edinburgh, 1792), pp. 8–11, 35–9.

VIII

THE DIDACTIC DILEMMA
IN SCIENTIFIC POETRY

MOST scientific poems of the early eighteenth century aimed at the sublime in their glorification of the orderly contrasting universes revealed by the telescope and microscope, and surprisingly often they succeeded. Even the lyrics and descriptive poems of the second half of the century traced the divinization of nature in terms of rural scenery so well that the best of them attained a permanent place in the hearts of English readers. When the didactic element is dominant and the illustrations of science become dominantly technical, however, it is inevitable, by the very nature of things, that the sublime element should dwindle until finally the poems might even reach the extreme bathos of a pedestrian versifying of science and technology.

A few example from the early part of the century will illustrate my point. Abel Evans's *Vertumnus: an Epistle to Mr. Jacob Bobart* (1713) is mediocre poetry but a good history of the early study of botany at Oxford. J. T. Desaguliers' *The Newtonian System of the World* (1728) is a mathematical account of the recent discoveries of Newton, 'that incomparable philosopher', clumsily allegorized into a compliment to George II. Although he tried to justify his choice of medium ('Thus have I tack'd my poetry to philosophy, to make it go down'), the aesthetic dilemma becomes apparent from his description of the influence of the sun on the planets:

'He turns their motion from its devious course, / And bends their orbits by attractive force.'

Most of the early didactic poems on science were in Latin, and the collection of Latin poems called *Musae Anglicanae* was full of them. One of them, Tipping Silvester's Latin poem on the microscope, translated in 1733, is an amazing compilation of the wonderful world of the little: insects, crystals, fluids, botanical specimens, and the teeming life in a piece of mouldy cheese, alongside such curious sights as cloth, hair, razor, needle, and a magnificent flea with a gold chain of 100 links who, unlike Pope's chained flea, 'struts, and triumphs in the chain he wears'.[1] Many such Latin poems are on medical subjects, which find an English counterpart in *A Poetical Essay on Physick, inscrib'd to Dr. Pellet* (ca. 1735), a thoroughly didactic poem that attempts to trace in couplets the history of medicine from the ancients to Harvey, Sydenham, Sloane, Mead, Boerhaave, and Garth.

Other early didactic poems show how science can be brought casually into poetry of all kinds. John Philips mixes botany with patriotism in *Cyder* (1708). William Somerville in *The Chase* (1735) interrupts his explanation of hunting to digress on instinct in animals to explain the scent of hounds, on the scientific study of nature to demonstrate the universal goodness of God, and on the majesty of the astronomical universe 'where Newton leads the way'. Dr. John Armstrong gives good advice and considerable medical history in the heavy verses of his *The Art of Preserving Health: a Poem* (1744). There is more popularized science than poetry in this piece, whose four books treat, in turn, the subjects of bad air and extremes of climate, diet and intemperance, the therapy of bodily exercise, and the psychosomatic effect of 'the passions' on health.

We have already seen how two didactic poems, Dyer's *Fleece* and Grainger's *Sugar Cane*, combined natural history and travel lore, but the most remarkable natural history poem before Erasmus Darwin was Robert Dodsley's 'Agriculture', published in 1753 as the first of three proposed long poetical essays glorifying England.[2] This mixture of botany, animal husbandry, gardening, rural life, and nature description contains a fair amount of good

---

[1] *Original Poems and Translations* (London: J. Wilford, 1733), pp. 35–54.

[2] *Public Virtue: a Poem in Three Books. I. Agriculture. II. Commerce. III. Arts* (London, 1753). Presumably only Book I was finished.

poetry that lifts it a step above the usual didactic poem and makes
it worth a more extended analysis. The poem begins with an
appeal to the jaded city dweller to learn the ways of God by
pursuing natural philosophy through agriculture where Omnipotence 'unfolds the map of Nature'. Among the fruits and flowers
the poet, following the succession of growth with the four seasons,
can enter hand in hand

> With sweet philosophy, the secret bowers
> Of deep mysterious Nature; there t'explore
> The causes of fecundity, and how
> The various elements, earth, water, air,
> And fire united; the enlivening ray
> Diurnal; the prolific dews of night;
> With all the rolling seasons of the year;
> In vegetation's work their power combine.

Canto I ends with a rhapsody on the power of vegetation that
reveals the 'all-wise, almighty Parent of the World', first in a
scientific account of the flow of sap based on Stephen Hales's
Vegetable Staticks, and then in rapturous praise of England's
plants (hawthorn, cowslip, violet, carnation, and rose) and fruits
(grape, mulberry, plum, apple, peach, and pineapple), the gracious
gifts of the Supreme Creator.

Canto II treats at length several quasi-scientific subjects: the
chemistry of plant growth in different soils and the necessity of
keeping clay soil well pulverized; the contribution of manure to
the richness of soil; the various sources of fertilizer; the fine points
of horticulture, including the propagation of plants in a nursery
by grafting; a digression on the miracle of germination from
seeds; the various uses of England's trees, beech, yew, linden, birch,
ash, osier, chestnut, walnut, elm, and oak; and the problems
arising from drainage and irrigation. And then, as if on holiday
from didactic lessons, the poet lets the farmer enjoy the rural
beauty of wild flowers and the wild irregularity of an English
garden built to resemble nature, naming his flowers—arbutus,
almond, acacia, mezereon, laurustinus, and laburnum along with
more homely ones—with a love that comes from a knowledge of
herbals as well as horticulture.

Canto III begins with haymaking but soon digresses into a
passage on minerals and the technology of metals. The plants of
the wild countryside remind the poet of many useful herbs, such

as luteola, glastum, and rubia, for dyeing, and numerous others for medicinal purposes. Dodsley might well have read of the uses of sage, lavender, mint, valerian, angelica, chamomile, wormwood, centuary, althaea, eryngo, hypericum, liquorice, poppy, and thistle in a herbal or in Phillips' *Gardening Dictionary*, but the desire to include them in his treatise on growing things is a tribute to his interest in botany. And the entire poem shows how a mid-century poet could introduce into a long didactic poem various popular scientific interests of his time.

A favorite device for popularization of science was didactic poems that described the use of orreries and other ingenious mechanical devices used for instruction or experiment. An early example is Henry Jones's *Philosophy: a Poem address'd to the Ladies who attended Mr. Booth's Lectures*, printed separately in Dublin in 1746. The 'bricklayer poet' is concerned with the religious message as well as with instruction, as can be seen from his description of an orrery after describing experiments with color and electricity:

> Contracted here, by wond'rous art, is seen
> A boundless system in a small machine;
> Here human skill to proud perfection brought,
> The mortal mimic of omnific thought,
> Th'Almighty's model to the mind conveys,
> The universe, and all its pow'rs displays;
> How wander planets, how revolves the year,
> The moon how changes, and how comets glare. . . .
> Here godlike Newton's all capacious mind
> (The glory and the guide of human kind)
> Shows wedded worlds far distant worlds embrace
> With mutual bands, yet keep their destin'd space.

A similar planetarium appears in Edward Perronet's 'On the Wonders of Electricity, and other Branches of Natural and Experimental Philosophy' (1785), along with a description of machines for demonstrating artificial lightning and the force of magnet and pulley:

> Here restless meteors their long vigils keep,
> And roving comets in their orbits sleep;
> Or left at large, velocity immense!
> Elliptic fly, and range the vast expanse! . . .
> Go on, great bard, and shake the electric rod,
> Till fools grow wise, and atheists own a God!

Technology is the subject of several didactic poems. Coal mining is a favorite subject for economic and aesthetic reasons as well as scientific. In 1755 John Dalton's *A Descriptive Poem addressed to Two Ladies, at their Return from Viewing Two Mines near Whitehaven* describes the process of mining and the workings of a steam engine used to pump out water, though for the sake of the ladies the poet goes on to point out the philosophical value of exploring the secrets of the earth ('How intervein'd rich minerals glow, / How bubbling fountains learn to flow') and the aesthetic value of grand mountain scenery, especially in the wilder portions of the Lake District. Richard Jago also brings the beauty of mountains into the technology of coal mining and steel making in *Edge-Hill* (1767). And John Sargent enlivens *The Mine: a Dramatic Poem* (1785) with a description of fossil specimens based on Linnaeus.

Astronomy and botany are the subjects most extensively treated in didactic poems after 1750, and the very completeness of technical data in their halting verses furnishes the best example of the aesthetic dilemma that arises when pure science becomes too complicated to allow the poet to seize the sublime message behind the facts. Perhaps the impasse would not have been reached if Erasmus Darwin had been a better poet or a poorer scientist, but the problem is clearly stated even earlier in two poems on astronomy.

The first is a pedestrian poem with a sublime purpose, the anonymous *A Philosophic Ode on the Sun and the Universe* (1750). The prose preface states the aesthetic problem clearly: science can be used to excite the imagination and lead the mind to God by arousing wonder at the almost infinite variety of nature. Even with the naked eye copious instances can be found, yet with improved optical instruments the poet can use the discoveries of telescope, microscope, and prism 'to stretch his imagination to the utmost'. In this way 'the comprising a clear and succinct idea of the universe in a little poem, and interspersing some late discoveries therein' will make readers aware of the wonderful phenomena of nature to convince them of 'the majesty, goodness and omnipresence of the great Creator' and eradicate the prevailing debauchery and impiety. This lofty purpose stumbles sharply as the verses describe in didactic profusion the measurements of the sun and its satellites, the praise of Newton already noted, the probability of planets being inhabited, and the new discoveries on lunar tides, Jupiter's moons, and Saturn's rings. The information in the poor verses is reinforced with copious data in the notes, and it is only in the conclusion that the poet reminds us that all these mechanic wonders are the work of a divine architect who 'plac'd every system, kindled every sun, / And bade each globe its destin'd circle run.'

In 1781 Capel Lofft published the longest poem on astronomy of the century and the most prodigious didactic poem on science before Darwin. It is true that *Eudosia: or a Poem on the Universe* redeems its mountainous summary of astronomical research with occasional touches of the sublime that Lofft had put in his earlier poem, *The Praises of Poetry* (1775) in a description of nature at the creation: 'Thence tun'd the new-born stars their matin-song; / Thence the swift planets wheel their measur'd course, / And one harmonious force / Rolls their consenting orbs along.' Aesthetically, the 188-page *Eudosia* is inept, though not as great a failure perhaps as Darwin's more famous poem. The tedious technical versifying is only occasionally relieved by the poet's enthusiasm for science and his desire to conclude with his own version of the old theme of order in nature. At the same time it is clear that the very richness of scientific information available to him makes the subject more difficult to express in good poetry. This is an important aesthetic dilemma, for not even the numerous tributes to Kepler and his successor Newton, 'prince of revived philosophy',[3] can enliven the poetic rigor of six long books of astronomy and one of zoology. This poem is the first good example of too much knowledge and too little spirit that led Wordsworth to reject science as a subject for poetry. Since the book is inaccessible to most readers, let me show by extensive quotation what I mean.

Book I of *Eudosia* describes the earth, its relation to the other elements, its spherical form (reminding him of the contribution of voyagers, especially Captain Cook, to science), its measurements, and its place in the motions of the solar system. After three pages on the physical dimensions of the earth, the poet takes over to suggest its comparative smallness in the universe:

[3] The London, 1781, edition has not been reprinted. Newton references are on pp. 22, 32, 38, 39, 45, 61 (summary, mostly of *Principia*), 98, 127, 130, 140, and in the 48 pages of scientific notes appended.

> Even a point; an atom! Multiply
> The mighty aggregate of land and sea
> Ten thousand by ten thousand times; proceed
> Till computation faints beneath the toil,
> And industry herself cries out 'no more';
> Still, to a little portion of the whole,
> The amazing aggregate is like the mite
> To all the planetary worlds. . . .

Book II describes the planets with a richness of technical detail—distances, orbits, size, and physical composition—and a scarcity of poetic imagination. Even the religious conclusion is pedestrian:

> But fix'd their periods, and unchang'd their laws,
> Their motion constant, figure uniform;
> Remains that *one eternal mind* preside,
> Impel, direct, and limit all their course.

And the didactic descriptions show why too much knowledge is bad for poetry, as in this short example to explain why the quality of light varies with each planet:

> The planets own their several densities,
> Adapted to their distance from the sun.
> Five times in denseness yields vast Jupiter
> To Earth; and Saturn equals not a sixth;
> While Mercury not ill we may divine
> Of density superior to the Earth.

Book III describes technically the science behind the seasons, the signs of the zodiac, and the zones controlled by climate. Not only is the subject more suited to poetry, but the influence of Thomson on contemporary English poetry can be seen in Lofft's description of the seasons, in the harsh nature found in tropic heat and polar ice, in the digression on the blessings brought to Britain by a temperate climate, and even in the eulogy on Newton suggested by the poet's desire to name a new star for the great man who combined moral and natural philosophy.

Book IV on the fixed stars bewilders the reader with statistical data in a crushingly didactic catalogue of the constellations then known to astronomy. The poet pauses for a moment to give a total count of 3,200 stars 'seen by the unaided eye or telescope',

though they seem numberless because 'the multiplying power /
Of rich confusion, on the sense prevails.' Then he plunges into a
minute description of the rising of stars in different parts of the
world before the imagination seizes the idea of still greater knowledge to come from future astronomical research, when the telescope will 'open new heavens to thy astonish'd view'. By analogy
with what we now know of Sirius and Cassiopeia, there may be in
the skies 'thousand orbs, the imperial centres each / Of many
solar systems', part of 'thy glorious universe maintain'd by
harmony'.

Book V covers miscellaneous topics centering around the effect
of the sun and moon on the earth, eclipses, light and color from
Newton's *Optics* and the rising science of chemistry, the phases of
the planets, and the physics of ocean tides. Even in the description
of colors the poet is more interested in the physics of the spectrum
than in beauty, but the influence of Thomson can be seen in the
colors of flowers, trees, and birds, followed by a hymn to nature.

Book VI begins with an old subject of comets whose seemingly
erratic orbits have been explained by Newton and Halley, and this
reminds him of the devastations of nature, like earthquake, storm,
and pestilence, where we must remember that 'hid or reveal'd, the
Deity is one'. The elements of water and air remind him of the
old topic of capillary attraction in plants and the newer experiments with air and chemical fluids by Joseph Priestley. The description of the element of fire leads him from phlogiston, the
'quiescent state', to electricity, the state of universal agitation. He
takes the last six pages to versify electricity and its counterparts in
nature, lightning and the aurora borealis. The history of this
'recent wonder of our age' leads him from Thales to Benjamin
Franklin, whom he describes in his lengthy note as a mixture of
Newton and Solon.

Book VII tries to sum up the rest of the universe—human
anatomy, microscopic research, minerals, vegetables, zoophytes,
and animals—but, as if recoiling from the comprehensive task,
Lofft begins with his own version of the praise of nature in Job
and the Psalms, including Orion, whirlwind, the seasons, elephant,
crocodile, sun, moon, and rainbow. The climax of the human
physiology is the mind of man where imagination creates by
'ranging illimitable space' and reason leads in many directions,
one of which is that of technology (such marvels as raising waters,

building pyramids, levelling mountains, and diverting the ocean)
and science:

> Hence he deduces the protracted chain
> Of geometric reason; through the stars
> He walks; their distances, their magnitude,
> Their order traces; calculates eclipse,
> And estimates the tide: divides the ray
> Of light: and sees, with microscopic glass,
> The worlds included in the flowery dust. . . .

Numerous instances of microscopic experiment and a rather
general panegyric of medical skill bring him back to his original
attempt 'to retrace the mighty whole'. Nature's scale ascends by
gradation: minerals and the circulation of water, the vegetable
world from the 'thin green mantle of the sleeping pool' to varied
plant life, the combinations of vegetable and animal like the sensitive plant or the sponge, and the animal world in fish, amphibians,
insects, quadrupeds, and man. All 'the high study of great
Nature's works' ends in the Great Creator whose name fills 'all
his worlds with awe and sacred bliss, / Triumphant through the
boundless universe.' And so a tedious piece of protracted didactic
verse is partly redeemed by such occasional touches of the sublime.

The glorification of prosaic verse can be seen in a very learned
moral poem that makes extensive use of the didactic, Joseph
Wise's *The System: a Poem in Five Books*, the first three of which
were published in 1781. Wise adds prose notes that are scholarly
treatises on religious philosophy, and copious additions have
been made in manuscript to the British Museum copy of what the
Critical Review calls a 'very long and laborious work'.[4] Science
appears in Book III, poured out in didactic profusion, and reinforced with many notes. For example, the sun is 'the largest,
densest mass, / Ordain'd to wheel a vortex wide through space, /
Fix'd in the centre, turn'd upon his pole; / And rapid round made
Ether's ocean roll.' Numerous insects appear 'In crust or shell, in
silken tent or rind. / Penurious bees distend the waxen cell: /
Laborious ants in thatched grotto dwell.' With unintentional
humor 'the huge elephant resorts to feed; / His lythe proboscis
crops the savory mead: / The rude rhinoceros delights to lave /

---

[4] LIII (1782), 29–32.

His mail-clad sides in the rebounding wave.' With this inept use of didactic verse we are ready for the bathos of Erasmus Darwin.[5]

In 1789 there appeared the most widely known of all botanic poems, Erasmus Darwin's *The Loves of the Plants*, nearly 2,000 verses allegorizing the sexual system of Linnaeus in insipid couplets intended to edify but not offend the ladies. Two years later Darwin published the third edition of this poem as Part II of *The Botanic Garden*, with a new poem as Part I, *The Economy of Vegetation*. The verses themselves, reinforced by lengthy explanatory notes, contained a world of science but little poetry, and yet their popularity showed that the reading public was eager for botanizing in verse. The scientific achievement of Erasmus Darwin has long been recognized, especially as a predecessor of his more famous grandson in developing the theory of evolution. His poetry stirred for a time the intellectual interests of his scientific readers but seldom held their emotions, and so it remains a phenomenon of dryness, a didactic impasse that was made to be laughed out of even its temporary prestige by a burlesque *Love of the Triangles*.[6]

The Loves of the Plants begins conventionally enough with its display of English plants from the giant oaks 'to the dwarf moss that clings upon their bark'. After an invocation of the botanic muse led by Linnaeus, the parade of didactic descriptions of plants begins. In each instance the verse describes with confusing bombast the sexual life of the plant according to the system of Linnaeus. A concise footnote gives a prose explanation that makes the verses somewhat clearer. One sample will show what I mean.

> First the tall CANNA lifts his curled brow
> Erect to heaven, and plights his nuptial vow;
> The virtuous pair, in milder regions born,
> Dread the rude blast of Autumn's icy morn;

[5] Other scientific didactic poems of this period are John Walters, 'Botany' in *Poems, with Notes* (Oxford, 1780), pp. 107–34; *A Storm: with the Description of a Waterspout: a Shoal of Dolphins: and other Ominous Appearances* (Bury St. Edmunds, 1780); two medical poems, Hugh Downman, *Infancy: a Poem* (London, 1775), and William Lipscomb, 'Beneficial Effects of Inoculation', written in 1772 and published in his *Poems* (Oxford, 1784), pp. 9–16; George Cockings, *Arts, Manufactures, and Commerce: a Poem* (London, n.d.); and *The Rise and Progress of the Present Taste in Planting . . . in a Poetic Epistle to the Rt. Hon. Charles Lord Viscount Irwin* (London, 1767).

[6] See James V. Logan, *The Poetry and Aesthetics of Erasmus Darwin* (Princeton, 1936), especially pp. 136–47.

Round the chill fair he folds his crimson vest,
And clasps the timorous beauty to his breast.

Footnote: Cane, or Indian Reed. One male and one female inhabit each flower. It is brought from between the tropics to our hot-houses, and bears a beautiful crimson flower; the seeds are used as shot by the Indians, and are strung for prayer-beads in some Catholic countries.

The parade of plants continues monotonously, hundreds of Latin names that need some knowledge of botany to identify, and with each plant a laborious account of its sexual life. Occasionally, the monotony is relieved by a digression, as in the footnotes on philanthropy, or Mrs. Delany's collection of paper mosaics to represent flowers, or those curious freaks that seemed to ally the plant world with the animal, the Tartarian Lamb and the sensitive plant. After four cantos of approximately 500 lines each, the poem ends rather abruptly.

The Economy of Vegetation is by its very subject much livelier. In a way it is another physico-theological poetical essay, but instead of using all nature to proclaim the wisdom of God Darwin described those parts that play a part in the vegetable kingdom. Even though the scientist still surpasses the poet in this poem, there is a great deal more variety, less need of the straight didactic exposition, and a much more interesting subject than the sexual life of a plant. There is even a touch of the sublime in Darwin's account of the birth of the astronomical universe based on the recent discoveries of Herschel:

> Through all his realms the kindling Ether runs,
> And the mass starts into a million suns;
> Earths round each sun with quick explosions burst,
> And second planets issue from the first;
> Bend, as they journey with projectile force,
> In bright ellipses their reluctant course;
> Orbs wheel in orbs, round centres centres roll,
> And form, self-balanced, one revolving Whole.
> —Onward they move amid their bright abode,
> Space without bound, the bosom of their God!

Canto I continues with a sort of cosmic sweep that brings in all things having to do with fire, whether in the meteoric phenomena of the skies or the volcanic disturbances within the earth. With loving hand Darwin wrote of the new discoveries of steam and electricity and made exciting prophecies of the wonders that would soon come from their practical applications. Canto II undertakes the less sublime task of describing the mineral kingdom, beginning with the stupendous volcanic eruptions that gave birth to the earth and the moon, and ending with the springing of plants from the earth. Canto III treats a number of miscellaneous subjects that have to do with the element of water, whether in underground streams, the ocean, or streams and lakes on the surface of the earth. Here he introduced scientific subjects that had interested earlier poets, like the flow of sap in plants or the analogy of the human circulatory system to the cycle of sea, vapor, rain, springs, rivers, and sea. But mostly he described more recent topics like maelstrom, monsoon, geyser, and hot springs, or the mechanical improvements in inland navigation or fire engines. Canto IV is devoted to the element of air and its enormous influence on vegetation, but the account of new scientific discoveries allows the exciting digressions to absorb the main interest of the reader: the meteorological phenomena of sirocco, simoon, and tornado; the barometer, air-pump, and Joseph Priestley; the balloon and Mongolfier's flights; the 'sea-balloon' or early submarine made possible by Priestley's discoveries; the new stars discovered by Herschel; and the riches of exotic botany displayed in Kew Gardens. The poem ends with a call to England to excel in medical botany, a subject dear to the physician from Lichfield. *The Economy of Vegetation*, with its variety and its occasional touches of the sublime, somewhat redeems the didactic dilemma of the earlier *Loves of the Plants*.

The Temple of Nature, or the Origin of Society is Erasmus Darwin's best poem, but it did not appear until 1803 and therefore lies outside the limits of this study. This combination of science, philosophy, and poetry is nevertheless in the tradition of those longer poetical essays that used scientific illustrations and imagery in a lofty manner that often reached the sublime. Certainly *The Temple of Nature* treats a sublime subject, the evolution of life from 'the first specks of animated earth' in the primeval ooze under the sea through the development of plants and animals in the natural world to the human mind and the struggle between good and evil in human society. The poem is a belated example of what I have tried to show happening throughout the eighteenth century, that scientific material treated in a philosophical manner often lent a sublime element to the poetry of otherwise quite ordinary writers. It may not be the 'noble poem' that Elizabeth Sewell finds it, yet her fine analysis of it in *The Orphic Voice* shows that it contains many noble passages. We may believe, with her and other recent critics, that *The Temple of Nature* deserves to be rescued from the unjust condemnation that has arisen from its association with *The Loves of the Plants*.[7]

The Botanic Garden seems to prove that science, especially botany, had by 1790 become too technical to be treated as a suitable subject for poetry. Science can speak effectively in poetry at this time only in the gentler aspects of nature, the catalogues of flowers and birds in nature description or the idea of divine wisdom and order observed in the natural history of rural England. The didactic impasse of *The Loves of the Plants* marks the end of an era, but before Blake's vigorous attack on science as an enemy of the spiritual, Cowper and some interesting lesser poets more suitably marked the end of an era by their acceptance of the old theme, the divinization of nature, with newer poetic variations. It is they, and not Darwin, who furnish the real prelude to pantheistic nature in the great romantic poets. It is fitting that they should have the last word.

[7] *The Orphic Voice: Poetry and Natural History* (New Haven, 1960), pp. 237–52. See also Desmond King-Hele, *Erasmus Darwin* (New York, 1963), pp. 120–32, and Irwin Primer, 'Erasmus Darwin's *Temple of Nature*: Progress, Evolution, and the Eleusinian Mysteries', *Journal of the History of Ideas*, XXV (1964), 58–76.

IX

END OF AN ERA: THE PRELUDE TO WORDSWORTH

THE end of one era merges into the beginning of another, for in the writing of literature there is more continuity than our literary histories allow. The last quarter of the eighteenth century, as we have seen, reached a sort of inglorious climax in the didactic and satirical aspects of scientific verse, but the natural history poetry carried the influence of Thomson into the nineteenth century, through descriptions of changing flowers and birds with the seasons, gentle philosophizing on nature, and localized rural scenery in topographical poems. Thomson faded with the new genius of the *Lyrical Ballads*, yet the continuity of theme became apparent as we examined more closely the almost forgotten poems that reflected the influence of *The Seasons*. The carry-over becomes even more obvious in those later poets, including William Cowper, who wrote about science in its more general aspects, describing, like the older physico-theological poetry, other branches of science besides natural history.

By far the best of these general poets is Cowper, and so we can begin with him as an example of the transition from one era to another. This mild poet loved nature and enjoyed using the latest discoveries of science as far as his limited knowledge allowed, but when he saw what he thought was arrogance and growing atheism among the scientists of his own day, his mildness vanished and he showed his rebellion with evangelical passion. The conflict in Cowper's troubled mind, paradoxically, was often healed by physical therapy in gardening and by mental consolation in allowing nature to exert its power to soothe, delight, and instruct. He showed this resolving of the conflict as early as 1782 in the poem *Retirement*. Here as in many similar poems early in the century, the happy man who has retired to the country can pursue his leisurely study of science, 'trace, in nature's most minute design, / The signature and stamp of power divine'. He can contemplate the variety of insect forms, the underground source of ten thousand rivers, and the majesty of sun and moon and countless stars. He can repeat the theme of God in nature, and few in the century did it better or more sincerely:

> These are thy glorious works, thou Source of good,
> How dimly seen, how faintly understood!
> Thine, and upheld by thy paternal care,
> This universal frame, thus wondrous fair;
> Thy power divine and bounty beyond thought,
> Adored and praised in all that thou hast wrought.

In the writing of *The Task* Cowper relieved the tensions of his tortured mind, and in the process unintentionally summarized the old and pointed to the new in scientific poetry. The old is there in the revelation of divine order in all nature from planets to insects, and Cowper's way of saying it is more sublime than most. The new is there in the sympathetic observation of English trees, flowers, and birds, even in the didactic description of his own cucumbers and exotic plants, done in the manner of Thomson but with better expression and more imagination. The old and the new are mixed in Cowper's attitude toward science, what appears to be a dichotomy of violent satirical attack on the one hand and praise showing God in nature on the other hand. The apparent conflict is considerably softened when we remember the skeptical theme of the limitations of science that continued from the seventeenth century until after Cowper, yet the vigor of the attack reminds us of Blake's rejection until we place the satire alongside the praise of science for revealing the divinization of nature.

Cowper was no scientist, though his poetry shows a handbook knowledge of botany and we know that he read about general

science in current periodicals.[1] Yet there was no doubt in his mind
about the value of science to reveal God to his schoolboy friends
when he told the Unwin boys in *Tirocinium* that science was able
to show God in

> Yon circling worlds, their distance, and their size,
> The moons of Jove and Saturn's belted ball,
> And the harmonious order of them all;
> To show him in an insect or a flow'r.
> Such microscopic proofs of skill and pow'r,
> As his from ages pass'd, God now displays
> To combat atheists with in modern days.

The importance of science to religious philosophy is even more
powerfully expressed at the end of *The Task*. To see how the poet
arrives at this clear statement after mingled description, satire,
therapy, and philosophy, it is necessary at this point to analyze
some of the passages in *The Task* that deal with science.

Book I, for example, illustrates Cowper's love of the natural
history around him in the country, shown by his description of
color, leaf, and odor in English trees, contrasted with his scorn of
mechanistic science among the learned city folk. He will not let us
forget that God made the country, and man made the town, for in
London the riot and incontinence of daily life are matched by the
eagle eye of philosophy that counts the spots on the sun and with
exact implements calculates 'all distance, motion, magnitude, and
now / Measures an atom, and now girds a world.' Book III ridicules the scientist who tries to explain the disease of nature in
earthquake and hurricane when religion treats such harshness as a
part of divine providence. The same book contains a charming
digression in somewhat didactic terms on the growing of cucumbers in a hot frame, a list of exotic plants in a greenhouse, and the
techniques of pruning and other phases of gardening. It is true
that this amateur expedition into botany is part of the poet's
therapy: 'O blest seclusion from a jarring world,' he cries in
momentary exultation, 'which he, thus occupied, enjoys!' But the
enduring rapture comes from the religious teaching of nature
through science:

[1] The fullest account of this is in H. P. Kroitor, 'William Cowper and Science in
the Eighteenth Century', unpublished dissertation, University of Maryland, 1957,
a part of which appears in *Journal of the History of Ideas*, XXI (1950), 511–26.

And she that sweetens all my bitters too—
Nature, enchanting nature—in whose form
And lineaments divine I trace a hand
That errs not, and find raptures still renewed,
Is free to all men—universal prize.

Cowper was clearly torn between a distrust of the rapidly changing physical sciences and the desire to know enough about natural history, especially botany, to understand the gentler rural aspects of nature. This conflict is well put in Book III in a long passage on the vanity of human knowledge, which he illustrates with the dreams of science 'giving laws / To distant worlds, and trifling in their own', building systems that will vanish like smoke, and speculating on geology and astronomical mechanics. And yet, he adds, religion and science were once friends when Newton, the 'childlike sage' was a 'sagacious reader of the works of God'.

Cowper affirms his faith in the ability of science to show the wisdom of God in nature when, at the end of Book V, he sums up lyrically many of the scientific poems of an earlier period. God is to be seen in his works, in the telescopic and microscopic universes, in the insect's wing as well as the rolling worlds in the sky. Revelation can see through the opaque veil of nature the author of her beauties, even though the 'impure' present-day scientists deny his power with their mechanical philosophy. Cowper here approaches the sublime when he speculates on stars invisible to man 'and systems of whose birth no tidings yet / Have reach'd this nether world.' He reaches the sublime when he says what many other poets had been trying to say, that God is revealed by an understanding of his works that comes from scientific study,

A ray of heavenly light, gilding all forms
Terrestrial in the vast and the minute—
The unambiguous footsteps of the God
Who gives its lustre to an insect's wing,
And wheels his throne upon the rolling worlds.

The noblest expression of Cowper's interest in science is in Book VI, where ridicule is laid aside as the poet arrives at poetic generalization through details of botanical observation. The poet takes his winter walk at noon and muses on the miracle of germination that defies winter. The vital energy that moved in summer 'through the imperceptible meandering veins / Of leaf and flower' now sleeps in winter, but in spring this uniform drabness of seed and dormant plant will burst into a bewildering variety of colors. Laburnum, syringa, rose, lilac, woodbine, hypericum, mezereon, althaea, broom, jasmine—all are touched by the poet's descriptive magic as they become illustrations of 'nature's progress' from death to life. 'Nature is but the name for an effect, / Whose cause is God', he concludes, and then, as if to refute the philosophers of his day who used science to postulate a clockwork instead of God's personal supervision of his creation, he continues, 'He feeds the secret fire / By which the mighty process is maintain'd'. The final answer is in the great variety and fecundity of nature in the rural England he knows so well, where, to him at least, it is clear that God

> Rules universal nature. Not a flower
> But shows some touch, in freckle, streak, or stain,
> Of his unrivalled pencil. He inspires
> Their balmy odours, and imparts their hues,
> And bathes their eyes with nectar, and includes,
> In grains as countless as the seaside sands,
> The forms with which he sprinkles all the earth.

There is a touch of Thomson in *The Task* but poetic genius has carried Cowper farther than those many versifiers of his time who imitated *The Seasons*. We agree readily with John Aikin, who had declared the aesthetics of natural history in poetry, that while Thomson deserves first place as a pioneer in 'delineation of natural objects and the incidents of rural life', Cowper's 'powerful imagination was equal to those creative exertions which are perhaps the highest triumph of poetry'. Cowper was no scientist but he used the rhetoric of his poetic powers to summarize the popular science that he knew. He was no philosopher but he was able to persuade others that the wisdom of God was still revealed in nature.

Many other poets, in the last quarter of the eighteenth century, were saying much what Cowper said but not so well, in moral poems and lyrics illustrated with general science as well as in those Thomsonian georgics already described as poems of natural history. Even the hard-pressed poet-laureate William Whitehead looked to the imagery of winter for his New Year Odes and of summer for the birthday odes to George III on every June 4 after

1761, and once, in a poem 'On Ridicule', paid his tribute to science as he described 'mighty Newton with an augur's hand, / Through heav'n's high concave stretch th'imperial wand'.

The miscellaneous nature of scientific poems of this period can be seen in the witty occasional poetry of Samuel Bishop, head-master of Merchant Taylors School.[2] The subject of light, for example, reminds him of prism, electricity produced by friction, water of underground streams, evaporation, hydraulic machinery, ocean waterspouts, and colors of nature in the spectrum. He names his flowers and shrubs, imagines a trip to the moon in one of the new balloons, and tries to recall the ten descriptive categories for his specimen beetle. He envies the astronomer in his easy-chair and philosophizes on the day-fly's brief existence as 'proof of th'Omnipotent Goodness'. He shows respect for science in 'Natural Philosophy', a survey of science from the ancient world to modern England:

> There all her stores to Bacon Nature spread;
> There her own hand in Newton's rules she read;
> There hand in hand with Boyle she lov'd to stray;
> And led, and met Experiment half way. . . .
> Thro' earth, air, sea, discovery's range extends;
> And only stops it—where existence ends.

And he recalls Thomson, too, in 'Hymn on the Spring' where all nature reminds him of God's 'unerring skill' revealed in the 'vegetable scene' of the seasons, in the stars that 'roll constant thro' the liquid space', in snow and thunder, and in aquatic creatures and insects.

In longer reflective poems the same general scientific ideas and images can be found. The anonymous *Nature: a Poem* (1790) piles up scientific commonplaces to show a kind of pantheism in nature: gravity ('the high impulsive force' that keeps celestial bodies in their orderly courses); the growth of plants from seeds by 'balmy juices' in pores and vessels; the 'thousand little monsters' in a drop of vinegar or stagnant water; the glorification of instinct in animals and reason in man, 'matter rich, / Sublim'd into the highest purity'. He looks back to the idea that full knowledge comes only in cosmic voyages after death. He looks forward to

---

[2] *The Poetical Works of the Rev. Samuel Bishop*, I (London, 1796), 48–53, 95–305. Since he died in 1795, the poems were probably written over many years. Cf. Fairchild, II, 221–3.

Wordsworth in defining nature as a secret force whose energies that 'clothe with life and beauty / This varied earth' cannot be explained by science, and in describing the serenity that comes to thinking man through contemplation of 'hoary wood . . . the cataract's wild roar . . . the rustling breeze of twilight'.

A long philosophical poem that combines science, religion, and georgic is *Contemplation: a Poetical Essay on the Works of the Creation* (1776) by Richard Fayerman, an obscure village parson in Norfolk and chaplain to the Earl of Bute. From the vegetable world of spring flowers, though studied in an irregular garden with Linnaeus in hand, he plunges into the microscopic world that he seems to know intimately. He combines moralizing with didactic detail in his favorite experiments with 'wheel animals' rotating to seize smaller insects that 'in their whirlpools swarm', or with peach-flies whose colors defy the beauty of flowers, paintings, or even the rainbow. He describes the hundreds of thousands of 'puny insects' in a drop of water swimming 'as freely and as much at ease, / As the Leviathan in spacious seas', and then draws moral conclusions on 'these breathing atoms to perfection wrought':

> The microscope apply'd where e're we will,
> We find great Nature's symmetry and skill;
> While endless wonders, that long dormant laid,
> Now charm the sight delighted by its aid.

The metamorphosis of the butterfly from 'her mean reptile state' reminds him like other poets of the flight of man after death among unknown worlds where 'boundless wonders croud upon the view'. An insect's sting and the circulation of blood in a frog's foot are common examples of the flawless work in the museum of 'nature, God's art' that surpasses human art and 'leads the enamour'd mind still high'r and high'r'. The rest of nature—the singing of birds, the cries of animals, the myriads of celestial bodies—becomes a general prelude to his long moral conclusion that the 'book of nature' speaks to the heart and invites us to observe this evidence of 'God's pow'r and goodness extant every where'. This country parson did not become as famous as Gilbert White in Hampshire, but he was more poet than the curate of Selborne.

A popular moral poem that attracted the attention of Gibbon and was often reprinted, *Sympathy: a Poem* by S. J. Pratt (Courtney

Melmoth),[3] combines older scientific commonplaces with natural history. The moral theme is a combination of Thomson and Gray, in which the unfamiliar scientific ideas are easily recognizable for instinct ('dimly it gleams on insect, fish, and fowl') and order in the Chain of Being:

> To lowest insects, highest pow'rs, a part
> Widely dispens'd to ev'ry beating heart;
> A due proportion to all creatures given,
> From the mole's mansion to the seraph's heav'n.

Swarms of insects, 'the wing'd legions which at noon-tide play', illustrate the social law of sympathy, for 'not an atom takes its flight alone'. All creatures are 'born to share', and an impressive list of examples is produced from natural history: unwieldy sea monsters, wild beasts of the forest, 'the viewless tribes that populate the air', fish, and many birds, including the larger rook and eagle and such songbirds as lark, nightingale,

> The glossy blackbird, and the echoing thrush,
> The gaudy goldfinch which salutes the spring,
> Winnowing the thistle with his burnish'd wing.

The touch of Thomson can also be seen in pictures of realistic rural scenery, in the rude savage of 'scorching sunshine' or 'worlds of ice', and even in tales of a mad woman or a distressed sailor.

Glimpses into the history of science appear in odd places in these later poems. James Kenton, *An Essay on Death* (1777), along with his vivid use of the Lisbon earthquake to illustrate providence, neatly summarizes the activity of scientists while he deplores the futility of their knowledge:

> Yea, even the learned, the sagacious men,
> That heav'nly secrets labour to explore,
> Who scan the orbs of light in yonder skies,
> Who track the stars thro' their extensive paths,
> And measure their immense circumference. . . .
> The sons of science with laborious toil,
> And strict researches thro' all nature's form,
> Dive deep for knowledge with assiduous care,
> And thro' the whole of wide creation's store,
> With fix'd attention as for hidden spoils,
> Their ev'ry power and faculty employ.
> But vain their efforts; all their curious art.

[3] The edition used here is the expanded 6th, London, 1782.

George Crabbe studied botany, as did Thomas Gray, for a pastime without putting much of it into his famous pictures of village realism. There is a passage in *The Library* (1781), however, that summarizes scientific books and prophesies of Erasmus Darwin. In the collection of contemporary books Crabbe places science first:

> Our guide through Nature's works, and in our own;
> Who place in order Being's wondrous chain,
> Save where those puzzling, stubborn links remain,
> By art divine involv'd, which man can ne'er explain.
> These are thy volumes; and in these we look,
> As abstracts drawn from Nature's larger book.

In these books appear first gems and minerals, then vegetable life, as interpreted by 'the sexual system of Linnaeus':

> Which, when the spring calls forth their genial power,
> Swell with the seed, and flourish in the flower:
> There, with the husband-slaves, in royal pride,
> Queens, like the Amazons of old, reside;
> There, like the Turk, the lordly husband lives,
> And joy to all the gay seraglio gives;
> There [the Class Cryptogamia], in the secret chambers,
>   veil'd from sight,
> A bashful tribe in hidden flames delight.

In his description of the Class Dioecia as bolder brides expecting 'their distant lords', Crabbe sounds like Darwin's later *Loves of the Plants*, but fortunately he goes on to other phases of science:

> Next are the tribe whom life and sense inform,
> The torpid beetle, and the shrinking worm;
> And insects, proud to spread their brilliant wing,
> To catch the fostering sunbeams of the spring.

He uses the migration of swallows as his example of bird lore and passes over 'the scaly myriads of the ocean' to let his scientist trace 'the sullen people of the savage race'. Aside from this passage and some satire on physicians, however, Crabbe pursued his science and his poetry quite separately.

In 1781 there also appeared the third edition of *Elegy on Captain Cook, to which is added, An Ode to the Sun*, two poems of the versatile Anna Seward which show that occasionally she could put into verse the scientific interest that was sharpened by her acquaintance with Erasmus Darwin at Lichfield. Cook's expeditions to the South Seas had added immeasurably to scientific knowledge, and Miss Seward informs us in verse and notes of the tragic story as well as of exotic flora and fauna, silk, poi-bird, and giant bat. In her *Ode to the Sun*, with which she won a prize in 1779, she hails the 'life enkindling light' that gives color to shell and fin and diamond, and life to the farthest reaches of the earth:

> From the dwarf coral, with his vermeil horns,
> Or sea-moss, matted round her briny caves,
> To the broad oak, that Albion's cliff adorns,
> And bears her sons triumphant o'er the waves;
> Each stem, root, leaf, fair fruit, and flowret bright,
> Lustre and fragrance drink from thy all-chearing light.

An example of an occasional poem that aids the history of science is Percival Stockdale's 'A Poetical Epistle to Sir Ashton Lever', describing the finest of many private science museums. In praising Lever's generosity for making known to scientists 'the various wonders of the globe' from Siam to California, the poet insists nevertheless on the moral that a study of this 'varied and magnificent store' serves to unfold further 'the world's harmonious plan'.[4]

The history of poetry and the history of science merge in a remarkable Scotsman, Francis Garden, Lord Gardenstone, who is best known today for the social experiments that resulted in the economic prosperity of his village of Laurencekirk. His most interesting writing on science is in his prose descriptions of his own extensive collection of shells and minerals and the large private museums visited in his three years of travel in Europe from 5 September 1786.[5] His best verse is the satire on science already described, but a serious poem, 'The Dignity of Human Nature', uses natural history to furnish images for the moral analogies be-

[4] Stockdale, *Three Poems* (London, 1784), pp. 17–23.
[5] *Travelling Memorandums, made in a Tour of the Continent of Europe, in the Years 1786, 1787, and 1788, by the Hon. Lord Gardenstone*, Vols. I, II (Edinburgh, 1792); Vol. III (1795, prefaced by a biography). The value of his comments can be seen in an excerpt from his visit to M. Sprungle near Geneva (II, 8–12): "He has in his collection 240 birds of species quite distinct. He says that there are yet ten more to be found in Switzerland. He is in search of them, but he has not yet been able to find them, as they are birds of passage and rare." On his "testy and discontented" old friend Smollett, see I, 5: "even his oddities are entertaining."

tween animals and man, where herring, camel, pheasant, lobster, turtle, dolphin, gannet, shark, bear, duck, frog, seal, viper, boar, crocodile, whale, and blackbird, in that bewildering order, are added to the traditional ant, bee, dove, beaver, and elephant.[6]

The numerous poems described in these last four chapters clearly indicate that scientific poetry of the second half of the eighteenth century covers a multitude of subjects in a bewildering variety of style and prosody. From the earlier poetry the moral themes of order, providence, and the divinization of nature continue, along with imagery from the telescopic and microscopic universes and a respect for Newton as the symbol of scientific discovery that reveals the wisdom of God. Besides the miscellaneous character of the poems, the new look appears in the imagery of natural history reflected in verses imitative of the descriptive element in Thomson's *Seasons*. The irony of this new rhetoric for science is that, while science itself was making tremendous advances in chemistry, physics, and geology, there was no poetic symbol to replace Newton, only an occasional uninspired mention of Linnaeus, Priestley, Herschel, and Franklin. The changes in the practical application of science in technology, especially in the inventions that led to the Industrial Revolution, found no imaginative outlet except in the protests of Goldsmith's deserted Auburn and Blake's 'dark Satanic mills'. The continuity lay only in the themes of providence and the divine wisdom in nature which by this time had already been rejected by the philosophers. Even these themes were largely illustrated by imagery from the gentlemanly sciences of botany, zoology (especially ornithology), and entomology, all grouped under the term 'natural history' and bound together by the new science of Linnaeus. The new look can be seen even in the general poems described in this chapter, for they combine with nature poems to furnish the prelude to Wordsworth though at the same time they look back to earlier scientific poetry.

The new look is in Cowper, and before him in less pure form in William Hayley, whose *Beauties of Spring* (1781) shows the wisdom of God in the lowly phases of nature by the flow of sap through 'a thousand plastic tubes' and the perfection of structure in microscopic creatures. In the 'mighty whole' of stupendous creation

[6] *Miscellanies in Prose and Verse* (2nd ed. rev., Edinburgh, 1792; first edition, 1791, was not for sale), pp. 21–4.

everything is suited to its place in the scale of being, 'every blade of trodden grass / Is perfect as its parent power the sun'. God is a master mechanic:

> How admirably various and complex
> Is every plant's machinery! far beyond
> The clouded ken of philosophic eye.
> How delicate its texture! Not a bud
> Swells on the branch, but in its folds contains
> Sublimer wonders than the human race,
> In all their monuments of art, can show!

James Fordyce shows the new look in many short lyrics included in his *Poems* (1786), whether 'amidst immensity's dread space' or in the harshness of storm and earthquake or in the skylark that 'on joyful wings, / Sublimely soars, and soaring sweetly sings'.

The last decade of the century produced a number of poems that, except for poetic quality, could easily be mistaken for Wordsworth juvenilia. Among those already described, the touch of Thomson that appears in the nature description, the religious themes, and the localized rural scenery of topographical poems also seems like a prophecy of *Lyrical Ballads*. A few poems of this decade that reflect general science rather than natural history will serve as a sort of transition to mark the end of one era and the beginning of another. Henry Moore of Liskeard wrote poems of this sort that were not published until after his death in 1802, of which 'A Lyric Rhapsody' is an excellent example:

> The strong and restless energy of mind,
> That roves the fields of science unconfin'd,
> That spreads its darting plumes from pole to pole,
> Wherever trumpets rage, or oceans roll,
> Explores the secrets of the realms on high,
> Draws the red lightning from the low'ring sky,
> Bids seven-fold light its magic dyes display,
> The blended glories of the golden day,
> Treads the bright path the circling planets run,
> Sports in the living splendors of the sun,
> Or far outflies the comet's blazing race,
> And seeks new systems thro' the wilds of space.[7]

---

[7] Moore, *Poems, Lyrical and Miscellaneous* (London, 1803) contains a biography by John Aikin and a poem on astronomy and Newton published as *Private Life* in 1795.

Alexander Campbell reflects the transition in his ode on the harmony of nature seen in the seasons, the power of light and heat to ripen fruit and flower, and the countless orbs viewed in his cosmic voyage after death.[8]

Two books of poems published in 1790 seem to be such a natural transition from Thomson and Cowper to Wordsworth that I should like to end with them. The first of these is by a friend and benefactor of Wordsworth and other young poets, William Sotheby, whose miscellaneous verses are scant in science but rich in nature description. His descriptive tours of Wales, where he said wild nature was bolder than the paintings of Salvator Rosa, must have had a special appeal to his younger proteges with their combination of melancholy, romantic mountain scenery, and sentimental humanitarianism. The collection printed at Bath contains two poems that remind us directly of Wordsworth, though they have nothing to do with science: the tragic love story of Lucy, and the loss-compensation theme in the description of Netley Abbey, where the poet finds that the ruins which in youth inspired in him romantic dreams have now faded into 'sublimer truth'.

The other poet, Francis Webb, is more profound. In the first of three long poems in the 1790 Salisbury *Poems*, Wisdom comes from the mouth of God to instruct men in those workings of nature which science had demonstrated:

> The mighty frame of this stupendous world,
> The sun's fix't centre, and the rolling orbs,
> Which, by th'almighty word their circuits keep;
> The comet's fiery track thro' endless space,
> And all the operations of the world,
> From the beginning to the end of time;
> The change of seasons, and the golden chain
> That links the year, and leads the ages on
> And joins them to eternity; the laws
> Of that exalted harmony which reigns
> Throughout the whole, and tunes the heav'nly spheres.

In this rather sublime blank verse, Webb goes on to paraphrase the Bible in ecstatic praise of the rainbow and hails 'with joy the

[8] *Odes and Miscellaneous Poems by a Student of Medicine in the University of Edinburgh* (Edinburgh, 1796), pp. 17-23. This collection also contains the only poem I have seen on chemistry in the century, 'power combin'd, combustible, impure!'

renovated world'. The other physico-theological poem, on the deity, praises the 'Great Parent of the universe . . . essential goodness'.

The third poem, on genius, is significant in the aesthetics of scientific nature poetry. The prose preface argues vigorously that all great art comes from nature, hence when this principle is 'applied to the poetic art, in describing the works of nature, they constitute the beauty of descriptive poetry'. As the mind is led from 'external material forms' to ideas, so we 'are led from contemplating the works of Nature to the contemplation of Nature's God'. In the words of the poem, only those favored ones 'purg'd from earth's corporeal stain' can see remote connections' and

> From out confusion's lab'rinth draw,
> Full taught by Order's sacred law,
> Fair forms of harmony.

Webb looks back to the older poets when he summarizes what science has enabled the philosopher to see:

> Who from his works beneath have sought,
> The hidden God, and deep in thought,
> Tracing through all his works th'Almighty hand.

At the same time he pursues the newer psychology in a way that looks forward to Wordsworth on intimations of immortality, when he insists that we come to divine vision through perception:

> No fabled Daemon, but the pow'r
> That from the first, the natal hour,
> Within the mind itself had an abode,
> Tho' clouds of sense obscur'd the latent God.

By the end of the century other stars had risen in the world of poetry. In 1798 two young poets published a slim volume called *Lyrical Ballads*. In 1800 a preface to the second edition showed the literary world that romantic poetry had come of age, though in the poems themselves it was already apparent that something new had been added to older themes that had been developing, with all the variations described in this book, for the past hundred years. In *The Rime of the Ancient Mariner* Coleridge portrayed a new kind of exotic nature beyond the novelty of albatross and water snakes. In *Lines Composed a Few Miles above Tintern Abbey* Wordsworth gave new meaning to the idea that nature has the power to bring a mystical joy to the mind. Yet these and other poems written later by Shelley and Keats and Byron and even Tennyson may now be looked on, I feel, as a continuation of what had been said, however feebly, in hundreds of scientific poems of the eighteenth century. The vogue of natural history in the second half of the century took away from the sublimity of the earlier telescopic and microscopic universes, but in doing so it demonstrated the wisdom of God in nature in the more intimate setting of English rural landscape. It prepared the way for the pantheism that is symbolized by daffodil and skylark, by the landscape of the River Wye or the change of seasons with the shifting west wind.

The new look was there several years before in the earlier poems of William Blake, but few readers recognized it. The unexplainable genius of Blake puts him, of course, outside any regular tradition. And yet the very paradox of his using the scientific idea of the wisdom of God in nature and at the same time attacking science can be better understood after seeing the older tradition. Pope and Smart and Cowper had earlier used the discoveries of science to glorify God but at the same time realized that in its arrogance science seldom admits its own limitations, its inability to explain the mysteries of nature. Blake rejected science more vigorously than they, because to him it was the enemy of the imagination. In his unique style he was able to dramatize an old idea in unforgettable terms.

Blake's attack on science took two forms. The first, and least important, is the youthful burlesque narrative, *An Island in the Moon*, written about 1785 in the tradition of Peter Pindar's ridicule of the Royal Society. The second and more important method was to use Newton in many serious poems to represent the mechanistic science that kills the imagination and deadens the spirit of poetry symbolized by Milton. Blake lumped together Newton, Bacon, Locke, and Reynolds as the antithesis of spirit, genius poetry, and art. Blake was aware that Newton had been praised by the earlier poets, and it may be that for this very reason he changed Newton from hero to scapegoat. As early as *Europe* he described Newton as a 'mighty spirit' before whose blast the angels fall like yellow leaves. In his poems, engravings, and notebooks, Blake built up the attack against science, which he called 'the Tree of Death' and symbolized with Newton, the oppressor of human mind and spirit. Later in the great epics it reached artistic expression in

Urizen, who is 'in part Blake's vision of Newtonian nature—cold, remote, mathematical, empty'.[9]

Though Blake attacked science more vigorously than any other poet of the eighteenth century, still he affirmed with consummate lyric skill what admirers of Newton and other scientists had been saying with a thousand variations before him: the wisdom of God is seen in nature. He would perhaps not have agreed with them that the harmony of nature is best revealed by the discoveries of science, but he repeated the main theme with lyric perfection. It is ironic but true that perhaps the most refined distillation of eighteenth-century scientific poetry can be seen in Blake's series of questions about the tiger's fearful symmetry, or in his motto to 'Auguries of Innocence':

> To see the world in a grain of sand,
> And a heaven in a wild flower,
> Hold infinity in the palm of your hand,
> And eternity in an hour.

Surely the rhetoric of science has devious ways to perform its magic.

[9] Jean Hagstrum, "William Blake rejects the Enlightenment." *Proceedings of the Conference on the Enlightenment*, Geneva, July, 1963, pp. 91–108.

EPILOGUE

WHEN science and religion meet in poetry, as they did in the eighteenth century, the result is often lofty and sublime. The examples paraded in this book show how the imagination of even little men was stimulated by the new discoveries of science that seemed made to order to justify the wisdom of God. In the poetry of Pope, Thomson, Smart, and Cowper, the result is startlingly good, but even the ordinary scientific poems of the century deserve more recognition than they have received. At first they repeated the Psalmist's praise of God for his works, but with an added fervor and conviction borrowed from recent scientific discoveries. Gaining confidence the poets launched into longer and more profound 'poetical essays', versifications of physico-theology based on the popularizations of science applied to religion. The science was at third hand, out of Derham and Wollaston who themselves went back to Newton and Boyle. But that did not matter, for the main purpose of the physico-theological poetry was to show how science revealed the attributes of the Supreme Being—power, goodness, omniscience, eternity, providence, and such—in short, to proclaim with poetic fervor the wisdom of God in nature.

The new science proved mathematically what the philosophers and theologians had surmised, that the universe was orderly and harmonious. Improvements in the telescope opened up a vast universe, where new stars proved to be suns for new systems, and so the earth shrank to a mere speck among innumerable worlds. Yet the poets also found much on the earth that revealed the wisdom of God, not only in the natural world of animal, plant, and mineral, but also in the physiology of the human body and the psychology of the human mind. The most spectacular field of the newer scientific exploration was in the little world under the microscope, where man by mechanical aid was able to see as far in the direction of infinite little things as he had already seemed to do with the telescope in boundless space. The effect on the imagination was staggering: if man could now see so much that was hidden only a few years before, there must be still much more left undiscovered in a universe that seemed infinite in both directions. And all of it was orderly, because God watched over it. The plenitude of forms, the incredible variety in nature, merely served to declare the glory of God, and with a new emphasis.

There were scientific puzzles, of course, such unanswerable questions as the origin of instinct in animals and reason in man, or the source of that attraction that kept celestial bodies in an orderly course, or the peculiar behavior of the sensitive plant that acted like an animal. These and many other things that scientists could not explain led many poets to point out the limitations of science, raising doubts about science obtaining the ultimate answers but at the same time praising science for what it had accomplished.

The puzzle that should have been the hardest to answer seemed to offer no difficulty to a generation that believed in the benevolence of God. Violence in nature, that harsher side shown in earthquakes, hurricanes, wild beasts, plague, and the extremes of climate felt in tropical and arctic regions, seems to be evil but actually, orthodox religion maintained, it is only a part of the general scheme of providence. The seeming discord of violent nature, as Pope put it, is 'harmony not understood', and partial evil is but a part of the universal good unknown to man.

Two other popular ideas continue from the seventeenth century but with a new zest added by scientific imagery: the amateur scientist in poems on retirement, and the happy man who explores the secrets of nature in a cosmic voyage after death. But the main religious themes treated in scientific poetry in eighteenth-century England are order, providence, and plenitude. And naturally the most sustained serious treatment of them is in the poetical essays of the first half of the century. This has been called Newtonianism because Newton became to the poets the symbol of the new science that demonstrated order and harmony in the universe and therefore revealed the wisdom of God in nature. Newton lent his mathematical genius to proving order by tracking the paths of the wandering planets, measuring the orbits of comets, and giving assurance of harmony in 'millions of suns with planets circling round'.

Even in the first half of the century, as I have amply demonstrated, the poets inspired by Newton used other scientific discoveries to prove that the glory of God is shown in his works. The microscopic study of small animals in their orderly world and of the circulation of sap in plants and blood in animals furnished the imaginative counterpart for the new world of astronomy revealed by improvements in the telescope. Natural history was encouraged, not only by the continuing research in botany inspired by the exotic plants imported from foreign lands and the practical need for herbs in medicine, but also by the study of birds and fishes made to fill out the picture of animal life for the classification schemes of John Ray in the seventeenth century. The minute world used by the poets to contrast with Newton's order in the skies also included the fascinating world of insects, for immortality itself was often compared to the metamorphosis of the beautiful moth from the ugly caterpillar that they called 'reptile'. Physicians like Blackmore added to their poetry the marvels of human physiology to show the wisdom of God in the creation.

Newton was only part of the picture even with the earlier poets, but he was the symbol of science to them, and his death set off a train of scientific poems that had a lasting effect on English poetry. His changing reputation in the latter part of the century, particularly in France with the revival of the influence of Descartes after 1735,[1] was little noticed by English poets until Blake. Scientific poetry suffered when Newton's orderly universe gave way to natural history, but the poets almost consistently refused to connect him with the mechanistic philosophy that he had unwillingly aided the Cartesians to establish even in England.

During the second half of the century the poems influenced directly by science were numerous but shorter and less philosphical. The tremendous popular vogue of natural history after 1750, aided by the discovery of new species in all parts of the world and by the new classification scheme of Linnaeus, changed

---

[1] A summary of scholarship refuting the famous conclusions of Carl Becker's *The Heavenly City of the Eighteenth-Century Philosophers* (New Haven, 1932) is in Henry Guerlac, 'Newton's Changing Reputation in the Eighteenth Century', *Carl Becker's Heavenly City Revisited* (Ithaca, N.Y., 1958), pp. 3–26.

the subjects of scientific poetry from the dominant metaphors of the telescopic and microscopic universes to emphasis on the gentler world of nature that could be observed close at hand, the kind that needed no elaborate experimentation or puzzling mathematical formulas. Botany and ornithology were genteel subjects, and even zoology could be studied in books and museums without too much fuss or bother. The tremendous output of colored plates of flowers, birds, and other phases of natural history during the second half of the century catered to this new taste and at the same time encouraged the poet's love of color and the Englishman's love of rural landscape.

The combination of art and science and religious moralizing was a powerful one that gave new zest to the georgic tradition that had for centuries brought the English landscape into English poetry. The religious themes continued, with only slight modifications, throughout the century, but the scientific examples used to illustrate God's presence in nature changed from celestial systems to English flowers and birds. The English countryside, it is true, did not lend itself to the sublime so well as the astronomical universe but it was much more suited to the English poet who could enjoy nature while he scientifically observed it.

This blending of science and the georgic tradition in the poet's use of natural history becomes more understandable in the light of the continuity of religious themes in eighteenth-century scientific poetry. It also helps to explain why the predominant imagery of nineteenth-century romantic poets is that of natural history, where nightingale and skylark, primrose and daffodil, are the most familiar of the multitudinous species observed in landscape and identified in science handbooks. Thomson's *Seasons* had a continuing, and even accelerating influence on this scientific georgic poetry. The blend of nature description and philosophic meditation in Thomson leads directly into the romantic poetry of the nineteenth century.

Meanwhile, scientific study in other fields than natural history had become too advanced and too complex for the amateurs, and most poets were certainly amateurs. Even the numerous compendiums and encyclopedias could not simplify for them the new discoveries of physics, astronomy, chemistry, mathematics, or even geology, the recent upstart in science. Most of the poets ignored these branches of science, but a few distrusted what they considered mechanistic and cold research. The orthodox Cowper, for example, did not like the way science attacked the authenticity of the Bible. The sensitive Blake rebelled openly against science as the destroyer of poetry, and Keats followed him in protesting the dissection of a rainbow. Wordsworth said in his preface to the 1800 *Lyrical Ballads* that he would gladly use science if it were more suitable for imaginative poetry, yet he showed an anti-intellectual attitude of hostility to science when he endowed his simple philosopher (scientist) with the ability to absorb knowledge by wise passiveness, sitting on a stone. Only Coleridge and Shelley among the romantic poets knew and loved science.

And yet the hostility of Keats and Wordsworth, to a certain extent even of Blake, is only on the surface, for their main theme is the physico-theological one of the wisdom of God in nature, which the scientific poets of the eighteenth century had brought to them in varying and sublime examples. They distrusted the science that they could not understand, and by 1800 much of it must properly have seemed to them cold, materialistic, and forbidding. Furthermore, the sublime had gone out of most scientific poetry, especially in that most notorious example near the end of the century, Erasmus Darwin's *The Loves of the Plants*. It is a far cry from unnumbered worlds in unmeasured space to a violet by a mossy stone, but images from natural history lead just as surely to an understanding of divine order in nature as those from astronomy. The imagery changed from blazing comets and the orderly world in a drop of pond scum to an impulse from a vernal wood, but the change did not obscure the underlying continuity of ideas.

CHECK-LIST OF SELECTED
SCIENTIFIC POEMS

(N.B. If not otherwise noted, the place of publication is London.)

I. Poems of General Scientific Interest, including Didactic

ANON.   The Book of Nature: a Poem. 1771
   A Philosophic Ode on the Sun and the Universe. 1750
   A Poetical Essay on Physick, Inscrib'd to Dr. Pellet. n.d. 1735?
   The Vanity of Philosophick Systems: a Poem addressed to the Royal
   Society. 1761
[AKENSIDE, MARK]   The Pleasures of the Imagination: a Poem in
   Three Books. 1744
ARMSTRONG, JOHN   The Art of Preserving Health: a Poem. 1744
BAKER, HENRY   The Universe: a Poem intended to Restrain the Pride
   of Man. n.d. 1734?
BISHOP, SAMUEL   Poetical Works. 2 vols., 1796
BENGER, ELIZABETH OGILVY   The Female Geniad: a Poem inscribed to
   Mrs. Crespigny. 1791
BLACKLOCK, THOMAS   Poems. 2nd ed., 1756
BLACKMORE, RICHARD   The Creation: a Philosophical Poem in Seven
   Books. 1712
BOWDEN, SAMUEL   Poetical Essays on Several Occasions. Vol. I, 1733;
   Vol. II, 1735
BRERETON, JANE   Poems on Several Occasions. 1744
[BROOKE, HENRY]   Universal Beauty. 1735 (six separate parts)
BROOME, WILLIAM   Poems on Several Occasions. 1727
BROWNE, MOSES   'Essay on the Universe', Poems on Various Subjects.
   1739
BRUCE, MICHAEL   Poems on Several Occasions. Edinburgh, 1782
BULLOCK, RICHARD   An Hymn to the Creator of the World. 1750

[CAMPBELL, ALEXANDER] Odes and Miscellaneous Poems by a Student of Medicine in the University of Edinburgh. Edinburgh, 1796

CARTER, ELIZABETH Poems on Several Occasions. 1762

CHATTERTON, THOMAS Works, ed. by G. Gregory. 3 vols., 1803

CHUDLEIGH, MARY Essays upon Several Subjects in Prose and Verse. 1710

[COLLINS, RICHARD] Nature Display'd. 1727

COOKE, THOMAS 'To Dr. Woodward', Miscellaneous Poems and Translations, published by Richard Savage. 1726

COWPER, WILLIAM The Task. 1785

DARWIN, ERASMUS The Botanic Garden. 1791

DALTON, JOHN A Descriptive Poem Addressed to Two Ladies at their Return from Viewing the Mines near Whitehaven. 1755

DESAGULIER, J. T. The Newtonian System of the World, the Best Model of Government. Westminster, 1728

[DIAPER, WILLIAM] Dryades: or the Nymph's prophecy. 1713

DODSLEY, ROBERT Public Virtue (I. Agriculture). 1753

DONN, BENJAMIN 'On the Usefulness of Natural Philosophy: a Poem', An Epitome of Natural and Experimental Philosophy. 1769

DOWNMAN, HUGH Infancy: a Poem. 1775–76 (3 separate parts)

EDWARDS, SAMUEL The Copernican System. Cambridge, 1728

[EVANS, ABEL] Vertumnus: an Epistle to Mr. Jacob Bobart. Oxford, 1713

FAWKES, FRANCIS Original Poems and Translations. 1761

FAYERMAN, RICHARD Contemplation: a Poetical Essay on the Works of the Creation. Norwich, 1776

FOOT, JAMES Penseroso, or the Pensive Philosopher in his Solitudes. 1771

[GAMBOL, ROBERT] The Beauties of the Universe: a Poem by a Gentleman of the Navy. 1732

GARDEN, FRANCIS Miscellanies in Prose and Verse. 2nd ed. corr, Edinburgh, 1792

GRAINGER, JAMES The Sugar-Cane: a Poem in Four Books, with Notes. 1764

HERVEY, JAMES Meditations and Contemplations. 1747. Poetic version by Thomas Newcomb, 2 vols., 1764

HIGGONS, BEVILL A Poem on Nature: in Imitation of Lucretius. 1736

HILL, AARON The Judgment Day. 1721

HUGHES, JOHN An Ode to the Creator of the World. 1708; The Ecstasy, 1720

JAGO, RICHARD Poems Moral and Descriptive. 1784

[JENYNS, SOAME] Poems. 1752

JONES, HENRY Poems on Several Occasions. 1749

LEAPOR, MARY   Poems on Several Occasions. 1748

LIPSCOMB, WILLIAM   Poems. Oxford, 1784

LOFFT, CAPEL   The Praises of Poetry (1775); Eudosia, or a Poem on the Universe (1781)

MALLET, DAVID   The Excursion: a Poem in two Books. 1728

MASTERS, MARY   Poems on Several Occasions. 1733

MOORE, HENRY (of Liskeard)   Poems Lyrical and Miscellaneous. 1803

NEEDLER, HENRY   The Works of Mr. Henry Needler. 2nd ed., 1728

[PERRONET, EDWARD]   Occasional Verses, Moral and Sacred. 1785

PRIOR, MATTHEW   Solomon on the Vanity of the World. 1718

[PYE, HENRY JAMES]   Beauty: a Poetical Essay (1766); Faringdon Hill, 2nd ed. with odes, elegies, and miscellaneous pieces (Oxford, 1778)

RACK, EDMUND   Poems on Several Subjects. 1775

RALPH, JAMES   Night: a Poem in four Books. Dublin, 1728

REYNOLDS, JOHN   Death's Vision, represented in a Philosophical Sacred Poem (1709) expanded in 1725 as A View of Death: or the Soul's Departure from the World

ROBINSON, MARY   Poems. 1791

ROWE, ELIZABETH   The Miscellaneous Works in Prose and Verse. 2 vols., 1739

SAVAGE, RICHARD   The Wanderer, a Poem in Five Cantos. 1729

SCOTT, JOHN (of Amwell)   The Poetical Works of John Scott, Esq. 1782

SILVESTER, TIPPING   'The Microscope', Original Poems and Translations. 1733

SMART, CHRISTOPHER   (see chap. II, note 10)

STEPHENS, EDWARD   Poems on Various Subjects. 1759
The Birth-day: a Pastoral, with other Poems. Ipswich, 1765

STILLINGFLEET, BENJAMIN   Miscellaneous Tracts on Natural History. 1762

TASKER, WILLIAM   Poems. 1779

THOMSON, JAMES   (for revisions in *The Seasons*, 1726–46, see Chap. IV)

WALTERS, JOHN   Poems, with Notes. Oxford, 1780

WERGE, JOHN   A Collection of Original Poems, Essays, and Epistles. Stamford, 1753

WHATELEY, MARY   Original Poems on Several Occasions. 1764

II. Poems emphasizing Natural History: the Influence of Thomson

ANON.   On Beneficence: a Poetical Essay. 2nd. ed., 1764
The Muse's Recreation, in four Poems. 1762

BARBAULD, ANNA LAETITIA AIKIN   Poems. 1773

BLAMIRE, SUSANNA   Poetical Works, now for the first time Collected by Henry Lonsdale. Edinburgh, 1842 (written ca. 1771)

BOWLES, W. L.   Sonnets written chiefly on Picturesque Spots, during a Tour. 2nd ed., Bath, 1789; Monody written at Matlock. Salisbury, 1791

BROWN, W. L.   Essay on Sensibility. 2nd ed., 1791

CARY, HENRY FRANCIS   Sonnets and Odes. 1788

[COLVILL, ROBERT]   On the Winter Solstice: a Descriptive Poem. Edinburgh, 1765

COTTLE, JOSEPH   Malvern Hills. 1798

CUNNINGHAM, JOHN   Day, and other Pastorals. Edinburgh, 1761 Poems, chiefly Pastoral. Newcastle, 1766

[DRAPER, W. H.]   The Morning's Walk, or City Encompass'd. 1751

HAWKINS, WILLIAM   Dramatic and other Poems, Letters, Essays, etc. Oxford, 1758

HURDIS, JAMES   The Village Curate: a Poem. 1788

[MAURICE, THOMAS]   Grove-Hill, a Descriptive Poem. 1799

MENDES, MOSES   'The Seasons', A collection of the Most Esteemed Pieces of Poetry. 2nd ed., 1770

MICKLE, W. J.   Poetical Works. 1806 (written before 1788)

MUNDY, F. N. C.   Needwood Forest. Lichfield, 1776

SEWARD, ANNA   Original Sonnets on Various Subjects, 1799; Elegy on Captain Cook, 1773

SOTHEBY, WILLIAM   Poems. Bath, 1790

[WALLACE, GEORGE]   Fragments of a Prospect from a Hill in Fife. 1754 (BM 11602.h.13)

WHEATCROFT, W. G.   The Powers of Fancy: a Poem. 1790

WOODHULL, MICHAEL   Ode to the Muses. Oxford, 1790

WRIGHT, GEORGE   The Rural Christian: or the Pleasures of Religion. 4th ed., 1794

III. Moral Poems that emphasize Science

ANON.   Hymn to the Deity. 1750 (BM 840.k.4)
  Hymn to the Power of Harmony. 1763 (BM 840.l.15)
  Miscellany Poems on Moral Subjects. Chester, 1750 (BM 11602. gg.29)
  Nature, a Poem. 1747 (BM 11630.c.1)
  Nature, a Poem. Edinburgh, 1790 (BM 11602.h.13)
  Order: a Poem. 1737 (BM 643.m.15)
  Poetic Essays on Nature, Men, and Morals. Essay I to Dr. Askew of Newcastle. Newcastle and London, 1750 (BM 840.k.4)
  Retirement: a Divine Soliloquy. 1722
  Solitude: an Irregular Ode inscribed to a Friend. 1738
  The Vindication: or Day-Thoughts on Wisdom and Goodness: occasioned by The Complaint. 1753

AMHURST, NICHOLAS   Poems on Several Occasions. 1720

BEESTON, SAMUEL   Immanuel, an Evangelical Paraphrase: a Poem. 1789

[BOYSE, SAMUEL]   Deity: a Poem. 1739

BROWNE, ISAAC HAWKINS   De Animi Immortalitate, 1754, in several English translations

[CATESBY, THOMAS, LORD PAGET]   An Essay on Human Life. 1735

CODRINGTON, SAMUEL   The Beatific Vision: a Poem. 1735

COOPER, JOHN GILBERT   The Power of Harmony: a Poem in two Books. 1745

DAWSON, WILLIAM   The Atheist: a Philosophical Poem. 1723

DENTON, THOMAS   Immortality: or the Consolation of Human Life. 1754

[DUNCAN, JOHN] An Essay on Happiness, in Four Books. 1762

GRAVES, RICHARD   The Love of Order. 1773

[HARTE, WALTER]   An Essay on Reason. 1735

[HILL, AARON]   Free Thoughts upon Faith: or the Religion of Reason, a Poem. 1746

HOBSON, THOMAS   Christianity the Light of the Moral World: a Poem. 1745

[KENRICK, WILLIAM]   Epistles Philosophical and Moral. 1759

KENTON, JAMES   An Essay on Death: a Poem in five Books. 1777

LANGHORNE, JOHN   Enlargement of the Mind. 1763

MELMOTH, WILLIAM   Of Active and Retired Life: an Epistle to H. C. Esq. 1735

MEREDITH, JAMES   An Essay on the Divine Attributes. 1738

[MORELL, THOMAS]   Hope: a Poetical Essay on that Christian Grace. 1745

[MORRICE, BEZALEEL]   An Essay on the Universe. 1733

OGILVIE, JOHN   Providence: an Allegorical Poem in three Books. 1764

[POPE, ALEXANDER]   An Essay on Man. 1733–34 (four separate parts)

POTTER, ROBERT   Retirement: an Epistle. 1748

ROBERTS, WILLIAM HAYWARD   A Poetical essay on the Esistence of God. 1771

A Poetical Essay on the Attributes of God. 1771

STOCKDALE, PERCIVAL   A Poetical Address to the Supreme Being. 1764   Three Poems. 1784

INDEX

Minor references and references to notes are generally omitted. A subject index to the most common topics used in eighteenth-century poems may be found under *ideas, images and themes, natural history, Newton,* and *science.*

Index

Ritso, George 194
Roberts, William Hayward 171-2
Rowe, Elizabeth 47, 49-50, 68, 161-2
Royal Society 3, 30, 36, 38
  satire 4, 34, 66-7, 70-8, 195-8, 227
Russell, Thomas 191

satire on science 4, 65-78, 179, 194-9,
  215, 221, 226. *See also* Banks, Royal
  Society, virtuoso
Sargent, John 204
Savage, Richard 103, 117-19, 120
science. *See also* astronomy, botany,
  natural history, Newton
  definitions and general history 4,
    14-19, 36-7, 39-40, 84, 87, 107, 117,
    122, 129, 135, 223, 232
  hostility 1-2, 4, 65, 214-15, 227, 233.
    See also ideas: skepticism
  popularization in poetry 86, 131-2,
    134-6, 207-8, 218, 220, 223
Scott, John, of Amwell 186-8
Seaton Prize poems 53, 148, 164-8
Seward, Anna 191, 221-2
Sewell, Elizabeth 212
Shadwell, Thomas 67-8
Shaftesbury, Anthony Ashley Cooper,
  3d Earl of 27, 90, 96, 108, 123, 129,
  147, 148, 149
Shakespeare, William 2, 3, 183
Shelley, Percy 171, 175, 227, 233
Silvester, Tipping 201
Singleton, J. 193
Sloane, Sir Hans 4, 70-2
Smart, Christopher 44-5, 53, 63, 76-7,
  133, 136, 148, 159, 164-8, 176, 179,
  227, 229
Smedley, Jonathan 75
Solander, Daniel 195
Somerville, William 201
Sotheby, William 225
South Seas, voyages to 194-5, 221-2
Sprat, Thomas 8, 37-8, 41, 66, 80,
  86
Stephens, Edward 177
Stillingfleet, Benjamin 19, 168-9
Stockdale, Percival 184, 188, 222
Stuart, David, Earl of Buchan 185
sublime, the 79-80, 91, 117, 119, 157,
  160-1, 210-11, 216, 233
Swift, Jonathan 4, 66, 73-4, 76, 198

technology 202, 204, 207-8, 209 n, 211,
  218

telescope. *See* astronomy, ideas, images,
  Newton
Tennyson, Alfred Lord 227
Thompson, William 46-7, 82-3
Thomson, James 2, 18, 27, 28, 54, 92,
  95, 96, 97-8, 115-20, 123, 124, 136-7,
  138, 146, 147, 148, 149, 155, 159, 217,
  218, 220, 223, 224, 225, 229, 232
  analysis of *Seasons* 107-15
  influence of *Seasons* 161-4, 168-70,
    173-80, 181-92
Tickell, Thomas 84
Tomlinson, Matthew 146
topographical poems 125-6, 176, 177-8,
  190, 204
Trapp, Joseph 52, 83, 103-4, 145
Tucker, Nathaniel 193

Utrecht, Peace of 90, 94

Vanity of Philosophic Systems 64-5
*Vindication: or Day-Thoughts on Wisdom
  and Goodness, The* 158
virtuoso, satire on the 4, 31, 65-78,
  195-9
Voltaire 29, 30

Watts, Isaac 53-4
Webb, Francis 225-6
Weeks, Nathaniel 193
West Indies 193
Whalley, Thomas 191
Wheatcroft, William 190
Whiston, William 11, 84
White, Gilbert 18, 31, 168-9, 180, 185,
  219
Whitehead, A. N. 1
Whitehead, William 217-18
Willey, Basil 140
Wise, Joseph 208-9
Wolcot, John (Peter Pindar) 195-8, 227
Wollaston, William 9, 13, 21, 22-3, 84,
  229
women poets and scientists 13, 14-15,
  18, 19, 23, 41, 61, 68-9, 161-3, 168, 176,
  179, 191, 212, 221-2
Woodward, Dr. John 68, 83, 91, 95
Wordsworth, William 171, 172, 179,
  205, 224-5, 233
Wright, George 184, 190
Wynne, John Huddlestone 186

Young, Edward 46, 50, 74-5, 102, 136,
  153-9, 160, 168, 174